THE 350-FOOT-HIGH LAVA BLUFFS OF PALISADE HEAD, LAKE SUPERIOR

ASPENS AND PAPER BIRCHES IN AUTUMN FOLIAGE

REEDS AND WATER LILIES ON SNOWBANK LAKE

MOSS, FERNS, BUNCHBERRY AND ASTERS NEAR GUNFLINT TRAIL

WHITE SPRUCES ON TOP OF A HARD-PACKED SNOW RIDGE, MANITOBA

A BULL MOOSE, ANTLERS SHED IN WINTER, HEADS FOR A THICKET

TIME LIFE BOOKS

THE GOOD COOK
WORLD WAR II
THE TIME-LIFE ENCYCLOPAEDIA
  OF GARDENING
HUMAN BEHAVIOUR
THE GREAT CITIES
THE ART OF SEWING
THE OLD WEST
THE WORLD'S WILD PLACES
THE EMERGENCE OF MAN
LIFE LIBRARY OF PHOTOGRAPHY
TIME-LIFE LIBRARY OF ART
FOODS OF THE WORLD
GREAT AGES OF MAN
LIFE SCIENCE LIBRARY
LIFE NATURE LIBRARY
YOUNG READERS LIBRARY

THE AMERICAN NORTH WOODS

THE WORLD'S WILD PLACES/TIME-LIFE BOOKS/AMSTERDAM

BY PERCY KNAUTH
AND THE EDITORS OF TIME-LIFE BOOKS

THE WORLD'S WILD PLACES

Editorial Staff for *The American North Woods*:
Text Editor: Jay Brennan
Picture Editor: Susan Rayfield
Designer: Charles Mikolaycak
Staff Writer: Gerald Simons
Chief Researcher: Martha T. Goolrick
Researchers: Angela Dews, Terry Drucker,
Barbara Ensrud, Rhea Finklestein,
Villette Harris, Myra Mangan,
Mollie E. C. Webster
Design Assistant: Mervyn Clay

Published by Time-Life International (Nederland) B.V.
Ottho Heldringstraat 5, Amsterdam 1018.

ISBN 7054 0164 2

The Author: Percy Knauth, a freelance writer and editor, has had a special affection for the north woods of North America since he knew them as a boy. He has returned many times, and he re-explored several out-of-the-way areas for this book. He has been a writer and editor for TIME, SPORTS ILLUSTRATED and LIFE, and served for three years as associate editor of the LIFE Nature Library.

The Consultant: Sigurd F. Olson is widely regarded as the dean of north woods naturalists. A former professor of biology and ecology, he has for many years devoted himself to the study and preservation of wilderness. He has been a long-time consultant to the Secretary of the Interior and the National Park Service, is a former president of the Wilderness Society and author of seven books, chiefly about the north woods. He lives in Ely, Minnesota, close to the forests of the Quetico-Superior lake country.

The Cover: A late spring dusk settles on a rain-soaked forest in northeastern Minnesota. This dense woodland along the river Baptism near the north shore of Lake Superior contains several species of trees found through the north woods. In the foreground paper birches, their trunks bent by the weight of winter snow, set off the two sturdier forms in the middle background, white spruce (*centre left*) and white pine (*centre right*). The smaller evergreens in the foreground are balsam firs.

Contents

A Land of Woods and Water

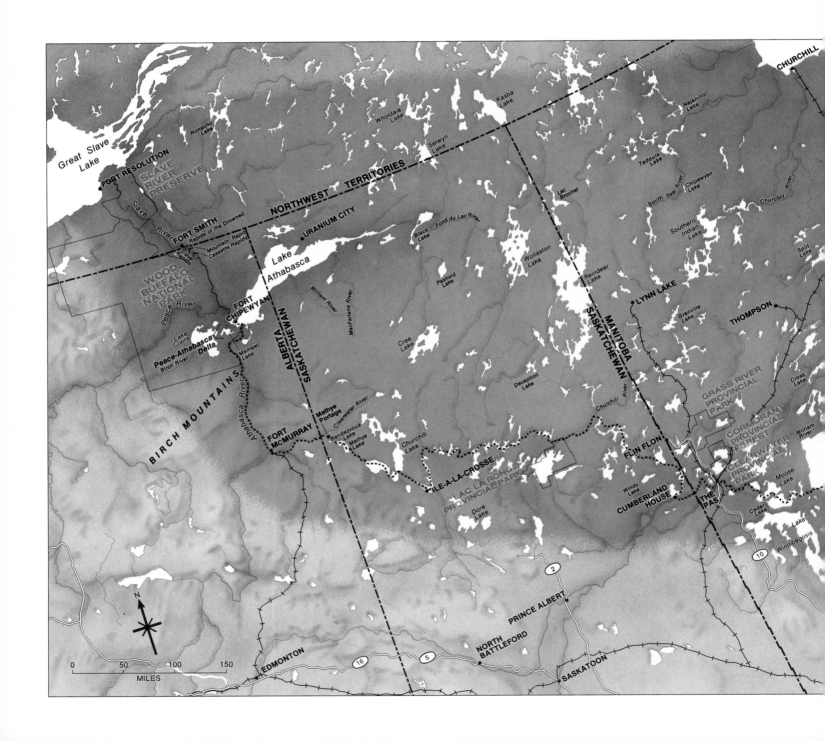

Lying about midway in the great coniferous forest belt that spans the North American continent from Labrador to Alaska, the north woods described in this book extend from northern Minnesota to embrace parts of four Canadian provinces as well as the Northwest Territories (green shading, right). As evident in the detailed map below, lakes and rivers abound in the region, giving it a look as much of waterscape as of forested landscape. A combined water-and-land route, some 2,000 miles long, helped foster the celebrated fur trade of the 18th and 19th Centuries; this historic Voyageurs' Highway, as it is known, is shown by a dotted line between its terminal points, Grand Portage on Lake Superior and Fort Chipewyan on Lake Athabasca in the northwest. Outlined in red and marked with red type are national parks, provincial parks and other protected wilderness areas.

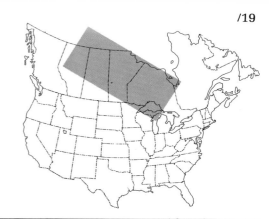

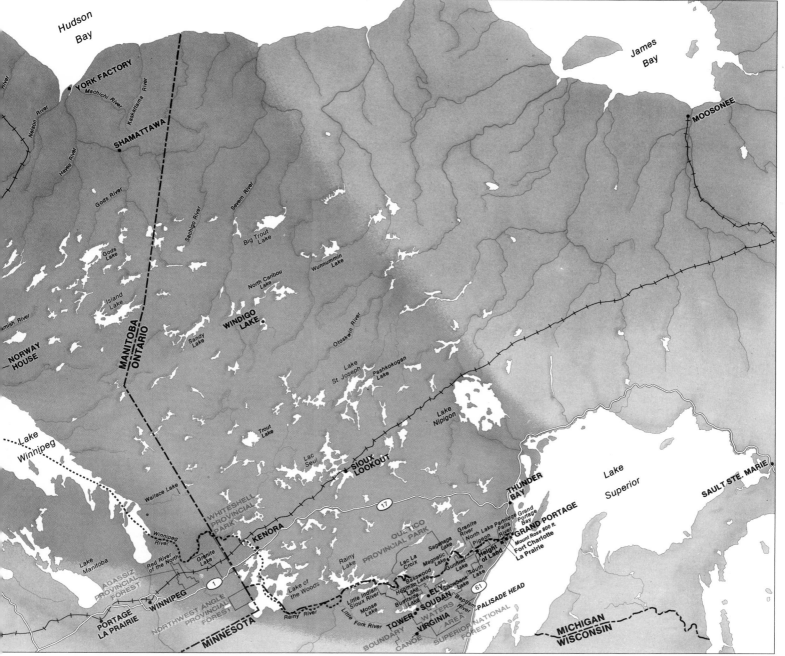

1/ An Infinity of Trees and Water

In the woods a man casts off
his years, as the snake his slough . . . .

RALPH WALDO EMERSON/ *NATURE*

Every man, when he surveys the places he has been in his life and reflects on the experiences he has had there, will choose one place above all others where he likes to be. Such a place, for me, is the north woods. This vast and marvellous land of forest, lake and stream has no precise boundaries, nor does it need any : it exists as much in men's minds as it does on the North American continent. My favourite north woods—with which this book will be primarily concerned—lie at just about the centre of the great forest belt that stretches from Labrador to Alaska. The part of it that most appeals to me begins on the northern fringes of the Quetico-Superior area, straddling the international border between Minnesota and the Canadian province of Ontario. From here it extends about 800 miles northwest to the western shore of Hudson Bay, from there west about 600 miles across the provinces of Manitoba and Saskatchewan to Lake Athabasca, and from there about 1,100 crow-flight miles southeastwards back to the Minnesota border. The shape of this domain is very roughly that of an enormous triangle, with one of the angles, fittingly, at the historic settlement of Grand Portage.

Where Grand Portage lies, at the edge of the great forest in northern Minnesota, Lake Superior beats with icy fingers against a rocky shore. A small creek flows out of the hills here, meandering past cultivated fields through groves of willow and aspen. Bearberries, blueberries and wild roses crowd in on the beach; beyond them, like clouds, soar the tops of sentinel pines. In a meadow by the shore, weathered and grey, stands the stockade of an old fort. These high spiked pickets and the buildings they enclose—reconstructed in modern times—commemorate a period, beginning more than 200 years ago, when the trail that starts here was the jumping-off place for one of the epic adventures in North American history. It was from here that the incredibly hardy breed of French Canadians known as the voyageurs challenged the most forbiding wilderness on the continent, travelling on foot and in birch-bark canoes, repeatedly making a 2,000-mile journey into the north woods in search of the furs that were to make other men's fortunes.

A small hill stands behind the stockade at Grand Portage, an 800-foot eminence known today as Mount Rose. There is a path that leads up it, wandering to and fro for perhaps half a mile as it climbs towards the summit, where in the old days lookouts were posted to shout the arrival of the canoe brigades. From the top, looking southwards, you see the seemingly endless expanse of Lake Superior. Towards the north, however, the view encompasses a haunting panorama: range upon range of dark-green forested hills, all of them bearing that ineffable stamp of the wilderness, an aura of solitude and of perfect peace.

When North America was first being explored by white men, the north woods stretched across the continent, forming an immense dark roof of spruces and pines. Where the climax forest stood, trees as straight and stately as the columns of a Gothic cathedral rose sometimes 100 feet and more; about half way up they branched out to form a canopy that the sun could penetrate only when it was low on the horizon. Below, the forest floor was carpeted with a thick, springy covering of brown needles that sifted down without a break from the branches high above; with no underbrush to impede the view, long dim vistas unrolled through the trees. Elsewhere, along streams and ponds and in the wetter areas of the forest, grew stands of such deciduous trees as the willow, aspen and, most important to history, the paper birch, *Betula papyrifera*. It was from this ghostly white tree, glimmering through the forest shadows, that the Indians—then the only inhabitants of the wilderness—fashioned their birch-bark canoes.

The north woods country is, indeed, the natural habitat of the canoe. No one knows when the first such craft was built or how it evolved, but the process was surely as inexorable as the one that, long ago and far away in a very different environment, brought forth the wheel. A boat is needed in a land of lakes and rivers and, since all the waterways do not always connect with one another, it must be a boat that can easily be carried overland—portaged. It must also be a boat that can cope with widely differing kinds of water, from the turbulent close quarters of rapids to the long unprotected stretches of large lakes where storms come suddenly, without warning, and whip a glassy surface into white-capped waves. Such a boat is the canoe, with its high bow and stern that smoothly divide onrushing waters, its broad midsection to carry heavy loads, and its light construction that enables its crew to take it on their shoulders and carry it when the waterway is blocked.

The canoe is one symbol of the north woods, and there is another: the beaver. This busy rodent is hardly the most imposing animal in a wilderness where black bears roam, where moose can be seen browsing in the shallows by day and the wolf's howl can be heard at night. But the beaver, more than any other creature, affected the history of this rugged land and indeed sometimes helped make it less difficult to traverse.

Many animals are capable of modifying their environment to suit their particular needs, but beavers are among the most successful at it. With the brushwood from the trees felled by their powerful incisor teeth, they build dams that back up streams, creating ponds where there may have been rapids before, eliminating cascades and other watery hindrances to travel. By raising the levels of ponds and rivers they can make an impassable water route passable. Far in the north, in Manitoba, there is a striking example of this in a shallow river that beavers made navigable across a height of land. Paddlers coming up that stream find themselves crossing one beaver dam after another, until finally they cross one more and discover that the river has now reversed its direction and they are paddling downstream. Long ago the Indians called this river the Echimamish, meaning the-river-that-flows-two-ways, and the name remains. But to keep the passage open, human hands eventually had to take up the beavers' work, because for a period of years the beavers disappeared from the area, their dams deteriorated, the water level dropped and the route became unusuable.

What caused the beavers to disappear—not only from the Echimamish, but from all over the north woods—was not any natural catastrophe but their wholesale extermination by man. From a population that once certainly numbered in the millions, the beavers were reduced by trapping almost to the point of extinction. They became exceedingly scarce in Minnesota, in southern Canada and, as their pursuit was intensified, in the more northerly reaches of the land.

The beavers are now coming back, though in nothing like their original numbers; the sight of their dams and ponds is now a familiar one in the forests north of Lake Superior. For today they are protected against excessive trapping by law, secure against a repetition of their earlier fate. That fate was the direct outcome of a single fact about the beaver: the desirability of its pelt. When men first came from afar to seek it, the wilderness of the north was probably the world's richest source of other fur-bearing animals as well—mink, ermine, marten, muskrat, lynx, wolverine, bear. These animals, too, were sought and caught, but the beaver, though its fur was less luxuriant than some of the others, was prized above all. The value of its pelt lay in its use not as fur but as the material from which felt was made—felt that was then moulded and pressed into manifold forms of felt hats. The attribute that commended the beaver pelt was the woolly underfur right below the outer layer. Each hair of this underfur was finely barbed, making the pelt tightly woven—a quality that was deemed uniquely suited for the making of thick, firm felt hats to grace the heads of the rich and the fashionable, men and women alike, all across Europe.

And so it was the glittering prospect of a bonanza in furs that led to the opening up of the north woods. Some of those who took part were primarily interested in pure exploration, and specifically in finding the fabled Northwest Passage to the Pacific. But eventually they were outnumbered by the fur traders. To the Frenchmen, Englishmen and Scotsmen who built up this trade, the sometimes deadly dangers it entailed were offset by the fortunes it promised: the value of a single year's fur cargo shipped back home could exceed a million dollars.

But the men who bore the heaviest burden of danger, who wrestled with the wilderness in all its unpredictability, did not stand to profit from the fur trade. These men were hired hands, toiling for a wage. It was they who worked the boats, who unloaded the cargoes at the start of a portage and reloaded them at the end, who between these points carried the cargoes on their backs, and who all the while coped with the endless exigencies that nature presents in uncharted terrain—a treacherous current that could capsize a boat, a stretch of swamp that could unbalance a man and his load, a path that proved a dead end and had to be laboriously retraced.

Of these men the most colourful, the most enduring in memory, were the French-Canadian voyageurs. They were in the employ of the North West Company, whose headquarters were in Montreal and which was eventually taken over by the Hudson's Bay Company, a British enterprise. The rivalry between the companies, before the merger in 1821,

THE GEOLOGIC TIME SCALE

For many years experts have argued about the dates to be assigned to the eras, periods and epochs of the geologic time scale. The scale generally accepted for many years has been founded on one that was devised by J. Laurence Kulp of Columbia University. But more recently a scale compiled for the Elsevier Scientific Publishing Company has gained wide acceptance. The scale used here in this book is an updated Kulp scale; its relationship to the Elsevier scale can be seen below.

	DATE MILLIONS OF YEARS AGO	
	Kulp Scale	Elsevier Scale
Paleozoic Era		
Cambrian Period	600	570
Ordovician Period	500	500
Silurian Period	440	435
Devonian Period	400	395
Carboniferous Period		
Mississippian Epoch	350	345
Pennsylvanian Epoch	325	310
Permian Period	270	280
Mesozoic Era		
Triassic Period	225	230
Jurassic Period	180	195
Cretaceous Period	135	141
Cenozoic Era		
Tertiary Period		
Paleocene Epoch	70	65
Eocene Epoch	60	55
Oligocene Epoch	40	35
Miocene Epoch	25	22.5
Pliocene Epoch	10	5
Quaternary Period		
Pleistocene Epoch		

Frothing white waters race along the shallow stream bed of the boulder-strewn river Little Fork in northwestern Minnesota.

was intense and often bitter. The Hudson's Bay Company venture into the fur trade started with a number of trading posts on the southwestern shore of Hudson Bay. At first no travelling was necessary; Indians wishing to exchange fur pelts for the assorted wares the company had to offer came to the trading posts. But as intensive trapping reduced the yields in the areas close to the posts the British, like the French before them, had to penetrate into the wilderness to get their furs. Working westwards from Hudson Bay, they used boatmen from their own country —stalwart Orkneymen from the islands off Scotland's northern coast. They also used a type of boat different from the canoe—a double-prowed wooden rowing boat, 28 to 40 feet long, with a wide, flat bottom. On the bigger rivers and lakes of the north country this craft—called the York boat, after York Factory, the Hudson's Bay trading post where it was built—proved to be workable and durable.

But the York boat, like the men who propelled it, lacked the romantic flair of the canoe and its crew of voyageurs. Cursing and singing and laughing in irrepressible Gallic good humour, the voyageurs made a special mark on the history of the continent. Their traces are to be detected even now in the north woods in the campsites they used and in the portages over which they carried their canoes and cargoes.

The wilderness that the voyageurs knew is much diminished today, the roof that once stretched across the continent pierced and decimated by the white man's civilization. In ecological terms it continues to exist as an entity: it is the topmost of three great forest belts that girdle the North American land mass, its mark of distinction the conifer. Experts in such matters call this coniferous belt the boreal forest—in honour of Boreas, the mythological Greek god of the north wind—or the taiga, after the Russians' word for the subarctic coniferous belt in Siberia and northern Europe. But whether it is called taiga or boreal forest or simply the north woods, the heavy hand of man has changed it. The push of population inland from the coasts, the onslaughts of loggers and miners, the inroads of power-plant builders, have sheared away vast sections of it. In areas where once only canoes could pass there are now shipping routes and railways and busy multi-laned roads.

But some of the great forest remains intact. From Grand Portage up the river Pigeon, past Gunflint and Saganaga and Rainy Lakes, down the river Rainy and into Lake of the Woods, and from here farther northwards past Lake Winnipeg—much of this is wild land still. The part most zealously guarded against the pressures of civilization lies within the 16,000-square-mile Quetico-Superior country. Within Quetico-Superior, the 1,029,690 acres of the Boundary Waters Canoe Area on the U.S. side and the 1,144,960 acres of Quetico Provincial Park on the Canadian side have been set apart by the respective governments as wilderness. Beyond Quetico-Superior, to the north and west, are other immense tracts unprotected by law but largely unexploited.

Viewed from ground level, even a small segment of the north woods looms as an infinity of trees—sombre, brooding, monotonous yet overpowering in their mass, a formidable citadel that appears all but impossible to breach. Within the woods one meets still further obstacles not readily seen from outside. Not until men learned to fly could the diversity and difficulties of the interior be fully perceived. From the air it is quickly apparent, for example, that much of the north woods is rock—mostly granitic outcroppings of the Canadian Shield, a portion of the earth's crust so old it dates back to the Precambrian Era, which ended about 600 million years ago. The rock takes forms often perilous to the traveller: sudden steep precipices, massive boulders, sharp ledges that jut out from the banks of a stream or lie concealed beneath it.

Water is a force even more to be reckoned within this wilderness. It is there in such abundance and variety—gently flowing, tumbling, cascading—that from a plane the north woods appear to be almost as much a waterscape as a forested landscape. The profusion of lakes alone stuns the mind; it is as if some giant brush had scattered droplets everywhere in careless abandon, again and again. Minnesota on its licence plates claims 10,000 lakes, Manitoba on its licence plates 100,000, and neither seems exaggerated. A few more formal statistics offer a hint—but a mere hint—of the number of lakes in the north woods. Within the 1,029,690-acre Boundary Waters Canoe Area alone there are some 2,500 lakes that are 10 acres or more in extent. Across the border, as one flies north, the same astonishing profusion of lakes unfolds.

It is difficult to see how anyone not equipped with detailed maps and accurate navigational instruments could ever have found a path through this labyrinth of water. The early voyageurs, of course, had only crude maps, if any, and little in the way of instruments beyond a compass. How, then, did they find their way from lake to lake? How could they have known where lay the portage that would carry them onwards to the next leg of their waterway? How did they know which river flowed northwestwards? Or which southeastwards? Or which river was passable, and which held rapids that could not be run? How did they find a pattern where seemingly no pattern exists, as one looks down upon this staggering plenitude of sparkling water?

Today, with the help of modern maps based on aerial surveys, the canoeist is prepared for some of the problems the voyageurs faced. One complexity with which they had to deal concerned currents. As they proceeded northwestwards from Grand Portage, they were paddling upstream against currents that flowed east or east by south; then for a while they had generally favourable currents; but in the second half of their journey, after they had passed Lake Winnipeg and were approaching the region of Lake Athabasca, they found themselves again fighting upstream on rivers and streams that flowed east or east by south.

The voyageurs found the pattern of the waterways by trial and error and by another equally effective means: they tapped the knowledge of the country possessed by the Indians. The French were the first white men to colonize Canada; by the time the fur trade began to develop, many of them were natives of the country—French Canadians whose homes were in peaceful villages along the Saint Lawrence Valley. An easy-going people, they had a talent for getting along with the Indians. They made friends with them, intermarried with them and in general treated them as brothers. Thus they were able to benefit from the experience of generations of hunting Indians who had long since developed their own canoe routes and portages. Most of the trails followed by canoeists today are portage paths trampled smooth by moccasined Indian feet centuries before the first white men arrived.

One vital lesson of the wilderness that the voyageurs had to learn at first hand concerned the climate of these latitudes. However familiar they might become with waterway patterns, the knowledge was futile unless it could be acted upon within the five months—roughly May 1 to October 1—between spring thaw and autumn freeze; the rest of the year their route was blocked by ice. Moreover, the time of thaw or freeze was never certain, and winter's premature arrival could catch a canoe brigade far from its base, forced to try to survive in some hastily improvised forest shelter.

To deal with this problem, the officials of the Montreal fur trade divided the 3,000-mile route from Montreal to Lake Athabasca into two stages, each travelled by a separate set of voyageurs. Some of the canoe brigades paddled from Montreal to Grand Portage, carrying trade goods, and from there back to Montreal, carrying furs. The fur cargoes were brought down to Grand Portage by canoe brigades that were based at Lake Athabasca or other northern outposts, and that would then return to these bases with the trade goods picked up at Grand Portage.

The 1,000-mile journey from Montreal to Grand Portage actually began a few miles upstream at the village of Lachine, at the head of a long stretch of fast water that barred the canoes from getting closer to the city. Here the goods that were to be traded to the Indians were wrapped in canvas in standard 90-pound bales. Included in the cargo were iron stoves, cooking pots, blankets, cloth of all kinds, needles, thread, pins, flour, salt, cheap trinkets, beads, guns, gunpowder, ammunition, brandy, rum, wine—all the blessings an advanced civilization could muster to tempt these Stone and Copper Age people who held the key to huge fortunes in furs. Fully three tons of cargo was loaded into each canoe —the great, 36-foot *canot de maître*, also known as the Montreal canoe, paddled by a crew of eight to 10 men. Whole fleets of these craft, built entirely of birch bark on a light cedar frame, set out in company, paddling up the river Ottawa until it turned northwards, then taking the river Mattawa to Trout Lake, then portaging over a height of land to Lake Nipissing, which led the voyageurs down the river French to Georgian Bay in Lake Huron. They paddled through the North Channel of that lake to Sault Ste. Marie, portaged around the rapids there into Lake Superior, and then faced 450 miles of treacherous north-shore water to Grand Portage. The trip took six to eight weeks: departing from Montreal just after the breakup of the ice around May 1, the voyageurs arrived at Grand Portage towards the end of June.

It is hard to believe that anyone could belittle this journey, but the voyageurs who came down from the northlands did so: they held the Montreal brigades in contempt as *mangeurs de lard*, or pork eaters, who spent their winters enjoying the softer life at home. The *hommes du nord*, or men of the north, as they liked to call themselves, spent their winters in the rugged outposts of the fur country, places like Cumberland House on the river Saskatchewan, or Ile-à-la-Crosse on the river Churchill, or Fort Chipewyan, the end of the line on Lake Athabasca. From these points, as soon as the ice broke up, they brought down the furs that had been acquired over the winter. Packed in the standard 90-pound bale, these were transported in the smaller, 25-foot North canoes, each with a crew of five or six men. If the ice broke up on the river Athabasca by May 15, the *hommes du nord* usually made the entire 2,000-mile trip to Grand Portage; if spring was late in coming, they would have to meet at Rainy Lake with a special detachment sent up from Grand Portage to take the furs (continued on page 32)

While mushrooms may be found in any area that supports plant life, including lawns and sand dunes, by far the favourite habitat of these fascinating fungi is a forest floor. Nowhere else do they thrive in such diversity of species, sizes, shapes and colours. The 11 different kinds of mushrooms shown at right and on the following pages are but a fraction of the hundreds of species that grow in the north woods. Some are delicious but deadly, others delicious and edible, but all share a vital peculiarity that explains the forest's attraction for them. Mushrooms lack chlorophyll, and so cannot use sunlight to manufacture their food. Instead they must feed on organic compounds: living trees, dead logs, and decaying leaves and needles —all abounding on the forest floor.

POLYPORUS ALVEOLARIS (HONEY-COMBED POLYPORE)

LECCINUM AURANTIACUM (ORANGE BOLETE)

MUTINUS CANINUS (DOG STINKHORN)

POLYSTICTUS TOMENTOSUS (HAIRY POLYPORE)

PHLOGIOTIS HELVELLOIDES (NO COMMON NAME)

SARCOSCYPHA COCCINEA (SCARLET CUP)

MYCENA LEAIANA (LEA'S MYCENA)

HERICIUM CORALLOIDES (CORAL HYDNUM)

LAETIPORUS SULPHUREUS (SULPHUR SHELF)

CLAVARIA PULCHRA (BEAUTIFUL CORAL)

CLAVICORONA PYXIDATA (CUP-BEARING CLAVARIA)

on down, since otherwise they would be unable to get back north before the freeze in October.

Usually, however, the final exchange of cargoes took place at Grand Portage in mid-July. This occasion was called the *rendezvous*, and the little fort on Lake Superior at this time played host to at least 1,000 roistering voyageurs and often twice that many Indians. When the *rendezvous* was over, the much-abused "pork eaters" took the furs back to Montreal in the big canoes, arriving just before the waterways froze and consigned them to the comforts of home. The furs were unloaded, sorted as to quality, and then shipped out to markets all over Europe.

The men of the north, meanwhile, marked the end of the *rendezvous* by setting out on that nine-mile hike up the Grand Portage trail that was the beginning of their journey north.

The Grand Portage trail was a special proving ground for the voyageurs, a place where they tested their strength against each other, where the men were separated from the boys. Each man was required to carry eight bales up to the river Pigeon, the first waterway on the route north; for anything beyond that load he was paid one Spanish dollar per bale. If a man took the normal load of two bales, or 180 pounds, that meant four round trips up and down the trail, a distance of 72 miles. To avoid this the voyageurs sometimes carried more, and sometimes they challenged each other to see who could carry the most. History has preserved, over a century, the name of one George Bonga, who on a wager once carried 820 pounds, or more than nine bales, one mile uphill. It is not likely that anyone ever managed to carry more.

The Grand Portage trail starts out innocuously enough, emerging from a gate in the southeast corner of the fort and following, for a while, the little creek that comes meandering out of the hills. It passes under the shadow of Mount Rose, through thickets of willow and aspen, then through a grove of pine trees and past fields that doubtless were already cultivated in the voyageurs' time. The people whom the hiker may see here today are probably not much different from those who lived in the area in those days, except in dress, for Grand Portage is now part of a reservation for the Chippewa tribe, once a proud race among whom many a voyageur found a bride. Today the Chippewa linger as a remnant, making their living out of souvenirs, or small-time farming, logging or fishing, and once in a while as guides.

Once past the fields, the trail begins to climb steadily towards a notch in the hills ahead that represents a sort of pass. From this height the voyageurs could look back a mile or so to Lake Superior, spreading out all silver in the distance. Here, too, they could take one last look at the bit of civilization represented by the fort below. Then the trail plunges into the forest, not to emerge again for eight miles, when it finally reaches the river Pigeon.

The Pigeon is a paradoxical stream. For most of its length it peacefully wanders past reedy banks over a bed of mud that on occasion is within inches of the bottom of the canoe. At such places, it is full of wildfowl, with ducks clattering up as the canoe rounds a bend, or kingfishers rocketing into its calm surface for their dinner, or a blue heron poking its long bill among the reeds. Mink and muskrat live along the banks; and beavers are there too, feasting on the succulent birches and aspens that grow along the shore. Then, suddenly, the river's mood changes: it goes berserk on rapids, or plunges abruptly over a precipice where its placid brown water turns to roaring yellow foam. Below the point where the Grand Portage trail reaches it, the river becomes completely uncontrollable, erupting in a series of wild cascades through gloomy, echoing canyons where no canoe could possibly survive. Few journals of the voyageur era mention this wild side of the river's character. Perhaps it is because this part of the river Pigeon is like a law of nature: there is no arguing with it, hence no point in discussing it. The Pigeon turns unnavigable; that is all anyone really needs to know.

Where the Grand Portage trail ends there are grass-covered mounds that mark the site of Fort Charlotte, an outpost on the river Pigeon that was the voyageurs' last contact with civilization. Here they beached their canoes when they came down from the north, turning them over against the rain. Here, on the way back north, they would reload the canoes with their cargoes of trade goods. A ton and a half to each 25-foot canoe—that was the standard load for the long journey into the wilds. And each canoe, before it was loaded, was overhauled and any damage from the previous journey carefully repaired.

Fort Charlotte today broods quietly beneath its sheltering pines and spruces, a place far off the beaten track and seemingly forgotten. But there are those who enjoy its history. On any summer weekend, a party of Canadian high-school kids from nearby Thunder Bay may erupt from the woods, having loped up the trail from Lake Superior in the manner of the voyageurs, who never walked when they could run; or a family from the States who have hiked up from Highway 61 may come trudging along and proceed to picnic there. At such times, with people poking animatedly about for relics, it is possible to imagine the fort as a going concern with its high stockade, its log buildings, the gaily painted canoes drawn up on the banks, the lithe voyageurs bending to their final tasks, arranging the 90-pound bales, shouting, cursing, singing snatches of the ballads they would later chorus as they paddled along.

A mile and a half upriver from Fort Charlotte is Partridge Falls, a sombre cascade where the river Pigeon, in one of its abrupt changes of mood, leaves its reedy banks and plunges about 50 feet into a ravine. There is a portage through the woods here, perhaps a quarter of a mile long. Alexander Henry the Younger, a North West Company partner who passed this way many times and kept a meticulous journal, mentions it as being "very slippery and muddy", which shows it has not changed much in the 170 or so years since he trudged up it. But another two and a half miles along is a place that every voyageur looked forward to with joy—*La Prairie*, or The Meadow, a wide, grassy place where the canoes could be beached for the night and a *régal* held. Here the men regaled themselves on rum or brandy to celebrate the start of the journey north. "All were merry," Henry noted of one occasion, adding that "there was plenty of elbow room for the men's antics."

From here on it was paddle and portage, paddle and portage, for two or three more days until Height of Land, between North and South Lakes, was reached. Here the upstream struggle ended for a while, for this is the Laurentian Divide, one of the great divides separating the northland's drainage basins. At Height of Land the voyageurs always held a ceremony that was their equivalent of the crossing of the Equator celebrated by salt-water sailors. New men in the brigade were sprinkled with water from a cedar branch dipped in lake water and were sworn to membership in the fraternity, which entitled them to supply drinks for all present. "At this place," noted Henry in his journal, "the men generally finish their small kegs of liquor and fight many a battle."

In a sense, Height of Land marked a jumping-off place: from now on the region through which the voyageurs moved would be subtly different. Rocky points and wooded points, islands innumerable and long vistas of blue water between rolling hills would pass before their prows. By day they might hear the screech of a bald eagle or see an osprey plunging into a lake. By night they would hear the loon's call, that marvellously evocative wilderness sound that at times seems to express unutterable loneliness and brings shivers to the spine, at other times rises to a chorus that blends and mingles the haunting notes much as the northern lights blend and mingle in a midnight sky.

Past Gunflint Lake, past Saganaga, past Basswood and Lac La Croix, the Voyageurs' Highway—as history has named their route—led to Rainy Lake and the river Rainy, and thence to the great Lake of the Woods and down the river Winnipeg to Lake Winnipeg itself. Everywhere there was the same landscape—the tall pines, the graceful spruces, the glimmering white of birches, the trembling silver of aspens. Rocks, cliffs, promontories appeared ahead and disappeared behind. The voyageurs swept down rapids where they could safely run them, and sometimes spilled where they could not. They grunted and swore over the portages. Beaches of sand and of rock received them when at last they stopped paddling at night; they slept exhausted, sprawled beneath their canoes.

From Lake Winnipeg onwards, the country into which they pushed was dark with distance, dim with the uncertainty of the unknown and unexplored. Here they encountered rivers—the Saskatchewan and the Churchill—that flowed eastwards towards Hudson Bay, across their path as they paddled northwestwards. Here, in this wilderness, the moose come down to the water unafraid, and Canada geese trace their course through the skies, their honking sound like a crying wind. The farthest point of the voyageurs' journey was Fort Chipewyan on Lake Athabasca. The north woods stretch even farther northwards, beyond Great Slave Lake to Great Bear. But this was beyond the distance that could be accomplished between spring thaw and autumn freeze in a freight canoe. In this far region it is winter more than half the year. What lies beyond is the Arctic, and that is a different story.

The voyageurs have been gone for over 100 years and their songs are heard no more among the tall, dark trees. But the woods in which they spent their lives and that they loved beyond any other place on earth —these are still wild, and so are the lakes and rivers that bore their canoes. In that rugged landscape lies the evidence of times long before the white men came, of times even before the Indians.

Fire in the Woods

When fire rages through deep woods in a storm of incandescence, its roar assaults the ear a mile away. No witness can help but respond with a sense of terror. More practically, men feel a deep responsibility to prevent the outbreak of fire and the destruction it leaves behind.

Yet in recent years many forest ecologists have come to believe that fire can contribute to the health and growth of the natural forest. The subject is a controversial one, however, and proponents admit that they need to know more about the long-term effects of fire. Opponents argue that although fire releases nutrients to the soil, a significant proportion of them is lost in runoff. Plant life may take as long as a century to recover, they say, and many forms of animal life may lose their grazing areas.

Other scientists, however, insist that the basic character of the forest is determined by fire. Certainly some trees such as the aspen, birch and jack pine, though vulnerable to the flames, survive hardily as species through periodic ordeals by fire; other species such as red pines and old white pines have evolved ways of surviving as individuals. For highly vulnerable species such as spruce and fir, healthy growth depends on the virtual absence of forest fire.

In the four north woods areas shown on the following pages—all near the Canadian border in Minnesota—fire has influenced the nature of the forest in ways that bear out the new attitude towards a force long regarded as an unmixed bane. Taken together, these areas show a progression of growth that makes clear the importance of fire.

Even a bad fire can have its beneficent side. A recent example was a serious outbreak east of the Little Indian Sioux river, shown on the opposite page and—in its aftermath —on pages 38 to 41. Driven by a relentless wind gusting up to 30 miles an hour, the Little Sioux blaze raged for three days, destroying nearly 25 square miles of woodland. The conflagration had been, in part, a crown fire—one that consumes the topmost foliage of trees. With their crowns burned off, most of these trees were doomed. Others would die because the fire had cooked their cambium, the layer of growing cells just beneath the bark. As the embers cooled, the scene seemed desolate.

But within months—and in some places after only a few weeks—fresh growth of pioneer species appeared on the site of the Little Sioux blaze.

Propelled by near-gale winds through the treetops, a crown fire consumes a century-old forest of balsam firs, white spruces and paper birches near the Little Indian Sioux river in Minnesota.

A year after the Little Sioux fire, charred trunks rise like toothpicks from the ashes. Now, however, with the destruction of the forest's

dense canopy, several hours of sunlight reach the forest floor every day, and new growth, visible beneath the dead trees, is proliferating.

A wild rose flourishes in the fire's aftermath.

Jack-pine seedlings grow next to a log.

A young ground pine—commonly found in shade—thrives on the Little Sioux blaze site.

Resurgent Growth on the Charred Floor

Within two weeks after the Little Sioux fire had been extinguished in late spring, Forest Service researchers spotted grasses, sedges and yellow bluebead lilies peeking upwards through the ashes. Around the end of June, bracken ferns and aspen sprouts began to appear, and jack-pine seedlings were germinating—in some areas at a rate of 20,000 an acre. Wild flowers and shrubs were also abundant. By the end of that summer, the entire area was covered with waist-high vegetation. much of which was young aspen sprouts that had shot up to an average height of four feet since the fire. A year after the holocaust had almost levelled the forest, the photographs on these pages were taken.

This phenomenal growth was a result of several factors. To grow, plants need nutrients like phosphorus, calcium and magnesium. Ordinarily, the bulk of these are locked up in the vegetation—either in the living plants and trees, or in the detritus decomposing on the forest floor. Fire rapidly breaks down these nutrients. Dissolved in rain water, some are lost in runoff. The rest enrich the soil, giving plants a burst of energy. In a brief period, fire can duplicate the work of years of bacterial decomposition. Simultaneously, the obliteration of the dense forest canopy by fire permits intense photosynthetic action to take place, stimulating sun-loving plants to surge from the exposed floor of the forest.

With its broad leaves opened towards the sun, a new aspen sucker stands against a stark background of fire-blackened tree trunks.

Aspens grow thickly where flames had devastated the woods 20 years before.

A Forest Blaze
Two Decades Later

In the 1990s, barring another fire, the site of the Little Sioux blaze will very probably be largely covered with jack pine and trees similar to those shown here. Photographed in Minnesota's Superior National Forest 20 years after an extensive fire, these are dense young stands of aspens and birches, both of which are particularly vulnerable to the ravages of fire. Their thin bark provides little protection during a blaze, and the trees die after their vital inner layer of cambium is subjected to the brief but intense heat of a forest fire.

But over generations of exposure to fire, both species have evolved in such a manner that they are always among the first trees to rise from the ashes. Stimulated by the warmth of the forest floor and encouraged by the new nutrients in the soil, the roots of burned aspens rapidly send out suckers, which become the stems of new trees. Similarly, new birches sprout quickly from the bases of dead parent trees.

Where they have been dominant before a fire, birches and aspens gain such a rapid head start on other trees that, 20 years or so after a blaze, they again become the dominant species, proliferating in such dense groves that sun-loving trees like red, white and jack pines have little opportunity for growth. In the shadows cast by the birches and aspens, only a few shade-tolerant species, such as spruce, fir and mountain maple, are able to flourish.

Paper birches share a woodland thicket with mountain maple shrubs resplendent in their autumn colours of orange, yellow and scarlet.

In shadow most of the day, a white-spruce sapling enjoys its brief exposure to sunlight.

A Competition Arbitrated by Fire

While species like aspen and birch have developed the capability of reproducing themselves after a fire, others have evolved means that permit them to survive a blaze. Chief among these in northern Minnesota are mature red pines and old white pines. Both have thick, insulating bark that protects their cambium from the fire's heat. Moreover, their foliage grows on top of tall trunks, remote from the tinder of the forest floor, and immune to practically anything but an intense crown fire.

Even when a stand of pines is incinerated, there is almost always a small number of survivors whose seeds, falling to a floor now burned clear of the thick litter of fallen needles that inhibits the growth of plants, can germinate to begin the building of a new pine forest.

But even when fire does not strike for years, the pine forest is not immortal. Beneath the pines' lofty, sun-shielding canopies, as shown in these pictures taken along the Gunflint Trail, such shade-tolerant species as white spruce and balsam fir find it possible to grow on the forest floor. Eventually, the pines reach old age, die and topple. Over their decomposing timbers will rise the new forest of spruces and firs—unless it is destroyed by fire before the pines die. In that case, the pines may return. Or, suited as they are to growth on blaze sites, birches and aspens may overtake the pines and become the dominant species.

Vulnerable to fire, balsams crowd fire-resistant 100-year-old white pines; without a blaze, the firs may well survive the ageing pines.

A Record of Ancient Fires

The north woods are full of sharply defined demonstrations of the pattern of fire's impact. In a grove of red pines on an island in Basswood Lake (*right*), where forest colossi 100 or 200 years old tower above the canopy, the periodic passage of flames can actually be dated. These great trees bear the scars of past fires; by boring sections through the scars and then counting the growth rings around them, scientists can produce a calendar on which the dates of ancient fires can be exactly calculated.

In other places where fire has recently passed, a brilliant swatch of reddish-purple fireweed frequently blooms, prospering in the soil of wood ash. Older blaze sites will be dotted with the light green of birches and aspens or the grey green of jack pines, and those older still with the deeper hues of red or white pines. Areas unmarked by fire for many decades will be revealed on the terrain by the dark, coniferous growth of spruces and firs, which become dominant only when there are long periods between blazes.

Increasingly aware through such observations of fire's crucial role in nature, ecologists are re-evaluating the fire-prevention programmes in the north woods and other wilderness areas. Although fire can have a devastating effect in the far north, it is controlled blazes, some suggest, that might help the preservation of the rich forest along the southern limits of the north woods.

Fire scars almost 100 years old mar 200-year-old red pines. At far left is a relatively young, unmarked offspring of one of the hardy giants.

2/ The Formation of a Landscape

*. . . this anomalous land, this sprawling waste of timber
and rock and water . . . this empty tract of primordial silences
and winds and erosions and shifting colours.*

HUGH MacLENNAN *BAROMETER RISING*

The wind is cold. The countless pools in the potholed rocks shine dimly. Herring gulls, pintail ducks and Canada geese fill the air with mournful cries. I am 800 miles northwest of Grand Portage, not far from where the boreal forest dwindles out in wind-battered fingers of black spruce and tamarack, near the place where the broad and powerful river Churchill empties into Hudson Bay. On cloudy days from this point the sea is like iron beneath an iron sky. This is the southern edge of the Arctic tundra, a stark, bleak land where winter rules pitilessly for more than half of the year.

Here, where the great, shadowy forest reaches its northern limits, I sit on an outcrop of rock on an autumn day and brood on the history of this ancient land. How different it is here from the sparkling lake country of northern Minnesota and the Quetico-Superior region! That is a land that lives vivaciously in the present, gay and beautiful, alive with the song of the white-throated sparrow, the wild cry of the loon, the peaceful labour of the beaver; a land in whose limpid river waters one can see the dark shadow of the northern pike, the swift rush of the walleye, the darting of trout over sun-dappled rocks on the bottom. Here on Hudson Bay, everything is instead evocative of the past; the very crying of the birds overhead seems an echo from a time long ago that no man ever saw. This is a place where geologic time is a reality, where 10,000 years are but a breath in the earth's slow pulsation, where the long history of this lonely land can be seen, felt and understood.

Hudson Bay, on whose shore I sit, is the remnant of the last of the great inland seas that successively inundated the north woods. The seas that preceded it disappeared hundreds of millions of years ago. The worn ledge that holds me is composed of the compacted remains of myriads of aquatic organisms that built up layers of limestone in those ancient seas. Through countless seasons waves pounded my ledge; rain lashed it; snow and ice covered it; Arctic temperatures cracked and split it; summer sun beat down on it; and now here it is, a listening post on a tumultuous past.

But my ledge is not really very old, perhaps only 425 million years or so. Within a day's hike from here I can find granitic outcroppings of far more ancient stuff—some of the oldest rock in North America, formed 1,700 million years ago, when life was still in a very primitive stage. And even this is not the oldest rock to be found in the north woods. Far to the south of Hudson Bay, on Burntside Lake near Ely, Minnesota, there is a point of land composed of rock that is more than 2,500 million years old—greenstone, it is called, and appropriately so. It is dark green in colour, and compact and solid as only a permanent buttress of the earth can be. It was originally formed of lava spewed forth from great fissures and fractures in the earth beneath the inland seas. Greenstone is found in many areas of the north woods—one two-mile-wide band of it in northern Minnesota stretches from Tower through Ely to Moose Lake, a distance of 40 miles. In places, this greenstone is 20,000 feet thick.

In close proximity to the Ely greenstone lie deposits of the rich iron ore of the Mesabi and Vermilion Ranges that brought untold wealth to those who discovered it in the last century and gave rise to such towns as Ely and Tower and Soudan and Virginia. Near the river Pigeon these deposits are so concentrated that they brought confusion to the compasses of early explorers and voyageurs, and still confuse the canoeist today; Magnetic Lake is named for this phenomenon. The name of Gunflint Lake in the same region bespeaks a different geologic inheritance. Flint, a sedimentary mineral that is yet another leftover from the inland seas, occurs here in such abundance that both Indians and white men named the lake to fix the spot where they could find the spark-producing stone that could be flaked into sharp tools.

All of these different types of rocks, and the myriad minerals of which they are composed, share a common heritage. All of them are part of the Canadian Shield, an ancient geologic formation that, in one area, has rock 3,800 million years old—only 700 million years or so after the earth itself came into being. Composed of the eroded roots of some of the earliest mountain chains that reared themselves above the earth's primal crust, the Shield reaches in a vast ellipse across the upper tier of the continent from the Atlantic to the Arctic Sea in the northwest, underlying 1,864,000 square miles of Canada and the Lake Superior and Adirondack regions of the United States. The Shield is thus the very lap of the earth to much of the north woods, and for the camper it offers particular advantages: wherever it crops·out, excellent campsites are to be found, properly elevated for good drainage, often with fine ledges of the granitic rock of which the Shield is primarily composed. On them, one can draw up a canoe, build a fire and sit comfortably before a tent pitched on level ground.

Only about one-tenth of the ancient rock of the Shield is exposed, but the Shield is very close indeed when one builds a campsite in the fragrant shade of spruce and pine and balsam. The soil of the north woods, the earth that nurtures all of its plants and trees, is seldom more than 10 inches deep; just below lies the Shield itself. That is a very thin covering for a place where trees grow 100 feet or more tall, and the effect of it can be seen on any tree, great or small, that has been toppled by a storm. No thick taproots probe deep into the earth and help to anchor the giant above; instead there is a tightly woven mat of roots and rootlets extending in all directions from the tree trunk. On ledges where the soil is especially thin, some of the rootlets find their way into cracks and fissures of the bedrock; often, as the tree falls, it pulls chunks of crumbling rock up with it. In such places the mat of the root system, peeling from the rock below, may lay bare a large area that has never reflected the sun. Once, on the river Granite north of Gunflint Lake, I slept in the shelter of a root mat: the rock beneath my sleeping bag was almost a pristine white, so cleanly had the earth been peeled back when the tree fell. I slept that night with my face turned upwards towards the clear, bright stars, and it was as though I were a part of the earth, and had grown up here with it, a living limb of that ancient rock beneath me that now, once more, lay open to the world.

But man is a latecomer to the north woods. The earliest time at which he might have inhabited them is thought to have been some 14,000 years ago; more likely, the first man wandered in around 8,000 years ago. Whenever he did come, he remained a part of the forest ecology for thousands of years, living in harmony with it until the first white men arrived. In the main, the north woods Indians did not progress

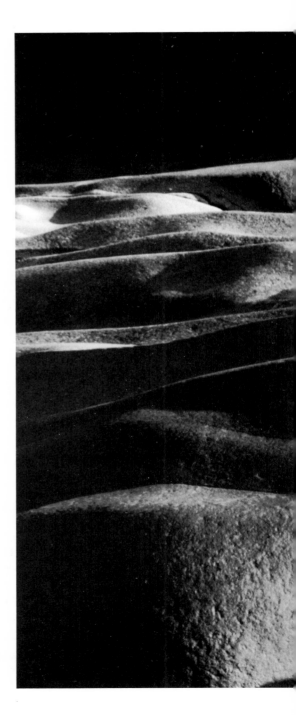

The contours of a limestone ledge on Hudson Bay's western shore reflect millennia of polishing and erosion by glaciers, sea and rain.

beyond the Stone and Copper Age until they were seduced by the wares brought from Europe by fur traders—and until they were corrupted by the white man's firewater, which undermined the Indian's mind and body, and his pride.

The north woods could not be inhabited at all, however, before the glaciers began to recede from the land 15,000 years ago. And it was the glaciers that made the north woods what they are today. These great ice sheets formed during the Pleistocene Epoch, which began perhaps two million years ago. The Canadian Shield was relatively stable by that time: its period of mountain building had long since ceased, and the inland seas had disappeared. The continent's outlines were generally similar to those of the present day, but the surface was in many respects very different. Most of the familiar geographical features, such as lakes and rivers, either did not exist at all or appeared in different forms. There were, for example, no Great Lakes to the southeast of the north woods; where these are now there were five great river systems. There were very few lakes in Minnesota and Canada, where they are found in such numbers today. Instead, there was a thick covering of forest, interrupted only by patches of bogs and grassy meadows.

This landscape was to be greatly altered by the onslaught of the Ice Age. For millions of years before then, the world had been growing colder. The temperature dropped only a few degrees in all, but in northern Canada that was enough to make the winters longer and more severe. Snow fell in masses over increasingly protracted periods of time; at last it fell nearly all year round, more snow than could possibly evaporate or melt and flow off in the increasingly short weeks of summer. And as it fell, it built up in the Canadian northland, layer by layer.

As time went by, the snow line advanced southwards into the temperate zone. But far more ominous was the fact that the snow gradually turned to ice. As the snowfalls piled up, one on top of the other like the sediments in ancient seas, they pressed down and compacted the bottom layers—metamorphosing them, to use the geologists' term. When the snow was thousands of feet deep, the weight of it was enormous. The bottom layers finally were transposed into a blue-white ice that was, in effect, a rock with a melting temperature of 32° F. And then the great ice sheets started to move, adding to their own mass the accumulation of rock and gravel that they picked up and carried with them.

The movement of ice is a force difficult for the mind to comprehend. It is slow—advancing from an inch to 10 feet a day in most cases—but its power is inexorable, relentless and absolutely irresistible. Only two things in the world can stop it: warm weather or the ocean water off a continent's shores, where the ice perforce breaks off and sails away in the form of icebergs. Everything else succumbs; hills, valleys, lakes, soil cover, gravel, rocks, forest are all altered by the pressure and movement of thousands of square miles of ice thousands of feet deep.

The basic force that drives an ice sheet is gravity. As the snow falls year after year it accumulates more deeply in some places than in others. It also continuously turns to ice and ultimately, under the steady pull of gravity, the bulging edges begin to move outwards in all directions. Ice moves when it reaches a depth of more than 300 feet, and because of its great weight—about a third as much as rock—it bends the earth beneath it as it goes. In this fashion Hudson Bay was formed during the Pleistocene Epoch by the great Laurentian ice sheet that covered all of northern Canada and ultimately advanced deep into the northern lands of the United States. Thus the ice shapes the earth not only by scraping, gouging and pushing material before it as it moves along, but by actually depressing the surface of the earth as well: its action might be described as that of a combination bulldozer, road scraper and steamroller, all in one unimaginably massive machine.

The glaciers of the Pleistocene Epoch—there were four major periods of glaciation, each lasting 100,000 years or so—scraped Canada almost bare. Forest, soil and rock debris were bulldozed away. The finer materials were picked up by the wind and deposited for the most part in what is today the American Middle West, where they formed the fertile fields of its farm states, extending as far south as Louisiana.

The marks left by a glacier's passing are everywhere to be found in the north woods today. Some of the evidence is small enough to be readily seen and understood. The river Granite, for example, has numerous islands and ledges that clearly show the planing and plucking action of the glaciers that passed this way: where the ice rode up on a rock ledge the surface is polished smooth, while at the other end, where the glacier froze to the ledge before moving onwards, the rock is broken and split and in its steep, clifflike faces gives evidence of how the ice tore off great chunks of it and carried them along. Much of the tumbled landscape of the river Granite area is due to glacial action. Everywhere can be seen debris deposited by the glaciers, from small pebbles to large, rounded boulders.

In some parts of the north woods, rock ledges show deep parallel groovings, like the claw marks of some ancient and gigantic bear. This

Pre-cambrian lava, spewed from the earth a thousand million years ago, formed this sheer cliff at Palisade Head, Lake Superior.

is so, for example, on the dark greenstone point at Burntside Lake. The grooves were made by the scraping action of the rock-bearing glacier that moved across the greenstone ledge perhaps 15,000 years ago. And higher up on this same point—as on countless others throughout the north woods—are boulders called "erratics", which were left when the glacier melted and retreated northwards. Some of these erratics are as large as houses and can be traced to their point of origin, which may be several hundred miles to the north.

These are traces that can be seen by the canoe camper today as he pitches his tent by some smooth ledge. But the full impact of what the ice age did to the north woods region can be best understood when one views the area from an aeroplane, or looks at a map that shows the thousands of lakes and rivers splashed across the land. For all of these glittering waters are the work of the glaciers. The channels of the rivers were gouged or hollowed out by the ice as it crept ponderously across the land. Some lake beds—kettle holes, these depressions are called —were created when enormous blocks of ice broke off from the main body of the glacier and were left stranded amid or beneath quantities of material also left behind when the glacier retreated northwards; when the ice melted, bodies of water were held trapped within the debris. Other lakes were formed when debris left by the glaciers dammed up a valley or depression, leaving, for the time being at least, no outlet for the melting water when the glaciers retreated.

As the ice receded, a fantastic landscape slowly emerged. Bare of soil and plant cover, part of the bedrock of the Canadian Shield of the north woods country reappeared, gleaming dully in the wan sunlight of the Pleistocene spring. Over thousands of square miles this barren landscape was dotted with clear lakes of the melted glacial water. No plants or organisms of any kind obscured these cold, crystal waters, for nothing had grown here for thousands of years. The lake bottoms glistened with granite pebbles and white quartz sand, as pure as the water that covered it. Immense boulders lay scattered about as though thrown in fretful impatience by a giant child. Only the water moved, and it moved everywhere, making outlets for the lakes and channels for the rivers, curling through valleys, brawling down rapids.

Much of what is today northern Minnesota, eastern North Dakota, western Ontario, southern and central Manitoba and east-central Saskatchewan lay beneath an enormous lake of meltwater that, sometimes expanding and sometimes contracting, spread at its greatest extent over

A prototypal north country panorama—dense woods of conifers interspersed with lake waters—unfolds in this view of Superior National

Forest. Such lake formations resulted when meltwater filled hollows dug by glaciers, or when drainage backed up behind their debris.

an area 700 miles long and 250 miles wide. Here the enormous weight of the icecap had depressed the earth's crust, leaving an immense watery basin. This lake, which geologists named Lake Agassiz in honour of Louis Agassiz, the 19th Century Swiss-American naturalist who first postulated the ice age, drained off slowly as the earth lifted again. What is left of this lake basin is now Lake Winnipeg and the lakes west of Quetico Provincial Park in Ontario.

Reminders of long-gone landscapes are all around me as I sit on my ledge of ancient limestone on the western shore of Hudson Bay. The cold wind blows down from the ice sheets of the Arctic as it did almost a million years ago. There are no trees; the forest has not returned here This is a primeval world; if I did not know that I was looking out at the grey expanse of Hudson Bay, I might well imagine that before me lay the waters of Lake Agassiz.

I am, in fact, in the middle of a perfect model of what the glaciers left behind—and also of what followed after their departure. The very rock on which I sit was shaped and polished by the glaciers. The ice scratched the long, parallel grooves in it. Turbulent water scoured its potholes; in them, in turn, are particles of sand and rock left by the glaciers. On such a barren landscape the Pleistocene sun shone 10,000 years ago when the last glaciers left the north woods. What a sight that must have been! Hundreds of square miles of scraped and scoured rock, much of it covered by glacial debris, stretching farther than the eye could see—a reborn world. And here before me, on the shore of the great cold bay, lay its duplicate.

To the south of Hudson Bay, life returned to this reborn world with the spores of lichens floating through the air, borne by the ceaseless wind. Where the spores landed on the sun-warmed rocks they found minuscule footholds and lichens began to grow. Red, rust-brown, grey, dark green, flaming orange, burning yellow, they brought colour, and life, back to the dead land.

Lichens are marvellous plants. They look like splashes of paint on the rocks, clinging as though they had dried there. But they are strong, unbelievably strong, and hardy. A combination of two primitive plants, fungi and algae, they were indispensable for the re-creation of these glaciated regions, for they can grow where nothing has grown for millennia, and they contribute to the production of the substance that advanced and complex plants need to grow on: humus, the decomposed residue of plant tissue, the life stuff of soil. The fungi and algae

Red sphagnum moss and green feather moss grow on top of the bare granite of the Canadian Shield near Lake Superior.

of lichen live symbiotically, each to the benefit of the other. The fungi draw some minute sustenance from the rocks and provide moisture to the algae, while the algae manufacture sugars—upon which the fungi feed—from the energy of the sun. And as the lichens spread, they help to break the weathering rock down into finer particles that seep into cracks and fissures and eventually play host to other plants.

Some of the weathered particles also fall into the pools of water in the rocks, adding to the material at the bottom. Here, in time, water plants take hold. Meanwhile, on the rocks the moss grows, adding its own remains to the slow accumulation of humus until grasses can germinate; then come plants like the fireweed, and finally the tiny beginnings of a tree.

Gradually, after the glaciers were gone, the soil accumulated on top of the rocks of the north woods. More mosses grew and then seeds drifted in, carried by birds or by the wind. The grasses came, and the herbs and shrubs, and the familiar birches, willows and aspens. Berry bushes arrived and prospered in a profusion that beckoned to animal life. Then came the lowly, hardy jack pines, the black spruces and the white, and finally, in the southern reaches of the woods, the towering white and red pines that would eventually dominate the forest until the axes of the white man felled them in their prime.

And gradually, too, there came the animals, migrating northwards as the plant cover grew and proffered the foods they needed. They were a different lot from the beasts that had been there before the ice came. They were also different from the animals of the ice age itself, like the mastodon and mammoth; most of these had almost gone, and many of their carcasses were entombed in ice or frozen swampland. Gone, too, were the camel and the tapir and other ungulates, and the great, sabre-toothed cats that had preyed upon them. Some of these animals had travelled southwards ahead of the ice and eventually reached the southern continent, where some of their descendants survive. But the beaver appeared in the northland, and the white-tailed deer, to feed on the tender shoots of the young deciduous trees; and the moose came to feed on the water lilies and other aquatic plants of the lakes; and the wolf came to prey on the moose and the deer, and in time there came the wolverine, and the mountain lion and the black bear. And so in time the north woods became populated with the animals that are there today.

The environment of the north woods—the forests, the lakes, the bogs —is very new in geologic terms, despite the great age of the rocks on which it is based. The 10 inches of soil that today cover the bedrock took 10 millennia to accumulate; as geologic time is counted, this is brief, a proof of how quickly nature can recover after a disaster.

And yet this land, like all lands, carries within itself the seeds of its own destruction. The disappearance of the north woods lakes, for example, is as inevitable as the seasonal ebb and flow of the water in their basins and in the streams that feed them. If they are placid lakes with little current, they gradually fill up with sediment; plants take over, moving outwards from the shore. Eventually the lake becomes a bog, and the bog in time fills up with soil and the forest takes it over. There are innumerable places in the north woods where one can see every stage in this process—from a bog in the making to a bog taken over by trees.

If the lake has a current, the water at the outflow will gradually erode the threshold, deepening it until at last the whole lake will drain out, leaving behind a river. If the climate turns dry, the lake will evaporate faster than it can be refilled. Born of geological accidents, lakes may die from them too: an earthquake, near by or distant, may change the drainage pattern of an area so that the lake will lose the sources of its replenishment.

Such a process, of course, may take thousands or even hundreds of thousands of years. Or it may take fewer. The floor beneath Hudson Bay, originally depressed by the glaciers, is gradually uplifting now that the enormous burden of ice has been removed. The shoreline is reaching into the water at the rate of two feet a century, and geologists calculate that within 40,000 years the entire 478,000 square miles of the bay—an area in which Texas and a few other good-sized states could be comfortably accommodated—will be reduced to a tiny inlet. In time, the forest will encroach upon parts of the former sea bed. But by then there may be still another ice age to bury the land, the lakes, the woods and the works of man and start the cycle anew. Thus the north woods, in all of their various aspects, are an affirmation of life—for through the long ages of their geologic history they have died many times, but have always come back again.

3/ The Voyageurs—a Legend

*Paddling and portaging their way westward . . . where
none but the hardiest could survive, the
highhearted voyageurs . . . opened Canada's rich hinterland.*

HUGH MACLENNAN/ *BY CANOE TO EMPIRE*

In the history of the north woods there are two undisputed heroes: the
legendary logger Paul Bunyan and the French-Canadian voyageur. Their
likenesses greet visitors in many roadside places: Bunyan, shown 10 or
15 feet tall, straddling a huge pine log on top of some filling station or
motel, arms akimbo in his checked mackinaw, face split in a gap-toothed
grin; the voyageur, small, stocky, hunched under a backbreaking load as
he is pictured trotting down some portage trail or paddling along some
wilderness waterway, his mouth open in full-throated song. They are the
very incarnations of the woods, these two, yet they stand for entirely
different things.

Bunyan's legacy is a wilderness that is drastically changed from the
one he knew. The lumberman's axe, which his storied army of loggers
wielded with such efficiency, rang through the Minnesota woods from
the river Pigeon to Rainy Lake, and from there on into Canada; and
where Paul's giant foot trod, there the land was devastated. Large-scale
logging began around 1870 and continued unchecked for about 50 years,
until it tapered off for lack of prized red and white pine as well as by reason of a belatedly awakened public conscience. John Szarkowski, in
his book *The Face of Minnesota*, sums up what Bunyan symbolized:

"In the mid-nineteenth century Minnesota contained thirty million
acres of virgin timber. The cutters began slowly; four thousand were in
the woods in 1870, forty thousand in 1900. The peak year was 1905:

nearly two thousand *million* feet were cut, 98 per cent of it white pine. Ten years later the yield was half as big; twenty years later, a fifth. Then the forests were gone. Remaining were the tales of Paul Bunyan, who levelled a section of pine when he sneezed."

The legacy of the voyageurs is quite different from that of the loggers. The voyageurs were content to leave the woods as they found them: dark, austere, abounding in mystery. Despite the hardships they endured, this was an environment they loved. Their attitude showed in their relations with the Indians, with whom they generally lived in friendship. "They accepted the Indian at his own evaluation, which was not low," writes the historian Grace Lee Nute, "whereas the American frontiersman could scarcely find words for his contempt of what he considered a thieving, shiftless, dirty race." Many of the voyageurs intermarried with the Indians and raised families of half-breed children that formed the backbone of the early north woods settlements.

The voyageurs were a class of men as distinct in their time as loggers were in theirs. They have sometimes been confused with those other romantic figures of the north woods, the *coureurs de bois*, or woods runners; but these were freelance trappers and traders who worked their traps alone and traded in furs without a government licence. The voyageurs were *engagés*, hired canoemen who signed on for a one- to three-year tour of duty, after which, more likely than not, they would sign right up for another. They were paddlers, not traders; they had no interest in the fur trade nor any ambitions to be rich or successful in anything but meeting the endless challenge of the wilderness. They were as tough as nails, they gloried in risking their lives in rapids, and they had their own peculiar pride in excelling at a way of life that strikes us today as not much different from that of a Roman galley slave. Grace Lee Nute quotes one voyageur:

"For 24 [years] I was a light canoe-man. No portage was too long for me. I could carry, paddle, walk and sing with any man I ever saw. When others stopped to carry at a bad step I pushed on—over rapids, over cascades, over chutes; all were the same to me. . . . Were I young again, I should glory in commencing the same career. There is no life so happy as a voyageur's life, none so independent; no place where a man enjoys so much variety and freedom as in the Indian country. *Huzza! Huzza! pour le pays sauvage!*" And this from a patriarch who still, in his seventies, longed to paddle.

The life of which this old man spoke so fondly was almost inconceivably rugged. Travelling in birch-bark canoes that had to be handled as gently as eggs, squatting or kneeling among the bales of freight, the voyageurs paddled for 15 to 18 hours every day, stopping only for five minutes or so at the end of every hour to have a quick puff at their pipes. They usually ate but two meals—breakfast, after three or four hours of pre-dawn paddling on an empty stomach, and supper, often as late as 10 o'clock at night, consumed by the light of a campfire. The voyageurs had scant protection against the swarms of black flies and mosquitoes that tormented them day and night, nor were they shielded against the weather. They paddled in pouring rain, high wind, burning sun; only snow and ice could limit their exertions.

But the most trying of all the hardships the voyageur endured were the portages, the overland trails they had to traverse between navigable stretches of water. The ordeal began with the unpacking of the canoes. Because of their fragile birch-bark skins these could not be dragged up on the bank for unloading, so the men had to leap out into water that was often waist deep and carry the bales of cargo ashore. They would then sling the bales on to their backs and begin the arduous journey overland. And arduous is the word for it: each voyageur was expected, as a matter of routine, to carry at least two of the standard 90-pound bales on each portage trip, and often he carried three. Daily the men ran the risk of hernia from their burdens; more than a few of them died of this injury on the trail.

To help in carrying their loads, the voyageurs used a tumpline, a device adopted from the Indians. This was a broad leather strap, about three inches wide, that passed around the forehead and over both shoulders—bringing the powerful muscles of the neck into play—and down the back. The bottom, or anchoring bale, would be tied with smaller straps attached to the tumpline. Slung into the tumpline on top of this bale, along the carrier's spine, would be placed as many more bales as he could take—perhaps two more, for a total of 270 pounds. Stooped under this towering mass, the voyageur was always, it seemed, on the verge of pitching over forwards. Nevertheless, he would trot rather than walk, and at a phenomenal pace. One passenger on a canoe journey, a missionary on his way to an outpost in the woods, described how he had tried to keep up with the crew on a portage. "I ran faster than I chose," he recalled. When a voyageur reached the end of the portage, he would set down his load and immediately trot back to the start of the trail for another. If the portage was more than half a mile long the cargo would be moved along it in stages.

A late-19th Century voyageur, in working garb typical of the period, was sketched for the magazine Harper's Weekly by the American artist Frederic Remington on a north woods trek.

Meanwhile, the canoe also had to be carried over the trail. The Montreal canoe, used between Montreal and Grand Portage, weighed 600 pounds; the North canoe, used between Grand Portage and the north, weighed 300 pounds—in either case a formidable proposition. Aside from its weight, the canoe was clumsy to carry, yet required the most delicate handling. The bowsman and the steersman of the North canoe took charge of this task, carrying the craft upright. In the case of the Montreal canoe, it was borne bottom up by four men, their heads inside it, trying at the same time to see where they were going. Not long ago, portaging along the river Pigeon, a friend and I experienced firsthand the problems of carrying a canoe through thick woods. We had come ashore at a place where a well-marked trail appeared to lead inland from the muddy banks of the Pigeon. But we sank ankle-deep into mud at every step and within a few yards we found ourselves in a trackless tangle of fallen trees and willow and birch shrubs. While I scouted ahead to find the direction of the trail, my friend, carrying our aluminium canoe on his shoulders as if he were some giant silver turtle, stumbled along behind, unable to see anything except the ground immediately before his feet. As a result, he progressed in a series of loud bonging noises that rang through the woods as our canoe rebounded from tree after tree. It was a noise fit to wake the dead, though such was not our intention. A birch-bark canoe would have been smashed to ribbons; our craft, made of metal, survived. Later we decided that we had been misled by a beaver trail; the portage we were looking for lay on the other side of the river.

The voyageurs, of course, often had to scout and hack a trail out of the wilderness by themselves, and even on known trails the perils were numerous. Some portages were fairly easy, leading over level or gently rising ground. But other portages might lead through bogs or seemingly bottomless mud or deep sand that tugged at the feet with every step. Always there were rocks and roots on which one might stumble and perhaps fall with an ankle-twisting wrench. Some trails led over cliffs, where the only foothold was a series of steplike ledges. In all, along the 3,000-mile route of the fur trade from Montreal to Fort Chipewyan on Lake Athabasca, there were 120 portages to be negotiated, and every one of them required a sharp eye and a sure step.

The most notorious was the 12-mile-long Methye Portage, in what is now the Canadian province of Saskatchewan, between Methye Lake and the river Clearwater, not far from the voyageurs' northern terminus at Lake Athabasca. Peter Pond, a Yankee fur trader whose nasal

Connecticut twang still echoes through his phonetically written journals, was the first white man to discover this portage, and many were the voyageurs who wished he never had.

Most of the portage is innocent enough. Its first eight miles—still well marked today—lead in a fairly direct line across a comfortably smooth, sandy ridge, sparsely wooded and with no sharp elevations to surmount. Then the portage is interrupted by a small, sparkling gem of a lake—Rendezvous Lake, only a mile long. Here the voyageurs had to reload again, paddle across and unload for the second stage of the portage. Even so, Rendezvous Lake provided a breather; white sandy beaches border it and make excellent camping grounds. The second stage of the Methye Portage, however, offered the voyageurs no comfort. It is deceptively easy at first, climbing gently through rolling hills towards the river Clearwater, four miles away. But then, like a cornered beast, it suddenly turns vicious. Near its end, among hogbacked ridges and steep eroded gullies, the trail seems almost to disappear: it takes a precipitous 700-foot drop down a cliff.

From the top of the cliff the eye can see 30 or 40 miles down the narrow valley of the river Clearwater. The view is a memorable one. The great Alexander Mackenzie, the fur trader and explorer who was the first to complete an overland journey across the entire northern continent, reported that the cliff commanded "a most extensive, romantic, and ravishing prospect". But among the voyageurs, there were few who really appreciated it; their Herculean task was to get canoe and cargo down this cliff. Sledges were devised to cradle the canoes so they could be let down the precipice without damage. The cargo was let down on ropes, or slid along with the voyageurs as they scrambled down. Staggering as the job was, its difficulties were infinitely compounded on the voyageurs' journey southwards from Athabasca to Grand Portage, when everything had to be hauled up the cliff.

Understandably, the voyageurs preferred to avoid portaging wherever possible, and in order to do so they often risked a more deadly wilderness peril—running rapids. The gamble was a tempting one. Successfully pitting a canoe against even a brief stretch of wild water could save hours of sweat involved in a transit overland; besides, it held a certain zest that was wholly absent from the drudgery of portaging. There were some rapids that headquarters in Montreal flatly forbade the voyageurs to attempt, for the men in the home office included former *bourgeois*, traders who had accompanied the canoe brigades and who well knew the dangers that rushing waters posed for human life—and for precious cargo. But the voyageurs often failed to heed these instructions. They took the risk and the consequences, shouting happily if they completed the run, burying their dead sombrely if they failed. Each grave-site was marked with a cross for the man lost, and there are riverbanks in the north woods where, during the fur trade era, as many as 30 crosses stood clustered near the fast water.

If at all possible, the rapids were shot with every man and all the cargo intact in the canoe—the most timesaving though also the most dangerous method. Every man's life depended on the close and un-failing co-ordination of the bowsman and the steersman, and on their skill at skimming along between the eddies near the shore and the tur-bulent waves at the centre of the rapids. Sometimes the *milieux*, or mid-dle men, paddled too, for it was imperative to keep the canoe on course.

The task was considerably more complicated in the case of upstream rapids. To negotiate them, several methods could be tried. One was to "track" the cargo-laden canoe along the rapids. All of the men, except the steersman, would scramble to shore and tow the canoe along by means of a long line to which they harnessed themselves like canal hors-es; where the shore was difficult to walk along they had to wade in the icy water, struggling to keep their footing among the slippery rocks and rounded stones of the river bottom. Another method, employed where the stream was fairly shallow, was poling; the voyageurs stood in the canoe and pushed it with 8- or 10-foot poles. In particularly rough spots, the men might unload half the cargo on the riverbank; the half-empty canoe would then be paddled or pulled up the rapids, unloaded at the top, then guided down through the fast water to be loaded with the rest of the cargo and moved up again.

Sometimes in shooting rapids the canoemen escaped death against all odds. Alexander Mackenzie gave an account of one such incident that befell him and his crew of voyageurs. They had encountered a fear-some stretch of water that forced them to hack a portage trail out of the woods to circumvent it. This done, they embarked but found them-selves almost immediately facing another bad rapid. In order to lighten the canoe Mackenzie got out, but his men persuaded him to get back in. Within minutes, however, they were in deep trouble.

"We had proceeded but a very short way," Mackenzie's diary re-counts, "when the canoe struck, and notwithstanding all our exertions, the violence of the current was so great as to drive her sideways down the river." Mackenzie and the entire crew leaped into the water and at-

Pictographs painted by early north woods Indians, on a cliff face at Hegman Lake, Minnesota, include a godlike figure and forest animals. The artists used the earth's own pigments to adorn the sheer granite walls.

tempted to halt the canoe's downstream rush, but they could not keep their footing and clambered back in again. Meanwhile the stern had been shattered against a rock, and seconds later the bow met the same fate when it was driven into the rocks of the opposite shore. The bowsman grabbed at a tree to try halting the canoe; the tree bent almost in two and before he could loose his grip, he was catapulted in a great arc from the canoe across the foaming water to shore.

While the rest of the crew sat paralyzed and helpless, the canoe careened down the river, with sharp rocks ripping several huge holes in its bottom. Finally, when the gunwales were awash, the men went over the side again and managed to kick their way to an eddy where at last the downstream rush was halted. Here they were rejoined by the bowsman, who had made his way down through the woods. Surprisingly, the men were able to repair the canoe, but some days later, after several further spills, they had to abandon it and build another, which they did on the spot—in four days.

With very rare exceptions, the voyageurs were all small men; there was no room in a freight canoe for six-footers. Their faces were typically French: swarthy, thin, often deeply furrowed, quick to reflect emotion. Many of them also bore the stamp of rugged experience. A contemporary description of one crew tells of a man whose face "seemed to have been squeezed in a vice, or to have passed through a flattening machine; it was like a cheese-cutter—all edge". Another man had had one nostril bitten off in a fight: "He had the extraordinary faculty of untying the strings of his face, as it were, at pleasure, when his features fell into . . . a crazed chaos almost frightful." A third man had been slapped by a grizzly bear—"his features wrenched to the right".

The working dress of the voyageurs was highly distinctive yet utilitarian. They wore deerskin moccasins and deerskin leggings that reached to just above the knees and were held up by thongs attached to a breechcloth. The thighs and upper torso were left bare, although a short shirt of wool or deerskin was sometimes worn to fend off flies and mosquitoes. For special occasions, this basic uniform was embellished by such items as a red woollen cap with a tassel hanging down over one ear, a blue hooded jacket and a gaily coloured sash from which hung the voyageur's short clay pipe and his tobacco pouch. Often, too, he sported a bright scarf that, tied loosely around the neck, also afforded at least the pretence of protection against stinging insects. Always before arriving at his destination, the voyageur would fancy

himself up with a few brightly painted or dyed feathers stuck into his cap—for the ending of a journey was reason to rejoice, a moment of triumph after long weeks of travail.

But en route there was little time or cause to celebrate. The voyageurs' working day began well before dawn, usually around three in the morning. "Lève, lève, lève!" would come the shout—"get up, get up, get up!" Groaning and cursing, the men would stumble about in the darkness until they had loaded and launched the canoes. Then they would set off, without so much as a morsel of food, and paddle for about three hours until daylight came and a stopping place was reached. The canoes were moored offshore by laying long poles across the gunwales with one end on land, and the voyageurs would fall to their breakfast, prepared the night before by the cook of the canoe brigade.

The voyageurs' menu was short on variety but long on quantity and nourishment. For the men who travelled the Montreal-Grand Portage route, the basic dish was a mushy soup composed chiefly of dried peas or corn, boiled up in a big iron cauldron with water from a stream or lake until the mixture was thick enough for a spoon to stand upright in it; and since these men were the so-called pork eaters, the soup might be flavoured with a little salt pork. For the winterers—the men of the north—the main food was the Indians' staple, pemmican, a mixture of dried buffalo or moose meat and berries, pounded fine; sometimes the pemmican was cooked in a soup of water and flour, a concoction called rubbaboo. And if the voyageurs caught any fish or chanced to shoot some game in their brief periods of respite from the paddle, these too would be joyfully added to the pot. Occasionally there would be a disappointment in this regard. One journal records that on a summer day in 1775, on the river Pinawa above Lake Winnipeg, "The mosquitoes were here in such clouds as to prevent us from taking aim at the ducks, of which we might else have shot many."

Sometimes the voyageurs' diet was augmented by the unleavened bread the French still call *galette*. In its simplest form, this bread was made by pouring a little water into a sack of flour; this was then kneaded until it formed a dough. If birds' eggs were available, they were poured in too. The dough was finally shaped into small, flat cakes that were baked in front of the campfire, or fried in a pan with grease. Campers today eat much the same sort of thing when they whip up a mess of bannock, the bread that is standard fare all over the north woods.

Whatever the voyageurs ate they ate with gusto, and in the most primitive manner imaginable. While some had dishes or cups, those who did not poured their ration of soup into their caps or kerchiefs, or into a shallow depression in a rock—in which case they would go down on their knees and lap up the food, dog fashion.

Once breakfast had been eaten, the men climbed back into their canoes and the heaviest work of the day began. Hour after hour they bent to their paddles, stopping only for the mandatory brief pause for a smoke, with no time out for a midday meal. On and on they drove, far into the evening. Thomas McKenney, an American who spent some years on the fur trade routes before he became an official of the United States Bureau of Indian Affairs, wrote of one voyage in 1826. At 7 o'clock one night, he asked his men if it were not time for the evening meal. "They answered they were fresh yet," he writes. "They had been almost constantly paddling since three o'clock this morning . . . 57,600 strokes of the paddle, and 'fresh yet!' No human beings, except the Canadian French, could stand this." When McKenney's men at last laid down their paddles, it was half past nine and they had travelled, in the course of this one day, 79 miles.

The evening meal for the voyageurs was soup again—but not until the canoes had been unloaded and laid on their sides on the beach so that they could be inspected for leaks or weak spots. Each canoe carried a repair kit consisting of a ball of pine pitch, a roll of *wattape*—the tough, stringy rootlets of the spruce tree—and a sizable roll of birch bark, as well as some cedar planking in case the frame was broken. If a leak was found, it was repaired on the spot: pitch would be melted at the campfire, birch bark cut to cover the damaged spot; then the bark would be sewed on with *wattape* and the joint covered thickly with pitch. The men were experts at this work, which they had learned from the Indians; they repaired the canoes with a skill and patience born of the knowledge that their very lives depended on the care they used.

At night the men slept like the dead. Curled up under their canoes, they had no mattresses to ease the hardness of a rocky floor, and they usually had only one thin blanket each. Nonetheless, they slept so deeply that only a major calamity could have awakened them—all, that is, save the cook, who had to get up periodically to stir the soup he was preparing for the next day.

There was one aspect of the daily life of the voyageur that merits a special look: their habit of singing as they paddled along. Even as they set forth in the pre-dawn dark they would launch into a rousing chorus that echoed incongruously through the pitch-black woods, and they would continue to sing, hour after hour, throughout the day and into the evening. Their songs—gay and sad, moral and bawdy—were like magnets pulling them on. Probably this custom of the voyageurs helped to relieve the tension of having to be ever watchful in the wilderness, and certainly it had a practical use as well, for the rhythms of the songs set a pace for the sweep of the paddles.

In any case, the songs were absolutely indispensable to the voyageurs, and the man with a good voice who could lead the chorus was sometimes awarded extra pay. Some of the songs had been brought over from France by an earlier generation; some were of the voyageurs' own devising. Composed in a French that is now archaic, the songs are highly evocative of the singers' wandering lives. Many tell of home and sweetheart and of lost love. One that is still familiar on both sides of the border is "Alouette". Another, and certainly one of the loveliest, is "A la Claire Fontaine" ("At the Clear Running Fountain"), which became a sort of unofficial anthem of French Canada:

A la claire fontaine
M'en allant promener
J'ai trouvé l'eau si belle
Que je m'y suis baigné.
Il y a longtemps que je t'aime,
Jamais je ne t'oublierai.

The song tells of a voyageur who stops by a clear running fountain and finds it so beautiful that he bathes in it. As he dries himself beneath an oak tree, he hears a nightingale singing high in its branches, with a heart as gay as his own is sad—for he has lost his lady love. Why? Because one day he refused her a bouquet of roses that she desired. Now he regrets his refusal bitterly. He knows that he will always love her, never forget her, and he wishes that the roses that brought about his downfall were thrown into the sea.

Other songs of the voyageur deal with the immediacies of the life he has chosen, celebrating the virtues of his canoe, affirming his faith in the power of his paddle, reminding him of the dangers that always lurk. These are graphically summed up in "Quand un Chrétien Se Détermine à Voyager" ("When a Christian Decides to Voyage"), a sermon in verse, supposedly given by a priest as the men prepared to embark. The rhyming is lost in the English translation, but the import remains:

"When a Christian decides to voyage he must think of the dangers that will beset him. A thousand times Death will approach him, a thousand times he will curse his lot during the trip. . . . When you are on traverses, poor soul, the wind will come up suddenly, seizing your oar and breaking it and putting you in grave danger. . . . In the evening if the swarms of mosquitoes assail you unbearably as you lie in your narrow bed, think how this couch is the likeness of the grave where your body will be placed. . . . When you are in those very dangerous rapids, pray to the Virgin. . . . Then take the waves boldly and guide your canoe with skill. When you are on portages, poor soul, sweat will drip from your brow, poor *engagé*. Then do not swear in your wrath, rather think of Jesus bearing His Cross."

Such thoughts must have often been with the voyageurs on their long paddle northwards. Not long ago I stood on the point of rock where Fort Chipewyan, the voyageurs' northernmost trading base, was established in 1789 on the shores of Lake Athabasca. I looked across that immense desert of water and marvelled at the men who penetrated to this point in days when the closest contact with civilization was nearly 2,000 miles away.

Here in the far north, everything seems more lonely, more remote. The dark spruce spiral upwards towards the sky, and the aspen leaves twinkle in the chill wind. Wide rivers run their swift course, and the land through which they pass is home to lynx and black bear, wolf and moose—some of the wildest country left on the North American continent. Looking out across Lake Athabasca, I felt the wildness and the loneliness. The sense of something not only untamed but untamable —this is what the voyageurs left for later generations.

A Proud, Hard Life

Churning rapids, trackless forests, precipitous cliffs, mosquito-ridden marshes—none of these obstacles could daunt the French-Canadian voyageurs who paddled and portaged their canoes through thousands of miles of north woods wilderness during the 18th and 19th Centuries. Outwards bound, they carried goods to be traded to the Indians; on return trips they carried the prize pelts received in exchange —furs that enriched not the voyageurs but their employers: the North West Company, later absorbed by the Hudson's Bay Company.

In the course of their service for this English colossus the voyageurs came under the scrutiny of a remarkable woman who recorded their rugged way of life in oils and watercolours. Frances Anne Hopkins had little formal artistic training, but was the granddaughter of the renowned English portrait painter Sir William Beechey. At 21 she married Edward Hopkins, a Hudson's Bay Company official, and settled near Montreal in 1858.

Over the next decade the intrepid Mrs. Hopkins accompanied her husband on a number of wilderness expeditions, sharing the perils of the voyageurs' canoe brigades and their portages through the woods. From the sketches she made en route came a score of finished works that memorialized the rough-hewn faces and brawny figures of the voyageurs, the decorations of their birch-bark canoes, the ripples and reflections of northern waters. Among her works are the oils on canvas shown on the right and on the following pages.

Mrs. Hopkins' pictorial narrative, more evocative than the written accounts of the life of the voyageurs, also served as an epitaph for their valorous era. By 1870, when she and her husband retired home to England, diminishing numbers of these stouthearted men were plying the swift, turbulent waters of the wilderness and tramping through its dark woods. After more than two centuries the fur trade itself had begun to enter a protracted decline, giving way to more lucrative ventures such as lumbering and mining. Improved, if less romantic, means of transportation came to supplant the birch-bark canoe: steam-powered boats and, in time, the railway, whose ribbons of steel were laid down where once only footpaths existed. By the start of the 20th Century, the voyageur breed had totally vanished from the north country.

As the bowsman watches for dangerous rocks, voyageurs run a canot de maître, the so-called Montreal canoe, down a savage stretch of white water. The few passengers shown probably include the painter and her husband; the others are presumably Hudson's Bay Company officials.

A brigade of Montreal canoes moves off into the mist. In this work, which she entitled "Canoes in a Fog, Lake Superior", Mrs. Hopkins

The voyageurs and travellers take their seats, a hasty look is thrown around to see that no stray frying pan or hatchet is left behind, and the start is made. An effort to be cheerful and sprightly is soon damped by the mist in which we plunge, and no sound but the measured stroke of the paddle greets the ear.

HENRY Y. HIND/ *NARRATIVE OF THE CANADIAN RED RIVER EXPLORING EXPEDITION*/ 1860

and her spouse are seated in the nearest canoe. She has her sketchbook prepared, while Mr. Hopkins puffs at his pipe.

The pale light of evening reveals the lakeside camp of a company of voyageurs. Some gather firewood, others oversee the preparation of

Here we found waiting for the morn seven loaded
canoes and eighty voyageurs belonging to the Hudson's Bay
Company. . . . It was an uncouth scene. There was a semi-circle
of canoes turned over on the grass to sleep under, with blazing
fires near them, surrounded by sinister-looking long-haired
men, in blanket coats, and ostrich feathers in their hats, smoking
and cooking, and feeding the fires.   JOHN J. BIGSBY/ *THE SHOE AND CANOE*/ 1850

a meal, another scans the horizon, and one man, apparently exhausted after a day's paddling, slumbers beneath a canoe.

At night a voyageur crew repair their canoe. One man stitches a patch over a hole in the birch-bark skin while another melts pitch to

It now became necessary to consider how we should get
on but the Canadian Voyageur soon finds a Remedy
and our Men were immediately occupied in repairing
the Hole. The Woods furnished the material. Bark from the
Birch Tree Wattape from the Root of the Pine, Splints
made from the Cedar Tree and the Crossbars. In the Evening
all was ready to start in the Morning.   DIARY OF NICHOLAS GARRY/ 1821

waterproof the patch. The onlooker wearing the suit may be an agent sent out from the fur trader's home office.

4/ The Ways of the Beaver

*If one wants to have any idea of what the
world once looked like, one must remember that
it was inhabited by beavers.*

LARS WILSSON/ MY BEAVER COLONY

Through the trees I see a distant gleam of silver. I am looking for a beaver pond, and I think I may have found it: where the silvery sheen beckons I know there is a shallow valley between two low hills. Cautiously, I move towards it. I have the impression that I am walking as soundlessly as any Indian, but I must be crashing through the brush as noisily as a moose on the trail of a mate—for suddenly I hear a sharp crack up ahead, followed by a splash. If beavers are there, I have certainly alarmed them, for the way they signal danger is to slap their broad, heavy tails against the water, producing a sound like a rifle shot. Then I hear other cracks and other splashes, and I hurry as best I can, convinced now that there is a whole family of beavers diving to safety as they hear me coming.

I emerge from the woods to see a small pond of such exquisite beauty and stillness that I feel like a wilderness transgressor just looking at it. Spruces border it, their reflections utterly clear in the perfect mirror image of the pond. The water at the edge is black, but so limpid that I can see the pebbles on the bottom. Only an occasional whisper of a breeze stirs the surface, crinkling it into little silvery ruffles. Not a sound is to be heard; even the birds are silent.

A few yards away, jutting into the water at the base of a dead tree that stretches bony fingers upwards, is a big mound of sticks piled seemingly at random—a beaver lodge. Beyond it, at the lower end of the pond, is a beaver dam. As I walk along the water's edge to take a closer look at it, I notice the fresh prints of six-inch-long beaver paws in the mud at my feet. The dam, stretching perhaps 60 yards across the valley, is an old one, tightly compacted: grasses grow out of the tangle of sticks that an earlier beaver generation used in constructing it. At one side of the dam there is an obvious weak spot, and a trickle runs through it with tiny gurglings.

Tonight, after I am gone, the beavers will undoubtedly be out to work on the leak, small though it is. While some sort of spillway to relieve the pressure of backed-up water is as essential to a beaver dam as to a man-made one, this hydraulic necessity is of no moment whatever to beavers; so far as they are concerned, running water is there to be dammed. And a dam is vital to the beavers because of the pond it creates. This enables them to swim to trees on which they can feed after they exhaust the supply in the immediate vicinity. No less important, the pond provides near-perfect protection against enemies. The beavers usually build their lodge at the pond's edge with the entrance on the water side. As the water level rises, the lodge entrance is submerged. The beavers can make their way through this underwater tunnel; non-aquatic predators like the lynx and the wolf cannot. Security of food and shelter—this is what is represented in the laboriously fashioned dam and lodge I see before me at the small pond.

Beavers are among the most remarkable creatures of the north woods. They are unexpectedly big animals—the second largest rodents on earth, after the South American capybara, another aquatic animal that resembles a warthog. At maturity beavers range from 30 to 50 inches in length and weigh 30 to 40 pounds. Curiously, they never quite stop growing. Only death sets a limit to their size, usually after 10 or 11 years if they live in the wild or up to 19 years in captivity.

The hard-working habits of the beavers are of course legendary; they have become the very symbol of conscientious industry. This is because their dam-building and tree-felling activities seem extraordinary to man—as indeed they are. Once, on the river Pigeon in northern Minnesota, I saw a beaver-felled aspen that was at least 100 feet long. The tree was about 12 inches thick at the point where the beavers had neatly chewed it; it might have fed a beaver family for a month, what with all the succulent branches it carried. But unfortunately it had fallen away from the river instead of towards it, where the beavers could have chewed off parts to float them homeward. Moreover, the top of the

Standing amid its meal of water plants, a young bull moose with a spring growth of antlers enjoys the cool of a northern lake.

aspen was hung up in a couple of large black spruces, and the trunk leaned at about a 45-degree angle. I could see marks where the beavers had made their way a short distance up, but they are poor climbers, and the topmost branches remained beyond their grasp. The toppling of the tree was a formidable achievement, but it was labour lost.

To fell a tree, a beaver begins by biting lightly into the trunk all around; then, continuing to circle the tree, it bites off huge chips of the interior wood. To take these bigger bites it first locks its two upper incisors, which protrude an inch and a half past the lips, into the top of the chewing area. Below this point it uses its two lower incisors to cut a deep notch; then, with the upper incisors again, it finally pries off a large chip of wood—three, four or even five inches long. Thanks to its large loose lips—so loose that they can fold behind the teeth—the beaver is able to gnaw off such chips without getting a mouthful of wood. The same attribute permits it to gnaw wood under water without drowning.

A beaver's teeth are well suited to its needs. The front surfaces are coated with hard enamel, and as the uppers and lowers grind against each other and against the tough fibres of the animal's woody diet, they are constantly resharpened. Like the beaver itself, the teeth never stop growing. If the animal has little wood to chew—as is sometimes the case in captivity—the teeth will grow longer and longer, assuming weird curved shapes and eventually doubling back into the beaver's jaws until it dies a horribly painful death.

The speed with which a beaver works would put Paul Bunyan to shame. An inexperienced axeman like myself might well have taken half a day to bring down the river Pigeon aspen; for the beaver it was probably no more than a couple of hours' work. To cut through the soft wood of five-inch-thick willow takes the beaver three minutes flat. Speed, however, is not always of the essence. There are known instances of beaver-felled trees that have obviously required longer effort; they measure five feet or more in diameter. Why a beaver should attack a tree that thick is a mystery; the animal cannot possibly haul so big a trunk to its pond, whether to store as food or to use for dam repairs. The supposition is that beavers chew trees simply because millennia of evolution have programmed them to do so; but they have no way of knowing that one tree may be better situated than another for their particular needs, and they are certainly unable to make a tree fall in a specific direction. They simply chew around the trunk, usually a foot or a foot and a half up from the base, cutting a beautiful smooth notch. When the fibres start to give as the tree begins to sway, the beavers beat a hasty retreat, sometimes not hasty enough: occasionally, a beaver is found dead under the weight of a tree it has felled.

Despite such mishaps, the beaver's record of success is phenomenal, even more so in its activities as an engineer. The dams it constructs are veritable miracles of their kind. The naturalist and writer Sigurd Olson cites a beaver dam in Minnesota that was half a mile long and firm enough to hold a horse and wagon. There are many instances of dams a quarter of a mile or more long, and if they are old enough they will have compacted to the point where they will support almost any weight.

Beyond the fact that the dams are always built in running water, there seems to be no rhyme or reason whatever to their location. Sometimes the site selected is notably efficient for the beavers' needs, permitting the construction of a dam that backs up water for miles. In another site the dam appears to reflect nothing more than an excess of zeal; it is built across the widest part of a stream even though a narrower site may be just yards away.

In any case, the dams are usually elaborate affairs. The beavers start construction simply by poking sticks of all sizes—twigs, small branches, chewed saplings—into the mud in the stream bed of the projected site. Gradually they add sticks until a wooden barricade stretches from bank to bank. Since the sticks are not interwoven, water flows through at first. The beavers deal with this problem by periodically adding mud that they dredge up from the bottom and carry clasped to their chests with their front paws. They plaster the mud liberally wherever needed, patting it into place like children making mud pies. Later, drifting bits of debris pile up against the dam, further sealing it until the passage of water is almost completely blocked. But the beavers remain continuously at work, repairing the inevitable damage wrought by winter storms or spring floods. An old dam may reach as high as seven feet above the original water level, and it is impervious to just about anything except dynamite or a bulldozer.

In time its builders will abandon the dam and move elsewhere if they find that they have stripped the trees around the site of the food they need. But this takes considerable doing, for trees as far as 500 or 600 feet inshore from the beaver pond are within the animals' reach. This supplement to their food supply is made possible by a network of canals, each at least a foot and a half deep—the minimum depth a beaver requires to swim in. Some networks are very extensive, and on sloping ground they have what appear to be locks.

In a rare daytime foray, a black-masked racoon prowls a pond for crayfish. It usually dunks its food repeatedly before devouring it.

Whether these canal systems are the product of the beavers' deliberate planning or merely the result of chance is a subject of dispute among scientists. In earlier times such canals were hailed as proof of the beavers' ingenuity, and there are naturalists today who support the view that the beavers intentionally dig the canals and construct the locks. Other naturalists are sceptical. What actually happens, they believe, is this: the wet coats of the beavers dribble water along the paths they follow to the food trees, the animals churn the mud as they travel back and forth, the branches and sticks they drag move the mud to the sides of the runway, and soon a "canal" forms as water from the pond moves into the trench. This school of thought does credit the beavers for the locks in the canals, holding them to be small dams the animals have built to halt the movement of water. But otherwise, according to these scientists, the seemingly sophisticated canal and lock system simply represents the beavers' response to the presence of running water and loose objects. In fact, they point out, not even running water need be present to stimulate beaver activity: in captivity, a beaver will build a "dam" in the corner of its cage from anything lying loose—a food dish, a stick, even a keeper's dropped glove.

There is little scientific quarrel about another of the beaver's engineering achievements—the beaver lodge. Although to the eye of an inexpert observer it may look like no more than a casual heap of sticks, stones and mud, it is actually a snug and spacious shelter in which a beaver family can be completely protected against the sub-zero cold of a north woods winter.

The home-site is always near the water, and usually right in it; occasionally the chosen location is around the base of a large tree, which serves to anchor the building materials—sticks as well as saplings that the beavers have felled and of which they have already eaten part. In the early stages of construction, these materials are simply piled up helter-skelter in a rough circle to form a large mound that is perhaps three to five feet high. As building progresses, mud is used to fill the chinks and crannies of the mound to shield the lodge against wind and weather —a particularly effective device in winter, when the mud freezes. Because beavers are air-breathing mammals, air must have a way of entering, and this is made possible by minute natural openings in the roof of the lodge.

Building the lodge high makes for an interior living room commodious enough to house the beaver, its mate, and as many as eight kits. But the construction job is not yet done. The beavers now dig two or more underwater tunnels into the lodge, each invisible to predators and deep enough to permit the animals to swim about freely beneath the ice in winter. One tunnel is a straight runway for ordinary passage into and out of the lodge and for the transport of food. The other tunnels wind and twist and serve as escape hatches. Another finishing touch is a narrow feeding platform just inside the entrance, about four inches above water level. Here the beaver eats its meal of sticks, tossing the peeled remnants back down the tunnel when it has finished. Perched on the platform, it can also shake the water out of its coat and groom itself a bit before entering the living room. A pair of toes on each hind foot is especially adapted for the grooming process: the toenails are split so that they form a comb, and as the beaver combs its dripping fur, it simultaneously removes parasites and redistributes the oils with which its hairs are impregnated, so that its coat is again waterproof.

Ordinarily the finished lodge will last the beavers indefinitely. Years after the first occupants have moved away to more plentiful feeding grounds, a new beaver family may settle in and find the lodge entirely habitable. On the other hand, it may fail even its original builders. Sometimes, if spring floods are excessive, the beavers' near-by dam may break, and the pond will drain out. If so, the entrance to the lodge will appear above water, destroying the beavers' security. But except for such eventualities the beaver lodge remains proof against predators. A lynx or a wolverine will claw in vain at its three- or four-foot-thick roof. At the mere threat of enemy invasion, the beavers can escape through one of their underwater tunnels. As winter tightens its grip and a thick sheet of ice prevents the animals from moving in and out of the water freely, another protective device comes into play. Knowing instinctively that they must provide against the cold season, the beavers spend late summer and autumn accumulating sticks and branches and pushing this food supply into the mud close to the entrance tunnel. All they have to do in times of freeze or at other moments of adversity is to swim to the entrance and dip into the larder they have carefully prepared. And so life in the lodge is generally peaceful and secure, with little pressure from the outside world.

A beaver family is close-knit; beavers mate for life. Their kits—one to eight in a litter—arrive in the spring after a gestation period of approximately 100 days. The kits are born fully furred and with their tiny eyes open; they weigh about a pound, and are about 15 inches long, including a three-and-a-half-inch tail. Their front teeth—orange in colour like those of their parents and many other rodents—are amusingly bucked; with this toothy look and their silky brown fur, they are almost irresistibly appealing. Nor do they present problems of housebreaking; the kits excrete their body wastes in the water and keep themselves scrupulously clean. Instinctive swimmers, they may venture outside the lodge within a few days after birth, under watchful parental eyes. In these first days of their lives they are extremely playful. They sharpen their swimming skills with water-tag games, and it is obvious that they enjoy themselves hugely.

For six weeks or so the kits subsist on their mother's milk. After weaning, they feed on the bark of deciduous trees but, like their parents, they also vary this basic diet by eating underwater plants such as duckweed, eelgrass and water-lily shoots. They remain under the parental roof for two years. When the third annual litter arrives the first-born leave their parents, either voluntarily or under the threat of forceful measures. By this time, in any case, they are old enough to fend for themselves and start their own families.

As they move towards adulthood, kits are especially vulnerable to predators. When one approaches, the entire beaver family will flee the lodge through one of the tunnels, dive below the pond surface, and wait in watery safety until the enemy gives up and goes away. During this emergency the large lungs of the beaver—the means nature has given it to adapt to underwater living—are a particular boon. With this powerful equipment a beaver can swim as far as a quarter of a mile without coming up to breathe; it can stay submerged for as long as 15 minutes. Usually that is long enough to discourage any predator watching for it to re-emerge. In a pinch, it may sustain itself even longer, though if it goes too far beyond its limit it will, like any air-breathing mammal, inevitably drown. But a premature expression of curiosity may also prove its undoing. Sometimes a kit—or a parent—will poke its nose out of the water to see if the coast is clear and decide to emerge; at this point an alert carnivore can seize it.

A more efficient predator of the beaver has been man. During the heyday of the north woods fur trade he hunted and trapped the species almost to the point of extinction. Lately beavers have been making a comeback, although not in the numbers of the past. There have been relatively few human beings, it seems, who have viewed the beaver without the purpose of profit, and even fewer who have viewed it with gratitude. One such exception was John Colter, a guide on the 1804

The fastest and strongest member of the weasel family, the fisher, was misnamed by woodsmen who found it in fish-baited traps. But it seldom catches fish, preferring small forest creatures, which it stalks in trees (above) or outruns on the ground. It even preys on the porcupine, flipping it on its back to avoid the quills and attacking its tender underside. Vicious by nature, the fisher growls, hisses and snarls when provoked (right) and switches its fox-like tail menacingly.

Lewis and Clark Expedition, which blazed the first overland trail across North America. Colter reported on an experience he had at a beaver lodge in 1807, when he was on bad terms with a band of Blackfoot Indians. The Indians were intent on exterminating him and they all but had him when Colter suddenly saw a beaver lodge in a stream just ahead. Without pausing for an instant, he dived into the water, found the entrance tunnel to the lodge and swam right up into the beaver living room, where he remained hidden until the Indians had given up their search and departed.

Whatever the truth of Colter's story—and frontiersmen were given to fanciful accounts of their escapades—a more objective exploration of a beaver home was essayed in recent years by Leonard Lee Rue III, a naturalist and author. Rue was not being chased by Indians; he just wanted to see what the inside of a lodge looked like. It was a time of drought and the upper part of the entrance tunnel was above water. Rue stripped and slithered into the hole. He was half in the water and half out, in darkness that became absolute once he had rounded a corner about 12 feet in. At this point the roof of the tunnel sloped downwards, and a few feet farther on he could no longer keep his head above water. Rue sensed a somewhat larger space ahead of him, and tried to get there by somersaulting forward. To his dismay he got stuck halfway through the manoeuvre, with his head under water and his feet jammed against the ceiling. "The only thought that flashed through my mind," he recalled later, "was, 'My God, what a place to get it'." By superhuman effort he managed to reverse his somersault and get back upright again, after which he wriggled out of the tunnel backwards. The experience left him wondering what might have happened had he managed to get right inside and discovered a beaver family in residence. Normally the beaver is a very inoffensive animal, but a family of six or seven, armed with long, sharp incisors, could very effectively rout an intruder in the homestead.

To beavers intrusion spells danger, and they are unable to distinguish between a predator, an innocuous investigator or, in my case that day at the little pond, a friendly writer simply anxious to catch a glimpse of them. I walked out on their dam, which I found to be only six inches above the level of the water, yet very strong: the surface barely gave beneath my feet. No beavers were to be seen, and so I made my way back towards the beaver lodge. Wild flowers leaned out over the dark water, mirrored in the surface. A few ducks floated idly a little way offshore. As I walked along, wild rose bushes gently scraped at me, their dark red hips heavy and luscious against the deep green leaves.

There was nothing to be seen or heard at the lodge, and yet I had the feeling that beaver eyes were peering at me from somewhere. Finally I got close enough to see the food cache beneath the surface, between the lodge and the dam—an assortment of sticks and twigs, some with the green leaves still showing, piled at random like jackstraws. I waited there, listening hard for the sounds it is said one can sometimes hear coming up from the lodge below—the vague cries and whines of beaver kits or an occasional wail like that made by a hurt child. Hurt or frightened beavers sound almost like children, crying and moaning gently, while angry beavers hiss like cats. But I heard nothing. I was certain the animals were there somewhere, and just as certain that they felt safe from an interloper as unskilled as I.

I left my observation post as the sun was almost down. A few yards into the woods, in an aspen grove, I found a beaver feeding spot, littered with chips amid the stumps of saplings and young trees. All the older trees had been felled. I sat against one for a little while to rest before going on and watched the darkening pond. The sun glared at me like an orange ball from the mirror of water.

Then, all of a sudden, I saw movement on the pond surface. The tip of a small "V" was cutting across it towards the lodge. I stared in fascination as the "V", a tiny black spot at its point, grew and spread, forming ripples touched with sunset red. Then I saw other "V"s being traced in the water, growing, spreading—and disappearing in the direction of the lodge. I walked away through the woods with a sense of exultation: for some strange reason I felt as though I had just joined the family.

Around the Beaver Pond

When beavers dam a stream to create a pond, they do so solely out of an instinct to establish a watery forest empire where they can obtain food from handy deciduous trees and at the same time ensure themselves a haven against their enemies —both animal and human.

But another effect of the beavers' building activities is to change their part of the forest profoundly, turning it into a rushy, sedge-grown, semiaquatic world, part swamp, part lake. The shallow slow-moving waters attract a host of living things— from algae and plankton to fish and crustaceans. These creatures in turn have their own parasites and predators—from mosquitoes to hawks.

Yet even on bright spring days such as those that provided the pictures on the following pages, the beaver pond is deceptively calm. The few signs of life may include the soft splash of a frog leaping to safety from a patch of grass where a snake has surprised it, or a sudden ripple in mid-pond where a trout has struck at a caddis fly that was hovering too close to the water.

What cannot be seen are millions of microscopic plants and animals teeming beneath the placid surface —basic links in the food chain for nearly all other animal life in the pond. The beavers pay no more heed to them than to most of the other creatures with which they share their world. But in a sense the plankton are as dependent on the pond's beavers as the beavers, through the food chain, are ultimately dependent upon the plankton. For though the beavers may live in the pond for years, they will move on when they consume all the food trees in their reach. And just as they created ideal conditions for other forms of life while they remained, so they set the stage for the death of the pond when they leave. Their abandoned dam slowly disintegrates and releases its impounded water, the level of which drops. Supplies of oxygen and nutrients fall below the point where they can support aquatic creatures, large and small. Finally' the pond dries out, to be succeeded by a stream-cut meadow.

The meadow in turn invites the encroachment of the forest. In a matter of decades, a new growth of willow and aspen will appear. And if the stream does not dry up, the combination of fresh food and running water will almost certainly attract a new family of beavers to begin the cycle once more.

A pond created by beavers near Ely, Minnesota, reflects their dome-shaped lodge in its waters. The spruces along the shore, though rejected by the beavers as a food source, will in time be felled by them for use in mending the lodge as well as their near-by dam.

A BEAVER FEEDING ON WILD CALLA

Signs of Spring in a Secluded Realm

As lord of the beaver pond, the animal that created it is unobtrusive in its dominance. Even after a long winter in the lodge on a diet of twigs and bark, it is rare to see a beaver feeding out in the open at pondside (*left*) on the calla leaves that surge up with the arrival of the first warm days of spring.

At this season, the most visible evidence of the beavers' renewed activity is the number of freshly felled trees around the fringes of the pond. Branches from such trees—which may be as big around as the two-foot aspen trunk pictured at right—provide both food and building materials. After the bark of the tree is stripped off and eaten, the twigs are used to fashion nests for the spring litters of kits. Longer branches go to build up the dam, thus helping to ensure a water level high enough to seal off the underwater tunnels that lead to the lodge. By this means predators are thwarted and protection is afforded the kits in their vulnerable first months.

Despite such precautions, danger still lurks for the beavers. Their worst threat is the otter, an agile swimmer that can negotiate the entrance to the lodge. At a hint that an otter—or any enemy—is in the vicinity, a beaver will slap the water noisily with its broad tail (*bottom right*), sounding an alarm to the other beavers and giving them enough time to dive to safety, hopefully far beyond the foe's reach.

A FRESHLY FELLED ASPEN

A BEAVER SLAPPING ITS TAIL IN ALARM

WILD CALLA

WATER LILY BLOSSOMS

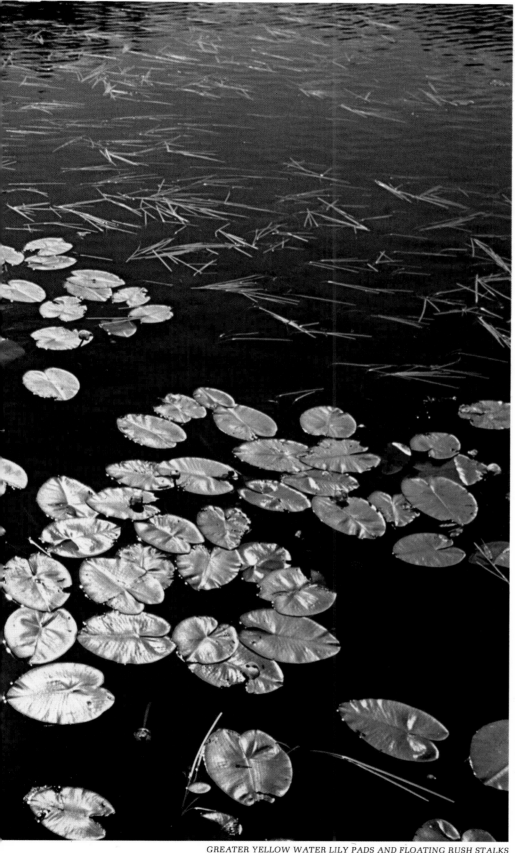

GREATER YELLOW WATER LILY PADS AND FLOATING RUSH STALKS

A Savage Struggle Behind a Placid Facade

As the eye sees the plants and creatures of the beaver pond, and as the camera has caught them at left and on the following two pages, they reveal little of the intricate and frenzied pattern of competition and interdependence that rules their lives.

On a sunny spring day, the delicate yellow blossoms of the water lilies in the shallows charmingly offset the translucent blooms of the calla growing near by. Yet gentle as they appear, these lilies can prove lethal to other plant life at the pond. Where they spread their wide pads, sunlight is cut off from other emergent plants, such as bulrushes, that are reaching for the surface. The first plants to capture a space survive on the pond's limited resources, but those that fail are numberless.

The struggle for survival is as fierce among the creatures of the pond. Seen in isolation, none of them seems either threatening or threatened. Yet the insect larvae that dot the surface of the water furnish the mink frog with the protein it needs to shake off the lethargy of winter. The frog in its turn may make a meal for the garter snake. Grass spiders, water scorpions, leeches and caddis flies all lead hazardous lives as potential consumers—and victims.

Transient though their individual lives may be, however, their kind will inevitably be back for another spring's struggle to share the pond with the lilies and the beavers, which endure from year to year.

A GRASS SPIDER ON A LILY PAD

THE SHED PUPAL SKIN OF A CADDIS FLY

A LEECH ON A SANDY BOTTOM

A WATER MITE AT PONDSIDE

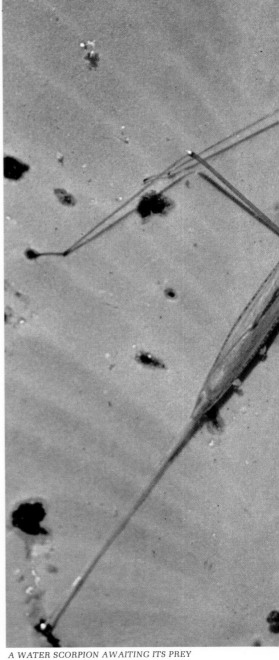

A WATER SCORPION AWAITING ITS PREY

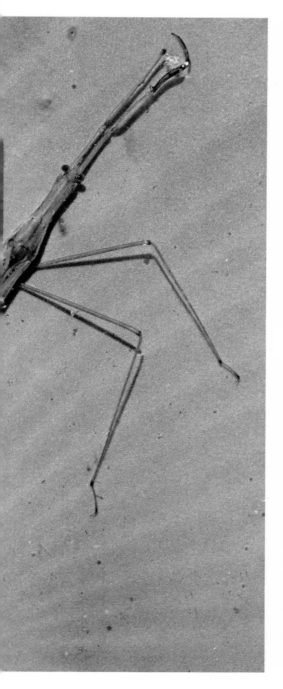

AN AROUSED EASTERN GARTER SNAKE

A MINK FROG ON THE MOVE

A BEAVER CANAL AT THE POND'S EDGE

A Perilous Venture in Search of Food

The need for food will often lure beavers beyond the pond's edges into the forest, a journey they make by means of a system of canals. Some zoologists believe that the beavers carve these channels inadvertently, simply by dragging their bodies through the swampy fringes of the pond; others credit the beavers with building these convenient passages purposely. In either case these channels serve the beavers well, providing access to fresh supplies of aspens and other food trees and serving as sluices in which bark and twigs can be floated from the outer boundaries of the pond to be eaten at the beaver lodge.

The tall grasses and thick woody growth through which the beaver canals wind support their own great variety of plants, insects and birds, some of which are pictured at right and overleaf. Birds build their nests in the area's grassy camouflage and their newly hatched young feed on a protein-rich diet of the pond's insects, which are attracted by the scents and spots of colour provided by wild flowers. But hospitable as the boundary region may be for these species, for the beavers it represents a place of peril. Their clumsiness on land exposes them to such fearsome predators as the lynx, the wolf and the bear, and so they make their forays to new groves of food trees only briefly, scuttling back down their canals as fast as they can to the relative security of the pond.

A RUFFED GROUSE ON ITS NEST

A CLUTCH OF SPARROW EGGS

A CRANE FLY

SAWFLY LARVAE ON A HAZEL LEAF

A SWALLOWTAIL BUTTERFLY

BUNCHBERRY

WILD IRIS

A MOCCASIN FLOWER

Confident as the relative safety of dusk descends, a beaver swims powerfully through the dim tranquillity of its pond's shallow waters.

Most active after dark, the animal faces a busy night's work of building, repairing and foraging for food before returning to its home.

5/ In the Grip of Winter

*I love the deep silence of the midwinter woods. It
is a stillness you can rest your whole weight against . . . so
profound you are sure it will hold and last.*

FLORENCE PAGE JAQUES/ *SNOWSHOE COUNTRY*

At 1 o'clock on a frigid January morning I stand in the woods above
Snowbank Lake in northern Minnesota, trapped by the silvery magic of
a full moon. The snow lies deep all around me; one step from the trodden path and I would sink in it up to my hips. The cold—it is 40° below
zero—presses in upon my goose-down parka, my felt-lined boots and
my mittened hands. The moonlight, astonishingly brighter than any big-
city street lamp, reflects on the delicate traceries of birch and aspen
branches, the sombre pyramids of spruce, the wayward bulk of jack
pines. The great shimmering curtains of the aurora borealis glide to
and fro like phosphorescent ripples in some mysterious sea. The stillness in the white-clad forest is eerie and beautiful.

In the north woods in winter, snow is the dominant force. It is an environment all its own, requiring radical adjustments in the lives of
people, of plants and, most notably, of animals. In all animals, the coming of snow triggers reactions that change their mode of living
fundamentally. Some flee southwards; others retreat to the deathlike
sleep of hibernation; still others change their food, their habits, even
their coats and their colouring. In this sense, every forest animal leads a
double life—one of spring, summer and autumn, and one completely
fitted for survival in the winter cold. What causes the changeover from
one life to the other is the onset of snow.

I had observed the first signs of winter four months before in late September, some 800 miles north of Snowbank Lake where the dwindling forest meets the tundra on the shores of Hudson Bay. Here the air at night had a razor's edge of chill to it, and in the early morning I could see slivers of ice forming along the mossy margins of a muskeg pool. At the tree line, the autumn colours were of an intensity I had never before encountered: flaming scarlets, vibrant greens, flaring yellows, rich browns. Wandering the area around the bay, I sensed an animal world in transition, poised to go southwards or withdrawing into itself for protection against what was to come. The air was alive with birds preparing for long flights. Canada geese, snow geese and whistling swans swept in ragged files across the lowering sky. Within the fringes of the woods, small animals were storing their food for the long siege that would begin when the first fine flakes of snow blew in.

Now, in January, snow lies everywhere in the north country, blanketing both its woods and its waters. Those most typical of summer sounds—the roaring of a waterfall, the rustle and burble of rapids on some river—are silenced. Here and there, where a stream's current is too swift to freeze, a whisper of movement may be heard from the depths, but that is all. The lakes, too, have changed their character: frozen hard, they now serve the caribou as resting places when the bands come out of the forest to seek the safety of an open space; they serve the packs of hunting wolves as a highway in their pursuit of caribou and moose and deer. The surfaces of the larger lakes are covered with wind-driven snowdrifts two or three feet high, crested like waves.

In every respect, because of the peculiar qualities of the omnipresent snow, the north woods in winter are a different world. Those of us who live in more southerly latitudes may find this hard to grasp; we tend to consider snow only as a passing phenomenon, sometimes giving us pleasure on the ski slopes, sometimes creating a hazard on our highways. In the north, however, its impact is so profound and all-encompassing that the study of snow as a natural environment in its own right increasingly interests scientists. They are learning more and more about how it can harbour as well as bury life, and about the transformations it works not only on the animals of the north but on their forest habitats. They are finding that snow itself—far from being the simple white stuff laymen believe it to be—is of different kinds. They are even developing a vocabulary to distinguish these varieties, borrowing from the languages of the Eskimos, Indians and Lapps, the people of the snow who know it best.

One pioneer in the field, William O. Pruitt Jr., a zoologist at the University of Manitoba in Winnipeg, employs these varied terms for snow not only in his learned papers but in his everyday conversation. *Qali* —the "q" pronounced like a "k", but with a glottal stop—is the word he uses for "the snow that is on the trees". Snow on the ground is *api*. The bottom layer of *api* is *pukak*, which provides a winter habitat for a host of small mammals. *Upsik* is the hard-packed, wind-driven snow of open spaces such as large lakes and bogs. *Siqoqtoaq* is crusty snow whose top layer has thawed and refrozen, sometimes so hard that it gashes the legs of moose and caribou that break through it; the crust can immobilize these beasts as effectively as an electric fence.

Each of these varieties of snow has important consequences for the areas on which it lands. Take, to begin with, *qali*. To most of us, snow that clings to trees seems merely picturesque, conjuring up visions of Christmas cards. That it could work major changes in a forest seems inconceivable. Yet *qali* plays a vital role in the cycle of plant succession, based on the simple but significant fact that snow on the trees represents a burden that eventually may become too heavy for them to bear. Piling up in the wind-still forest, the load of snow finally will break off branches or the tops of trees. When this happens, a break is caused in the forest canopy—a "forest window"—which is the beginning of a forest glade.

The effect of such a window is to change the ecological balance of the area where it has appeared. Through the opening left by the broken tree more sunlight reaches the trees still standing, and in time the branches on the glade side proliferate. This shifts the centre of gravity of the trees towards that side. Since more *qali* accumulates on the side with the heavier branches, the burden on the tree is increased until finally, some snowy winter, it falls. With each tree that is downed, the story is repeated until at last there is a glade of substantial size.

Dr. Pruitt has observed the creation of such glades in study plots in the subarctic forest over a period of several winters. He has also noted that when a forest window reaches a certain optimum size, the *qali* breakage stops. This, he believes, is probably due to the fact that at some point the wind becomes a factor: now that it can sweep into the glade, it shakes the *qali* from the branches so that heavy accumulations no longer occur.

Meanwhile, important things are happening on the ground. The dead and broken trees shed their needles on to the forest floor, choking out the moss carpet. Deciduous shrubs and trees invade and provide leaf litter, which decomposes into humus—and now a hospitable soil has been created for the seeds of spruce. In time, these take over, and finally a mature stage is reached in which the coniferous trees predominate, and the cycle of plant succession can start all over again.

Added to its key role in the life of the forest itself, qali plays a crucial part in denying or giving access to the food on which certain forest animals depend in winter. If the qali build-up is heavy, tree-living animals such as the red squirrel, the chickadee and the crossbill can no longer reach the spruce cones that are their chief source of sustenance. The squirrel must retreat to the forest floor and dig beneath the snow to seek out the cache of food it has prudently stored there, while the birds must fly off to windy hilltops where the trees are clear of qali.

Another familiar animal of the north woods, the snowshoe hare, finds qali a help rather than a hindrance. For its winter food it depends on the tender growing tips of birches and alders. These trees react differently to qali than do spruces. While spruces strive to remain upright and bear their growing burden of snow, the supple deciduous saplings bend with the weight, enough so that eventually their growing tips come within the hare's reach. Moreover, they provide the hare with a shelter beneath their bent branches during spells of extreme cold. In a classic example of interaction for mutual advantage, the trees provide food for the hare and the hare reciprocates by leaving pellets of fertilizing manure that help to nourish the trees when spring returns.

In some ways the hare has the best of all possible worlds in the winter woods. Its camouflage is superb; as autumn merges into winter, its brown and grey coat gradually turns snow white except for a thin rim of black at the tips of its ears. The snowshoelike hind feet that give it its name are another boon. When the hare can find no growing tips on which to browse and must subsist instead on the bark of birches or willows, it can rise on its hind legs and nibble all the bark within reach. At this point api, the snow that is on the ground, often comes to the hare's aid by building itself up another few inches and "elevating" the hare. Since the animal's snowshoe feet prevent it from sinking into the snow, it can now reach a higher level of the shrubs to browse on.

Api performs an even greater service in the case of small forest mammals and invertebrates. In the deep-freeze chill of northern winters its very presence makes it possible for animals of this size to survive, warmly sheltered beneath the snow itself.

To understand this, it is necessary to examine just what happens when snow falls on the forest floor. Where before there were mosses, lichens, a variety of small plants and considerable needle litter from countless conifers, there is now an insulating blanket that covers the forest floor entirely. Snow is one of the best insulators in the natural world: it is actually an emulsion of air and myriads of ice crystals. The basic shape of the crystals is a six-sided star, and because of this shape they are not able to nestle closely together. Hence the snow, when it first falls, is light and fluffy. As layer falls upon layer and as meteorological factors work upon each layer, the snow matures, and in the process many changes occur in its makeup.

The first change—the most important one to the small animals of the forest—occurs on the bottom layer, the *pukak*. The principal factors in this change are the warmth and moisture that flow from the earth. In the summer, the warmth and moisture simply radiate into the air and disappear; now they are trapped beneath an insulating cover. Warmed by the earth immediately below, the bottommost snowflakes begin to lose their water molecules, which flow off the attenuated rays of the six-sided crystals and gravitate to the colder crystals of the layers of snow above. Gradually, below the snow cover, an open space is formed that is interspersed with delicate crystals of ice, larger than most snowflakes and different in shape—hollow pyramids that hang together at their tips and form a delicate latticework of interlocking columns.

The *pukak* latticework may be as much as several inches thick —enough to offer a hospitable environment to any animal that may live there. Here, close to the base of the snow cover, the temperature is seldom more than a few degrees below freezing, no matter what it may be in the air above. In outside winter temperatures, small mammals such as the red-backed voles, the mice and the shrews would freeze solid in a short time; their bodies are simply not big enough to put out the metabolic heat needed to keep them alive. But in the relatively warm bioclimate of the *pukak* these animals can live, breed and reproduce. And they live in what any human being would regard as a veritable fairyland. The air is always warm and moist and still. The light that filters down through the snow cover is a pale bluish white. The only sounds are the scamper of tiny feet, the occasional tinkle of ice crystals falling from the roof of the *pukak* and the footfall of a predator stalking through the snowy woods above. Frigid winds may roar over the forest canopy; down in the *pukak* they are never heard. There is food aplenty, stored in the forest floor during the summer months, and there is seldom any need for vole or mouse or shrew to visit the world above.

Deep in Superior National Forest a September snowfall—first of the season—whitens a majestic stand of black spruces and balsam firs.

Once in a while, however, they must do so, and here again is demonstrated the balance of the winter world's ecology. In the layers of snow above the *pukak*, the maturation process is constantly taking place. There will probably come a time when a warm front, perhaps with a drizzle of rain, will briefly thaw the top layer of snow. When it refreezes, the snow cover will have a tough, crusty layer of ice on it, and this ice will impede the exchange of gases between the forest floor and the air above. Carbon dioxide formed by the decomposition of leaf litter will begin to fill the crystal halls of the *pukak* layer. When the carbon dioxide level becomes dangerous to animal life, the tiny mammals build ventilator shafts to the upper air. Through these, they can come up and catch a breath of cold fresh air—but this offers an opportunity to the little Richardson's owls that prey on them. The formation of a single layer of icy crust works to the benefit of these birds by bringing the mammals on which they feed within their reach.

The only other predator the voles and mice and shrews need fear in winter is the weasel, which is small enough to penetrate the *pukak* corridors. It may also happen that a fox passing by above will catch the scent of a *pukak* dweller and hear the tinkling sounds that signal a living presence below. The fox, jumping into the air with all four feet in order to come down hard, may try to break through the snow cover, but likely as not will only find itself in a snowslide from which it can get out only with difficulty. Or a moose or a deer may break through the cover with its hoofs, causing an avalanche of snow that blocks the *pukak* corridors. But soon the process by which the bottom layer of snow yields up its water molecules to the colder layers above will start anew, and in time the *pukak* will be as snug a habitat as before.

On frozen lakes and in open bogs, a different maturation process takes place, this one brought about by the wind. As the wind blows across the surface of the snow, it picks up the topmost layers of snowflakes and whirls them along, tumbling them over and over. As they move, the delicate snow crystals change their shape: the elongated rays break off, and instead of star-shaped snowflakes there are now countless millions of needle-shaped crystals of varying size. Blown along by the wind, these form side-by-side patterns, much denser than was possible with the star-shaped snowflakes. They then settle behind some protuberance—a crack in the ice of a lake, a rocky outcrop protruding through the peat of a bog—and drifts begin to form.

Where the wind blows fiercely and constantly, these drifts can be amazingly hard. Piled up five feet or more, the snow achieves a ce-mentlike toughness: when struck with the flat side of an axe it rings like a bell. It is solid enough to support the foot of a man or the hoof of a car-ibou, and the running wolf leaves barely a footprint in it. This is the snow called *upsik*; when it melts and refreezes into a crust, as it may after a warm front occurs, the tough icy layer is known as *siqoqtoaq*.

Both *upsik* and *siqoqtoaq* crucially affect the winter lives of the large mammals of the north woods, sometimes for good and sometimes for ill. The moose, for example, has stiltlike legs that generally keep the bulk of the beast above the snow level. But it is too heavy to walk on snow. Deep snow spells trouble, and heavily crusted snow can cause the moose to crash through and become trapped. To avoid the *siqoqtoaq* it either migrates to a region of thinner snow cover or stays put in a "yard" where food is plentiful, moving about as little as possible. If it exhausts the bark and twig supply from the trees and bushes around it, its only recourse is to rise on its hind legs, bring the weight of its body to bear on the tree and bend it down to where the higher food can be reached. Sometimes this will break the tree: a moose's yard in spring-time is usually marked by broken branches and tree trunks and—if the snow is crusty—by leg holes rimmed with blood.

In the case of caribou, *upsik* and *siqoqtoaq* serve a unique purpose that only now has begun to be understood, thanks to research by Dr. Pruitt. These two varieties of snow are determining factors in the strange, seemingly erratic migrations of the caribou—both the wood-land kind, which is rare now except in the northern forests of Canada, and the Barren Ground kind, whose habitat is the tundra. Once the car-ibou wandered from tundra to forest and back again in herds numbering hundreds of thousands; today, though much depleted, the herds follow the same general course. What chiefly influences the direction of these wanderings are "fences" of snow.

Dr. Pruitt has observed the migrations of woodland and Barren Ground caribou over a period of years, charting their courses in north-ern Canada and Alaska. By collating these observations with his studies of different kinds of snow he has found the explanation for the an-imals' sometimes inexplicable behaviour, notably in the springtime. Faced with warming trends that might be expected to lead them south-wards towards still warmer weather, the caribou head north instead—as if they wanted to stay in a wintry climate for as long as possible.

In summer caribou feed on sedges, grasses, lichens and the leaves of willows, birches and aspens. In winter, their deciduous food is gone; lichens and sedges are all they have left. To get these, they migrate to the woods and crop their nourishment from beneath the snow, pawing out "feeding craters" with their front hoofs so that they can reach down and get the food. Some types of snow—notably the light, fluffy *api* of the deep forest—make feeding easy for them. Other types, such as the dense, wind-blown *upsik* or the icy-crusted *siqoqtoaq* make feeding difficult. The caribou's migration thus has a double aim: to get them to places where they will find food, and to avoid areas where the snow makes feeding difficult or impossible.

Dr. Pruitt and his students have made extensive comparisons between areas where caribou are numerous in the winter and the types of snow found there. The animals are found in greatest numbers where the snow is light and fluffy enough to allow them to get at the food beneath it. They may not congregate in the same area the next winter; while the food may be there, it may be inaccessible because the snow is dense or crusty. Or there may be an area of ideal snow but with no food beneath it. And so the caribou push on, wandering aimlessly, it would seem, but actually guided by snow conditions—"fences"—fully as effective as any fence man might erect.

When the cold begins to loosen its grip and the sun sheds some warmth on the frozen earth, the topmost layer of snow may thaw and refreeze. The crust may get so thick that it cuts the skin of the caribou's legs, causing great discomfort and making feeding impossible. When this happens, the caribou herds head north—where the snow is likely to be still fluffy and soft. Sometimes, as spring nears, they find themselves squeezed between a fence of crusted snow that is building from the south and the open tundra, where the deciduous plants that are the caribou's source of summer foods are still deeply buried and weeks away from their budding stage. This is likely to be the most difficult time of the winter for the caribou. Such conditions, if they are unusually severe, may wipe out entire herds.

Whether they are wandering north or south, the caribou gravitate for their rest periods to the frozen lakes, whose surfaces offer a welcome refuge where they can chew their cuds and loaf and sleep. From these open spaces, too, they can spot the approach of their principal predators, wolves, and can bunch together and make a run for it with the easy, swinging trot that wolves cannot match. Wolves, for their part, must follow the caribou, a primary source of their food. Thus they, too, migrate from the tundra to the forest and establish hunting bases under the snow-laden branches of some large spruces. From here, in single

All hardy winterers in the north woods, the four species of owl at right endure the cold that other birds flee when autumn arrives. The snowy owl, the great horned owl and the great grey owl are of imposing size, with wingspreads up to five feet. Richardson's owl is small as northern owls go, with a wingspread of only two feet. In all owls, the wing tips are notched, allowing the free and relatively noiseless passage of air when the birds are in flight. Thus their search for prey is virtually soundless —a prime advantage for a predator.

GREAT HORNED OWL

SNOWY OWL

GREAT GREY OWL

RICHARDSON'S OWL

file, they make their trails through the snow, and almost always the trail will lead towards a lake, the caribou's resting ground.

Wolves do not stalk like lynx or mountain lion; theirs is a straightforward approach to the job of finding and killing their prey. If they spot a band of caribou on a lake, they will advance. When they are within sight, one of the caribou will spot them and instantly give the danger signal—a hind leg thrust out sideways. The band will spring up and, in a tight-packed bunch, explode into a clumsy gallop, then settle down to a distance-eating trot that they can keep up for hours.

When the caribou flee in this tight bunch, with no stragglers, the wolves seldom attempt to follow them, instinctively knowing they have little chance of success. But let one caribou hesitate or falter, out of indecision or because of age, sickness or injury, and that caribou is doomed. Such behaviour instantly triggers in the wolves the stimulus to kill. There is an old saying that "a wolf can catch any animal it chases" and it is true to the extent that the wolf usually will chase only an animal it thinks it can bring down. Wolves may test many caribou or moose before they encounter one whose flight reactions deviate from normal. Even so, unwittingly but with superlative efficiency, the wolves cull the caribou herds. By killing the weak and infirm, they help to maintain the quality of the herd and establish the fitness of the caribou to survive. This is a form of interdependence between wolf and caribou no less essential to both than that between spruce and *qali*.

There is only one documented instance in North America of a wolf attacking a human being; in 1942 a man riding a handcar at 10 miles per hour on a Canadian railway track was set upon by a wolf, which hung on for almost half an hour before three other men succeeded in killing it. The animal, however, was believed to be rabid. The rarity of such encounters is probably due to the fact that men do not arouse the pattern of stimuli required to cause a wolf to attack. My friend Sigurd Olson, who has lived in the north woods all his life and studied wolves in their own habitat, tells a revealing story in this regard. Skiing down a frozen river one moonlit winter night, homeward bound, he became aware that a pack of wolves was following him. He had no gun, just a hunting knife, but he also had his own knowledge that wolves do not normally attack man. "I had written a book that said that," he recalls with a grin, "but I didn't know if the wolves had read the book, so after a while I got a little nervous, realizing that what I had said about them not attacking man might well be put to the test that very night.

"Up ahead of me, reaching more than halfway across the width of the river, I could see a rocky point. I would have to ski past this, through a narrow gap, and I began to think to myself: 'If they're going to jump me, that's where they'll do it.' I slipped my knife out of its sheath and held it in my hand, thinking that if I had to die, I would at least try to take one of them with me. Now I could see the point clearly in the moonlight, and as I looked, two big wolves came out of the woods, trotted down the rocks and on to the river, and sat there facing me. There were probably more out of sight in the woods.

"I was perhaps within 30 yards of them, and not knowing what to do, I stopped. I stood still and looked at them, and they sat still and looked at me. Predator and prey, I thought; but which is the predator now, the wolf or me? The knife didn't feel very reassuring, but it was all I had, and I clutched it as though it were King Arthur's sword.

"We stood there and looked at each other for what seemed a long time. The eyes of the wolves—I could see them clearly in the bright moonlight—were unwavering. I didn't move a muscle. Finally the larger of the two wolves got up, shook himself, trotted up the rocks and disappeared into the woods. The other got up and followed him. And I skied down the river until I got to my cabin, which I then entered, being extremely careful to bar the door."

Was it the fact that wolves fear man that kept those two unmoving in the snow? Or was it the fact that the man who faced them stood unmoving, betraying no sign of fear or weakness that might provoke the deadly stimuli that unleash the wolves' attack behaviour?

I was thinking about this as I stood above Snowbank Lake on that January night when suddenly I heard the most beautiful, the most chilling sound to be heard in the north: the calling of the wolves. It came from over the ridge, probably from a half mile away. There was a single voice at first, rising in a long wail. Another joined it, then another; then the wolves were singing in harmony, as I had heard they often did.

The sounds aroused some stimuli in me. The hackles on my neck rose, a cold vice gripped my heart and travelled towards my stomach. Without thinking, I found myself walking quietly through the snow to the warmth and safety of my cabin, where I, too, barred the door.

The Bane and Blessing of Snow

Winter in the north country is a time of harshness. Daylight is brief and warmth scant. A none-too-easy environment for animal life even in milder seasons, the north woods can support even less life at this time of year, as temperatures plummet and the snow builds up, denying access to customary food supplies. Yet, paradoxically, it is the snow itself that helps forest animals survive the winter. For those that can exploit its characteristics, the snow can be friend and protector.

Certain animals—called chionophobes by zoologists, after the Greek word *chion*, or snow—cannot tolerate the snow at all. Notable among these are ground-feeding birds and waterfowl; they take to the air and migrate south at the first chill hint of winter. Other animals, called chioneuphores—moose, wolves and such small mammals as voles and shrews—make adjustments to the snow. Wolves hole up in soft snowbanks to conserve body heat when the cold becomes unbearable. Moose easily wade through depths of soft snow on their long stiltlike legs. Voles and shrews take up winter residence in crystal tunnels beneath the snow cover: the layers of snow serve as an insulator, trapping the ground

heat below the bottommost layer and affording these tiny creatures a haven in which the winter temperature seldom drops below 20° F.

A third group of animals, called chionophiles, or snow lovers, have made actual physical adaptations to winter conditions. The broad feet of the predaceous lynx enable it to move surely and swiftly across even relatively fluffy snow cover. The snowshoe hare possesses similarly well-adapted hind feet and also another advantage: a pelt that turns from brown to a camouflaging white as the snow cover builds up.

But despite adjustments and adaptations, life remains difficult in the north woods winter. Carbon dioxide occasionally fills the tunnels of the voles and shrews and compels them to surface for a breath of fresh air and to create ventilation shafts, risking a pounce by a hungry fox or owl. Moose and deer may break through crustings of snow, gashing their legs. The snowshoe hare, emerging incautiously from a warm burrow in the snow, may be seized by an alert lynx. Across the snow the trails and tracks of predators and potential prey attest to their perilous search for the food that will enable them to survive to see another spring.

A nameless island in Manitoba's frozen Wallace Lake catches the sunrise. At this hour, nothing is astir, but there is life here; nocturnal animals have retired to await another darkness, while diurnal creatures do not yet dare venture into early-morning gloom.

The Deceptive Delicacy of a Snow Called Qali

No variety of snow has a greater impact on the vegetation of the north woods—and thus on the animals that eat the vegetation—than *qali*, the feathery sort that rests on trees. Its branch-borne beauty is deceptive; *qali* is a potent force in the forest.

Its accumulating weight causes such deciduous trees as birches, willows and aspens to bend temporarily to the ground, making their tender tops accessible to the snowshoe hare. Conifers will not bend under the *qali* unless they are very young, as in the case of the jack pine at left. Instead, such trees will break, beginning with their branches. As more trees topple, a "window" is created in the forest canopy, allowing sunlight to reach the forest floor for extended periods and nurture the deciduous trees on which deer and moose can browse in later winters.

The big deterrent to *qali* is a strong wind; sweeping in through the forest window, it will prevent the pileup of snow. Snow and wind often work together to aid animal life, notably on the open spaces of lakes. The wind compacts fluffy accumulations, in time hardening the lake surface enough to permit such creatures as foxes, wolves and caribou to use it as a winter highway.

A young jack pine bends nearly to the breaking point under its burden of seemingly lightweight qali. Both the cold and the absence of wind have permitted the build-up of snow in these woods near Wallace Lake, Manitoba.

A solid highway for animal travel will eventually evolve on top of these fragile hoarfrost crystals on the surface of Wallace Lake. The crystals provide a base for falling snow, which strong winds then gradually pack hard enough to support even heavyweight animals.

A Final Round in the Contest to Survive

That most avid of snow lovers, the hare, is not without its troubles in the winter woods. If the snow is even slightly compacted, the snow-shoelike feet of the animal will carry it rapidly across the surface in search of food trees. But if the snow is too soft the hare will sink in. To cope with this dilemma it hops up and down to carve out trails to feeding areas. Each new soft snowfall, however, obliterates the trails—and the hares, impelled by a special behavioural adaptation, must leave their snow caves, usually at night, to re-establish their routes.

But as they engage in their frenzied hopping dance, the enemy lurks. The lean, furry lynx—the only cat adapted to the northern forest—can lie patiently and motionlessly for hours beneath the branches of a tree before striking. Like the hare, the lynx has enlarged feet that enable it to move swiftly in quest of a meal. The hare is the mainstay of the lynx diet, and when it ventures from the cover of the trees into an open area its movements can give it away despite its camouflaging white winter pelt. Quickly and efficiently, the lynx pounces. The cat's long teeth crunch through the hare's skull into its brain, killing it instantly.

A snowshoe hare falls victim to its classic enemy, the lynx. As a rule the foes are equally agile, but this hare made the error of taking a short cut through a clearing where its movements could be easily spotted.

Signs of Life in a White Wilderness

The visitor to the wintered-in north woods seldom sees any of its animal inhabitants, but evidence of their presence abounds in the form of trails and tracks. In the snow, prints of hoofs, paws, wings, tiny feet and whole small bodies not only betray the passage of living creatures but reveal much about their habits and methods of survival in winter.

Of the five animals whose tell-tale marks are shown here, the moose leaves the most heavily indented imprint, thanks to the long legs that enable it to move through deep snow; the tracks often lead to a "yard" of relatively open space where it can find succulent deciduous trees, the moose's favoured winter eating. The grouse, burrowing beneath soft snow for night-time warmth, makes both entrance and exit holes recognizable by an observer. The flying squirrel, seeking another food tree, drops from a branch in a glide, then scampers swiftly to its goal. Wolves, though they hunt in single file, following a trailbreaker through the snow, leave rough circles of paw prints after a kill or a period of play. The hopping feet of hares form a fairly direct line—a trail that takes them straight to their treasured sources of food.

Deep hoofprints in the snow cover mark the long strides of a moose, which has made its ponderous way towards an area in the forest in which it can stay put for a period and browse on branches conveniently near by.

Entrance (left) and exit holes denote a grouse's night-time burrow.

A glide and a skit of paw marks reveal a flying squirrel's route.

Tracks made by a milling wolf pack cover the surfaces of a lake.

The hopping of snowshoe hares marks a clear trail to their food.

The snow pyramid at right covers a mound-shaped beaver lodge and provides an added shield against predators. But the residents face a

new danger in winter. In the dark lodge, the beavers are deprived of the light they require for growth, they lose weight, and some die.

6/ The Burgeoning Spring

In the spring I look at the forest floor with excitement, no matter how dead it may appear to be, for life is there, waiting for the signal to emerge.

SIGURD F. OLSON AND LES BLACKLOCK/ *THE HIDDEN FOREST*

Spring, that sweet and so often romanticized season, is not universally beloved in the north woods. For man, it is a time of paralysis; he cannot move for days on end. The ice that provided his winter highways is crumbling now; he can neither walk on it nor go through it in a boat or a canoe, and not even bush planes can land on the thawing lakes and rivers. In the woods, trails turn treacherous with mud and flood. Slush is everywhere as the snow blanket slowly turns to water—slush that loads up skis and snowshoes until the feet can scarcely lift them. "Summer is too short to go through the hell of breakup," say oldtimers, and they retire to their cabins, stoke the fire and sit out the melting season.

Sometimes it seems as if the whole world is liquefying. Or so it seemed to me one early April day as I tried to cross a woodland meadow in Manitoba. The muddy path had been churned deep, probably by a moose's hoofs, and I decided to bypass it, stepping along the sides where patches of dried grass promised a more secure surface. But suddenly one of my feet sank to the ankle in ooze. I put my weight on the other foot in order to pull free; instead I pitched forwards. Somehow I managed to get my mired foot loose and took another step; this time I sank halfway to my knees in a gluelike mass of mud. And so it went for a while. Each time I put weight on one foot it would sink deeper as I tried to pull the other free. I could go neither forwards nor back, and I did not see how I was going to extricate myself.

In such situations large hoofed animals like moose or deer may become hopelessly ensnared as though in quicksand. But whereas in quicksand they soon sink out of sight and suffocate, in mud they linger, immobilized. They may linger thus for days until at last either a predator gets them or they succumb slowly and agonizingly to starvation. Whether this has ever happened to men I cannot say, but after this experience I could believe that it has. I finally rescued myself by the most delicate manoeuvres, shifting tentatively and precariously from one foot to another. I had only about five yards to go in the mud, but it took me all of half an hour, panting with exertion, to reach firm ground.

With the perils of spring thaw, however, there is also a joyous sense of renewal in the north woods. Amid the muted colours of winter splashes of brightness appear. Rocky slopes glint with the blue of harebells; silvery-pearl pussy willows dot the banks of a creek; flaming stems of red-osier dogwood fringe a marsh. The transformation is swift. Exploring along the river Peace in April 1793, Alexander Mackenzie noted in his journal: "The change in the appearance of nature was as sudden as it was pleasing, for a few days only were passed away since the ground was covered with snow."

Sounds as well as sights announce the northern spring. The long silence of winter is broken by the songs of whitethroats and marsh wrens, the drumming of grouse, the whine of mosquitoes aroused from their hibernation. But these are gentle sounds compared to two others that above all epitomize the start of the new season: the wondrous noises of ice breaking and of water unleashed.

Within the woods the dominant theme is that of ceaselessly running water, myriads of separate trickles joined in crescendo. As a balmy sun sheds hour after hour of radiation upon the earth, and a wind bereft of its knife-thrust chill blows warmth in among the trees, the ice crystals of the snow cover begin to melt. For the small animals that the snow has housed, this is a time of trial. Their tunnels collapse; more vulnerable now to predators, they are forced to seek haven elsewhere. But the melting goes on relentlessly. Water seeps everywhere, dripping from ridges and rocks, dribbling along the ground. Soon minuscule streams merge, perhaps on a trail, forming rivulets and finding a firm direction. For the final goal of all the running water in the woods is the river or the lake; the rivulets take their last leap from some stony ledge or mossy bank and unite with the waters of the shore.

In the open spaces of lakes and rivers the drama of spring thaw is more easily observed, an ear-piercing, eye-filling spectacle that once witnessed is not soon forgotten. On the rivers it begins when the ice, weakened at the edges by the flow of meltwater from the banks, reacts by trying to move. In the attempt it creaks and strains and shudders, but at first fails. With more runoff it succeeds—cracking, then ponderously getting under way. Now comes one of nature's most awesome feats: in a succession of thunderous roars, the ice mass breaks apart. Great blocks of it float free. The tumult continues as they collide and shatter and overturn. At sharp bends or other obstacles in the river, the floes pile up, screeching as if thousands of motor-car brakes had been suddenly and simultaneously applied. If the ice jam lasts more than momentarily, the liberated water behind it will back up and overflow the banks, flooding the woods. Even after the jam loosens the danger to the shore persists. Blocks of ice careening downstream will slam into the banks, uprooting trees, shearing off branches, stripping bark.

Sometimes the ice breaks up suddenly enough to strand an animal that happens to have been using it as a highway; spectators along the shore have been treated to the poignant sight of a startled doe passing by on a floe. In a big river, where the current is strong and swift, the breakup may come and go quickly, and people place bets on the length of time the process will take. I was at Fort McMurray, in Alberta, when the river Athabasca went out in 31 dramatic minutes, making one lucky punter richer by about $800. During the previous week, under a genial sun, I had watched the daily widening of the tell-tale dark band along the shoreline, evidence that the edges of the river ice were giving way to reveal the water below. On the day of the breakup itself, the powerful current swept the whole ice pan downstream in a rushing maelstrom of splintering floes that broke into ever smaller fragments until at last the river flowed high and clear. The effect was that of a violent explosion, except that it took place not in an instant, but in the relative slow motion of half an hour.

On the lakes, the breakup is more deliberate. One might describe it less as a melting than as a rotting process. At the same time the ice melts from top to bottom it also deteriorates internally. In the first stage, the warming sun melts the snow that covers the lake ice. When the cover has turned to slush and water, the sun attacks the ice directly. At this point the crystals of the ice undergo a structural change. Throughout the winter they had been lined up side by side to form a substance almost as hard as iron; now they form honeycombs through which water drips constantly as the surface ice melts. Gradually the walls of the honeycombs become thinner and thinner. The ice loses all of its inner strength; it may still be six feet thick, but the weight of a foot, either of man or animal, will collapse it: one breaks through the surface as readily as through a snowdrift, with a sound like the shattering of a thousand delicate glass goblets.

There are two phenomena particularly associated with the breakup of ice on a lake. One is the lifting of the ice; it may rise as much as a foot, sometimes with dramatic suddenness. The lifting occurs because the lake basin at the time of thaw fills up with meltwater above as well as underneath the ice cover; thus the ice, which is lighter than water, is subjected to two pressures—the weight of the water on top of it, offset by the stronger thrust of rising water from below. When the shore ice has melted and the ice can float free, it responds to these stresses by rising in turn. If the shore ice has melted unevenly, one side of the ice cover may tilt upwards while the other side is still held prisoner.

In time, of course, the warmth of spring prevails. At the final stage of melting, the lake ice darkens, and when this happens, oldtimers in the north know that its hours are numbered. The crystal honeycombs have now become so thin and fragile that they no longer reflect the light from above, but reveal the darkness of the depths below. If the wind is calm, the ice will simply vanish, sometimes in a single day: suddenly it is no longer there. If the wind is strong, it will drive the ice along until it piles up on shore; there, under the battering of the waves, it breaks into glittering shards that ride up on the rocks with a melodious tinkling. If the day is sunny, the beauty of the scene is breathtaking: the shoreline flashes as if blanketed with diamonds, and out on the lake whitecaps form like victorious battalions, inexorably advancing against those last remaining battlements of winter's cold.

With the final disappearance of the ice, one of the most fascinating of all the rites of spring takes place in the lake. Over the winter, the ice cover effectively seals off the vital exchange of gases between the air above it and the water below. Whatever oxygen remains in the water continues to be consumed both by fish and by decomposing plants and other underwater life. By winter's end, in relatively shallow lakes, this oxygen supply may be critically depleted, sometimes so much that the fish suffocate. The arrival of spring is a literal lifesaver, for with the departure of the ice the waters of the lake completely intermix, redistributing oxygen to every level of the lake.

This renewal occurs as the sun heats the surface water, newly freed of ice. When the surface temperature reaches 39.2° F., the temperature of all the waters in the lake, from top to bottom, becomes relatively uniform, and so does their density. It is this stability of conditions that permits a thorough mixing—when a strong spring wind blows. The turbulence produced by the wind makes the whole lake circulate, bringing oxygen-poor bottom water to the surface to become recharged.

In every level of the lake the fish begin to stir; they may now swim anywhere. Trout that in summer will elude the fisherman by staying in the colder depths appear among reefs along the shore, their golden brown and reddish hues plainly visible. I remember one spring evening at Wallace Lake in southern Manitoba. At one end of the lake there is a spot where the water is very low; it is a marsh full of water plants, cattails and reeds. Fish were not on my mind at the moment; I was hoping for the sight of moose. As I waited quietly in the woods just above the shore, I heard repeated splashes from the direction of the lake, as though fish were leaping out of the water after flies. But there were no flies around, nor any mosquitoes. I tiptoed to the shoreline and looked for the source of the sound. Finally I saw it: a spot where a tiny swirl of water was being pushed up like a bubble. The bubble was moving swiftly through the reeds, directly towards me. As I watched in rapt attention, I saw the slender, sinuous form of the fish beneath the bubble—a northern pike nearly three feet long. It swam almost to the shore, nosing about on the bottom as it did so; then with a swish of its tail—a movement that broke the surface of the water and produced a splash like those I had been hearing—it turned and was gone.

I have enjoyed the onset of spring in many places in the north country, but nowhere have I found it more interesting or more unusual than in the northeastern corner of the province of Alberta. Here, in a sprawling arc around Fort Chipewyan on Lake Athabasca is an enormous delta formed by three great rivers: the Athabasca, the Peace and the Slave. The Peace-Athabasca Delta, as it is known, covers 1.5 million acres, and has long been a wildlife paradise. But there are other wildlife paradises on earth; what makes the delta unique is that in the spring, as well as in the autumn, it serves as a funnel for every one of the four major flyways on the North American continent. Vast numbers of water birds that migrate back north after wintering in warmer climes travel through the delta; more than a million of them stay to breed or stop to feed there en route to Arctic nesting areas.

The singular hospitality afforded them by the delta was made possible by two natural factors: the flatness of the terrain and a remarkable

Doomed to disappear in a day or so, the disintegrating ice on Minnesota's Hegman Lake lies under attack by the warmth of a mid-May sun.

Harbingers of spring in the woods, cinnamon ferns will gradually unfurl their fiddleheads as the warmer weather persists.

hydrological relationship between Lake Athabasca and the rivers, particularly the river Peace. One might expect this river, powerfully coursing eastwards from the Canadian Rockies, to drain into the lake; instead, the lake drains into the river. The Peace veers north just before it gets to Lake Athabasca, and the lake water flows into it through two of the delta's many complex channels. Each year in late spring, swelled by the runoff from melting snow and ice, the Peace would rise to a level higher than that of the lake. For about 20 days the lake water would be blocked from its normal flow. As a result it would back off into the delta, flooding a considerable portion. The floodwaters would distribute their heavy load of silt and rich nutrients throughout the marshes and numerous smaller lakes and streams of the area, revivifying its plant life and providing a gigantic larder for its animal life.

Moose that have fed on low willows and other shrubs through the winter now have a plethora of water plants on which to browse. In the ponds and marshes muskrats gorge on eelgrass and bulrushes; these semiaquatic rodents have outstripped the beaver population that attracted the fur traders of old. Seen grazing in meadows, on the grasslike sedges, is the oddest looking of all the delta animals: the wood buffalo, a subspecies of bison. This shaggy, humpbacked brown beast is the largest land mammal in North America, weighing as much as 2,400 pounds. There are about 14,000 of them in the area; unlike moose, which tend to be loners, the wood buffalo move in herds. One bright morning, from the vantage point of a light plane, a friend and I spotted a small band of them peacefully chomping in an upland. As we flew lower for a better look, the animals stampeded into clumsy flight.

They had nothing to fear from us, nor for that matter from any man. As long ago as the 1890s, at a time when extinction threatened the entire bison species, the Canadian government legislated to preserve it from human predators, assigning the Northwest Mounted Police to enforce the law. The establishment of Wood Buffalo National Park, which includes most of the delta and millions more acres as well, has strengthened the protection. Throughout the park its namesakes roam wild, while overhead the bald eagle and the peregrine falcon, almost extinct elsewhere on the continent, wheel free and secure.

But it is the waterfowl, in all their astonishing variety and numbers, that make the delta most memorable for me. They appear as the weather warms, and the delta comes alive with their calling. Whistling swans fly arrow straight across the marshes, their wings beating the air with rushing sounds. All sorts of ducks and great gaggles of Canada geese oc-cupy the mud flats and shallows. There are herons and grebes, loons and cormorants. There are several species of gulls, and terns that de-fend their nests with the aggressive skill of fighter pilots. The delta is also the breeding ground of the white pelican, the strange bird "whose beak holds more than its belly can", as the old limerick has it.

If the delta visitor is really lucky, he may catch a glimpse of that rar-est of birds, *Grus americana*, the whooping crane. It is a very impressive sight, standing nearly five feet tall on long, spindly legs, its plumage a pure glossy white except for black face markings and wing tips. Its yel-low eyes, gazing fiercely upon the world, seem to reflect the spirit of the bird. It is rigid in its ways, unable to adapt to any habitat other than marshland that is rich in vegetation and small marine creatures.

Several decades ago—when fewer than 50 whooping cranes remained anywhere—efforts were begun to save the species. With the establish-ment of the Aransas National Wildlife Refuge, near Corpus Christi, Texas, a suitable wintering ground was provided, and it is there that the birds return, year after year, to spend the cold months. But where they went in the warm months was, until 1955, a mystery. Ornithol-ogists knew only that the place was somewhere in northern Canada. Then aerial surveys helped them pinpoint the exact location—Wood Buffalo National Park. The whooping cranes that arrive there in the wake of winter, coming down out of the sky with the wild bugling call that gave them their name, still number no more than about 80, but at least the species maintains its precarious hold on life.

To see the delta in springtime is to witness one of the world's great nat-ural sights. As far as the eye can probe there stretches a flat and sparkling mosaic that is both water and earth. The broad courses of the Peace, the Slave and the Athabasca seem laid out by design, so regular are their borders where the ice has melted. The innumerable smaller riv-ers and creeks meander in every direction across an immense sprawl of brown, yellow and pale green bog and marshland. From above it all looks like a child's painting, a mass of mixed colours through which experimenting fingers have drawn large swirls and looping trails.

But now a shadow hangs over the delta, a shadow cast by the works of man. In 1967, some 650 water miles to the west of the delta, a hy-droelectric dam went into operation on the river Peace. The harnessing of the river was probably inevitable; there is a continually growing de-mand for power all across Canada, and especially along its west coast.

Although biologists warned that construction of the W. A. C. Bennett Dam could lessen the annual rising of the river Peace, officialdom did not listen. Within a year it became evident that the effects on the delta's ecology might be very serious indeed. Coincidental with the fill-up of the dam's reservoir, the water levels in the delta have decreased. The dam appears to have controlled the flow of the river Peace in such a way that it can no longer be depended upon to rise high enough to make the waters of Lake Athabasca back up and flood the delta.

The results are beginning to be evident in creek and marsh and lake. Along the shorelines of lakes, now exposed to the sun, new growths of dwarf willows are pushing out the reeds and bulrushes on which muskrats thrive, and if this continues the muskrats will have to forsake these places. The wood buffalo, too, are affected. The sedges on which they feed depend for their growth on the annual flooding.

What will happen to the waterfowl no one yet knows. The ducks, for example, find in the delta an ideal habitat of small ponds and marshes; a single duck family stakes a claim to one of these as its own territory. Many ponds and marshes are beginning to dry out, and if this process persists the ducks may be forced to share the waters of the larger lakes with others of their kind and with other bird species as well.

Ecological disaster could engulf the delta, but there is strong hope that it will not. An intergovernmental task force, using small planes, helicopters, all-terrain vehicles and boats, has intensively studied every phase of the delta's complex life system. Hydrologists, biologists, chemists, geographers, engineers and experts in other scientific disciplines have taken part and have proposed solutions for the delta's dilemma. One solution would be the construction of small temporary rock-fill dams at strategic sites, impounding waters from the secondary rivers to raise the level of the lakes and ponds; one such dam, which would help to flood about 60 per cent of the delta, has already been completed. The birds and muskrats and moose and wood buffalo may yet take heart at the coming of spring; given the will and effort of man, their wilderness can be preserved.

NATURE WALK **/To the Virgin Forest**

PHOTOGRAPHS BY ROBERT WALCH

About a mile out in a lake in northern Minnesota, not far from the U.S.-Canadian border, lies a wooded island of priceless value to any lover or student of nature: an enclave that has never been logged. Today it is in private hands, secured against the power saw—a living testament to the virgin forests that flourished elsewhere in the north woods before they were wiped out by logging operations almost a century ago.

I have made the trip to the island a number of times. It is not a journey of heroic proportions: from the starting point on the lakeshore it covers a distance of no more than a few miles. It is, rather, a journey of the senses, in which increasing familiarity with a well-loved scene heightens my awareness of new growth and seasonal change. And so it was on my most recent venture to the island on a day in early June.

My trip began, as do so many north woods journeys, in a clearing at the end of a road. Before me stretched a typical second-growth forest, successor to a mature forest that the woodsman's axes and saws had destroyed. Slender birches interspersed jack pines and aspens. Two of the taller aspens had obviously provided a home for generations of pileated woodpeckers; towards the tops of the trunks I could count at least six nest holes that these large red-crested birds had bored. As I approached, two infant woodpeckers poked their heads querulously out of one nest, presumably awaiting their parents' return with food.

At the edge of the clearing, an old portage trail begins, leading through the forest towards the lake. Slowly I followed the ribbon of trodden earth through underbrush turned lush and green by spring rains. In the soggy ground along the trail, marsh marigolds bloomed in golden bursts, the waxy flowers shining in the bright early-morning sunlight that gleamed through the trees. The air was musty with damp and the smell of decaying wood. Black water stood in several deep holes left where trees had been uprooted in previous seasons. Afloat in these pools, mosquito larvae were slowly hatching in the warm sun; already the air was abuzz with mature insects seeking their warm-blooded prey. A few mosquitoes were caught in tree-hung spider webs that shimmered and swayed in the gentle breeze.

Thrusting up in thickets along the trail, most of the coiled new leaves of lady ferns had unwound, opening like fingers on an unclenched fist. Bracken ferns, and the horsetail so often found in their company, also flourished in profusion, prospering in the soggy ground.

As I approached the lake, the trail sloped downwards and the ground became even soggier. The surround-

MARSH MARIGOLD

ing underbrush was thick with willow saplings, supple shoots of alder and an occasional young red maple. Off to my left I glimpsed the ruin of a small cabin, built about 70 years before by a Finnish woodsman. The roof had fallen in long ago, but the walls were still sound. I briefly detoured, as on past trips, to take a look inside. Rocks were piled on top of the rusty remains of a crude stove. In the old days, when the stones were thoroughly heated and water was thrown on them, crackling steam would explode through the

room, well serving the Finn's purpose: he built the place as a sauna.

Near the lake, the old portage trail swerves on to a long neck of land that terminates in a rocky point. I walked past stands of white cedar, whose green fronds are a common sight in this area. White cedar has one of the

LADY FERN

most wonderful fragrances that I know of. Crush a frond in your hand and the pleasantly pungent scent will pour off it, the very essence of the north woods. Sprouting in and around the clumps of cedar were the broad-leaved shoots of another aromatic plant—sarsaparilla.

Along this stretch of trail I always seek out a tiny flower called goldthread. It has a starlike white blossom a quarter of an inch across, so frail that it seems ethereal. But the real beauty lies concealed beneath the soil—in the root. Dig with a care-

SECOND-GROWTH TREES ALONG THE TRAIL

ful index finger and you will find the root to be a long, slender thread the colour of purest gold.

The Lakeshore Landscape

A few steps more brought me to the lakeshore and a curving beach of fine white sand. Just back of it, in the higher, drier places among the pines, berry bushes grew in dense tangles: bearberry, blueberry, woodland strawberry, and my own favourite, Juneberry, which—despite its name—bursts into masses of dainty white blooms even before the month arrives, a true indicator of spring. All these varieties of berry were flourishing only a few yards from the water, in close company with juniper and dwarf dogwood.

Almost at the water's edge I found a memento of the voyageur era: a clump of fleur-de-lis, once the royal flower of France. A member of the iris family, the fleur-de-lis is believed to have been brought to the north woods by early French explorers and voyageurs who planted it nostalgically at their forts and, occasionally, at campsites along the canoe route to the north—from which places water-carried seeds spread the species. At this time of year the fleur-de-lis was still putting its strength into green growth, but in a few weeks its graceful yellow flowers would shoot up between swordlike leaves.

Also near the water's edge I came upon the lilylike leaves and yellow blossoms of clintonia. Only a few of the fragile flowers had opened to the warm sun; most of the buds were still tightly closed. Hugging the

JUNEBERRY IN BLOOM

A FLEUR-DE-LIS IN EARLY GROWTH

FLOWERING CLINTONIA

ground, shaded by the clintonia's leaves, violets bloomed, tiny splashes of cool colour that accentuated the rippling waters of the lakeside.

I continued along the shore towards the rocky point, skirting a large boulder deposited by a retreating glacier millennia ago. From trees closely overhanging the shoreline came the bell-like song of a thrush, accompanied by the excited whistling of nuthatches and chickadees.

A branch of one overhanging tree brushed my head. As I looked up, I saw a typical jack-pine cone, warped and twisted, sealed as tightly as if it had been dipped in hot wax. Someday, heat from a forest fire will break the seal and release the seeds, which will then be carried away by the wind. Somewhere a number of them will take root, for the jack pine is one of the toughest, most persistent species in the forest.

At the rocky point, a classic north woods vista unfolded. The rock is greenstone, and part of the Canadian Shield. The ledge shelved gently down into blue waters shaded by a lone red pine, standing sentinel-like at the tip of the point, its branches framing the view of a small wooded island just offshore.

The Trip across the Lake

From the point, I set out by canoe, paddling slowly to savour every inch of the way. Beyond the small island that I saw from the point two outcroppings of rock rise up from the lake. One has a bit of soil from which a solitary jack pine grows. I knew that in years past gulls had nested on this islet, and sure enough, a pair

A RED PINE AT THE ROCKY POINT

APPROACHING THE ISLAND

of them had taken up residence once again. As my canoe approached, the female gull winged up from a crude nest of twigs on the rocks; she was quickly joined by her mate. Frantically defending their unborn brood, they screamed and wheeled and made shallow dives at me with their beaks wide open. I paddled close enough to make an inspection of the nest. In it were three large eggs, dark brown with olive-green splotches. The mottled coloration very much resembled army camouflage.

I swung around another islet and saw my ultimate destination in the middle of the lake: a small island of about 10 acres, a place of cliffs and steep hills crowned by dense forest. Even from afar it has the look of virgin wilderness, a pristine little world

of its own that has managed to elude human alterations of any sort.

As I glided towards the shore, a rabble of ravens greeted me. Never had I seen so many of these big birds gathered together in one spot. From their perch on a large rock, two croaking ravens took to the air on sooty-black wings, and two more flapped awkwardly inland, out of sight beyond the trees. On the shore, other ravens assaulted the air with a raucous din, fighting furiously—perhaps battling for the remains of some small creature I could not see.

Slowly I circumnavigated the island. With every stroke, my paddle stirred golden pollen dropped by the minuscule blooming flowers of red, white and jack pines. At each breath of wind, more and more of the mar-

BRANCHES GROWING SKYWARDS FROM A FALLEN WHITE PINE

vellous powder was wafted into the water. The lake was streaked with gold, and where wavelets lapped against the shore they built up the pollen accumulation, forming what one poetic observer of the north woods has called "the yellow band of spring". Some of the pollen had blown across from the mainland; most of it, however, was drifting down into the water from the magnificent forest on the island.

A Study in Majesty

The forest reached all the way to the rocky shoreline, a dark green study in majesty, its maturity proclaimed by the size of spruces and red and white pines. There were no birches or aspens or other second-growth trees to be seen among these

A POLLEN-STREAKED LEDGE

splendid conifers. Along the shore several pines lay prostrate, felled by winter winds. One invincible white pine had somehow maintained a roothold in the earth after it fell, and though its top was buried in water, two branches had grown straight up from its recumbent trunk, seemingly trees on their own.

I put ashore on a low pollen-

WILD LILIES OF THE VALLEY AND CARIBOU MOSS

streaked ledge and started walking inland through the trees. The terrain rises and falls sharply; rugged hillocks are interspersed with swampy hollows and defiles lined by rocks. Most of the island is covered with a thick carpet of pine needles. Slick and springy underfoot, the litter is replenished year after year by a steady rain of needles from the canopy of pines above.

The Domain of the Lichen

Here and there, under my feet, the layer of needles was penetrated by pearly grey-green caribou moss, a lichen named for the animals that make it a major staple of their diet elsewhere in the north country. In turn heavy clumps of this delicate plant were themselves pierced by several other plants, among them the wild lily of the valley, with its bright, heart-shaped green leaves and thick clusters of fine white blossoms.

Lichens grew on weathered rock in many varieties and endless profusion. There was one striking variety with slender grey branches and a bright red top, for which it has come to be called British soldier. There were crustose lichens, with almost microscopically small orange and yellow tissues, that from a distance look like splatters of bright paint. There were foliose lichens of a more sombre hue, notably the *tripe de roche*, or rock tripe, once favoured by the voyageurs as an addition to their soup. Its broad lobes form a blackish-brown coating on the sunny sides of boulders and cliffs; in hot weather they are as brittle as scorched paper but, boiled in a pea-soup mixture, they become moist and fleshy and quite tasty.

At the centre of the island is its highest hill. Its granite flanks are covered with small, compact rock ferns, which grow even on vertical surfaces as if they had been glued in place. Higher up, the thick needle litter takes over again, sifting from the pines and softening the prostrate outlines of long-dead trees that are slowly crumbling back into the earth from which they came. The slippery needles made walking difficult, but after considerable exertion I finally reached the top of the hill. At my feet I found a cushion moss growing in a luscious, bright green mound as large as a Victorian lady's bonnet and just as decorative. Under a nearby spruce lay a fallen bird's nest —probably once the home of a tree sparrow. It had been blown down by the wind, which moans almost constantly through the trees.

A SPARROW'S FALLEN NEST

CUSHION MOSS

Even though it was a warm June day, the wind swept across the lake in gusts that I could almost see. Each gust enveloped the island with an enormous sigh and started the tree branches swaying in a massive but graceful ballet. Even the island's tallest tree, a huge white pine near the crest of the hill on which I stood, joined in the dance.

I walked a few yards downslope to inspect the giant pine. Its trunk was about 30 inches in diameter at the base, with bark that was thick and rough but pleasing to the touch. The tree soared straight upwards to a height of at least 100 feet. It must have been very old, possibly 300 years or more, to have grown so tall; I like to imagine that it stood watch on this hill as successive companies of voyageurs paddled by. The trees standing in the immediate neighbourhood seemed to have retreated from it in awe. Actually, of course,

BRITISH SOLDIER AMID PINE-NEEDLE LITTER

WINTERGREEN WITH BERRIES

its tremendous shadow has inhibited the growth of young trees near by, leaving a circle of open ground.

Continuing down the far side of the hill, I saw my first sure sign of a land animal: a furtive flurry of movement in the undergrowth near a red-berried wintergreen bush. I stopped short and stood stock-still, hoping that the creature would show itself. Most likely it was a red squirrel, which abounds in these parts. But it could have been a chipmunk or even a chocolate-brown mink; I had seen both animals here on previous visits. I had also heard that an occasional black bear or a porcupine swims over from the mainland.

For two or three minutes I waited motionless. But I was out of luck: the creature had managed to make good its escape.

Time and the Forest

Suddenly it was late afternoon, time to head back to my canoe. The hike was a slow one, down one needle-slippery slope and up another, through or around swampy bottoms and rocky crevices. The wind was abating. A hush settled on the long colonnades of trees, and the ruffled waters of the lake became still. Above, the ravens circled silently on motionless wings.

As I walked back through this rare and beautiful wilderness, I thought, as always, about its future. By a rough count of tree types from place to place, I knew that the pines outnumber the spruces. This means that the forest, though clearly a mature one, has not yet reached its climax stage, when spruces and balsams

RANKS OF RED PINE

will be the predominant species. In the north woods, a forest requires about 400 to 500 years of natural development to grow from pioneer seedlings to this final stage. The island wilderness will therefore reach its climax roughly two centuries from now—barring some disaster. If such does occur, it is likely to be natural rather than man-made, for private ownership of the island guards against the latter eventuality.

But nature does, of course, inflict calamities of its own. The trunks of several trees on the island bear deep scars left by a forest fire that was probably touched off by a bolt of lightning. The fire undoubtedly took place many decades ago, for the scars were nearly overgrown. The bark of these trees had formed thick scablike tissue around the wounds, but the burned wood nevertheless showed through. A certain amount of burning, however, furthers the natural development of a forest, enriching the soil with the materials it burns, and so I hoped that the island would get its fair share of fires—all of them minor. Certainly they would pose less of a threat than the dangers once posed by loggers.

Why this virgin wilderness escaped the depredations suffered by the forests around the lakeshore became apparent as I turned to take a last look from my canoe, now halfway across to the mainland. The island's good fortune has been its size and location. To the loggers, it was simply too small and too inconvenient to reach from the mainland for them to discern any profit in it.

FIRE SCAR ON A PINE TRUNK

As I paddled shorewards at dusk, I conjured up an imaginary scene that might have preserved the island's virgin state the last time it was in jeopardy. In my mind's eye, the foreman of a logging camp landed on the island to make a survey. Up through the gorges he struggled, up the hills and cliffs, stumbling and cursing as he slipped and slid among the deadfall. The tall pines looked down upon his efforts with disdain. Finally, sweating profusely, the foreman returned to the spot where he had tied up his canoe. With a last frustrated glance at the forest, he muttered: "It's more trouble than it's worth." And so he paddled off across the lake, leaving untouched a living museum of north woods history.

THE ISLAND AT DUSK

7/ The Canoe—Key to the Lakes

These days in a canoe brought life in a new dimension. In calm waters we seemed to glide somewhere between earth and heaven, silently and gently.

WILLIAM O. DOUGLAS/ *MY WILDERNESS: EAST TO KATAHDIN*

"It was not so much a test of the body," once wrote Eric Sevareid, the Columbia Broadcasting System commentator, recalling a canoe trip he had made into the north woods as a young man. "The body takes care of itself at that age. It was a test of will and imagination, and they too, at 17, have a power and potency which rarely again return to a man in like measure. I would follow shock troops across a hundred invasion beaches before I would repeat that youthful experience of the rivers." Sevareid's journey, undertaken with a high-school friend, Walter C. Port, who later became a department head in a Minnesota store, remains a classic in the modern annals of the north woods. In 1930 the two boys, in a secondhand canvas canoe, travelled from Minneapolis to Hudson Bay, a distance of 2,250 miles via interconnecting rivers, lakes and portages. Their voyage cannot be precisely duplicated today; there are too many man-made dams, locks and other obstacles between Minneapolis and York Factory, the old Hudson's Bay Company trading post where the two young voyageurs eventually ended their journey. But parts of the trip can be retraced; I have travelled over sections of their route myself, as have a number of others, and can testify that canoe trips in the north woods remain a challenge to the will and a delight to the imagination. They are, in fact, balm to the soul.

North woods canoeing today is far easier than it was when Sevareid and Port made their voyage. To be sure, there have been trips in modern times on which people have died—because of mistaken judgment in rapids, because they ran behind schedule and were caught by hunger or cold, or because they got lost in unknown territory. But this does not happen often: the experienced modern voyageur carries detailed maps and an accurate compass, and packs freeze-dried food that can be stowed so compactly that he can take a supply for many weeks. And with lightweight nylon tents and goose-down sleeping bags, he can survive almost any kind of weather.

Sevareid and Port almost did not make it. They lacked reliable maps, they had few woodland or navigational skills, and they were facing what was—and remains—some of the wildest country on the North American continent. The last 500 miles of their journey, from Norway House at the northern end of Lake Winnipeg to York Factory, led through territory virtually uninhabited and largely unexplored. Some Cree Indians lived there, visited on occasion by missionaries and Royal Canadian Mounties, and a few trappers still staked out their lines in the territory. But as far as anyone knew, there was not a man alive who had paddled those final 500 miles, via river Gods, clear to Hudson Bay. And before Sevareid and Port reached Norway House and the trackless labyrinth beyond, they had to traverse Lake Winnipeg—275 miles of open water known for the deadly treachery of its sudden squalls, and its wild north winds that could kick up rollers six feet or more in height, swamping a canoe or keeping travellers landbound for days or weeks on end.

Nonetheless, they went, over the initial protestations of parents and teachers. School was behind them, and they had an unshakable determination to accomplish some sort of impossible journey to someplace—to the North Pole or South Africa, or any spot that was hard to get to and far away. It was the sort of dream that most boys are fired with at some stage between youth and manhood, and this was the age of Charles A. Lindbergh, Admiral Richard E. Byrd and the first flights over the North and South Poles. The trip took from mid-June to the end of September, and by the time the two young men got to York Factory they were worrying about freeze-up. The story of their eventful experience is told in *Canoeing with the Cree*, a book Sevareid originally published in 1935.

A few paragraphs from the book illustrate the hardships that men can find in the north woods. It was early September, and the two voyageurs had been paddling for nearly three months: up the river Minnesota southwest, west and finally northwest to the Bois de Sioux, down its reedy channels to the river Red of the North, down the muddy Red for more than 300 miles to Winnipeg, up that fearsome lake to Norway House, the final jumping-off point. Civilization was many days behind them; unknown miles still lay ahead, and for days on end it had been raining. Winter, with all its dangers in the north woods, would soon be setting in.

"Drip . . . drip . . . drip.

"Every time we touched a branch, drops showered upon us. Twenty yards of pushing through the trees and we were drenched again. Now even birch bark refused to burn readily. Dry wood was impossible to find; only by painstakingly cutting out heartwood could we start a fire. We laid our blankets close to the fire, usually with a lean-to above us. Vainly we would try to dry our clothing. By the time it was half fit for wear, our eyes, aching from smoke and weariness, would refuse to stay open. We never failed to awake in pouring rain. Sleep lasted but a few hours each night. The dark hours were dreadfully cold.

"Each day we scanned the skies anxiously, watching for a break in the clouds. But day after day the leaden heavens lowered above. The icy wind blew directly against us time and again. Our faces grew raw and black from exposure. We could not shave, nor even wash our faces. All our wearing apparel was on our backs, day and night. We lost the heels to our rubber-bottom boots and walking over slippery rocks with the canoe over our heads was very dangerous. Once, as we were pulling the canoe along by rope, Walt slipped and slid backwards down a twelve-foot granite wall. Like a cat, he landed in the centre of the boat and by a miracle he did not tip it."

To eke out their dwindling rations, the boys determined to eat only a certain small amount each day. "The animals stayed well away from the river, hidden in their retreats. . . . We saw only a wolf, a black bear and occasionally smaller animals. In an attempt at diversion, we chased a loon two miles along the river one day. One night we sat upright, startled out of sleep by the unearthly scream of a lynx close at hand. We gripped the rifle and waited. But the scream was not repeated, only a low rumbling sound came to our ears and then ceased. Another morning, when we got up, we found the deep impressions of a giant moose in the clay of the river bank. The animal had come to drink that night, only twenty feet from our camp. . . .

"The portages were overgrown. It was evident that no one had gone through the region for many months. Our canoe began to leak badly.

Ragged but erect, three jack pines cling to a small rocky island in one of the myriad lakes in Minnesota's Boundary Waters Canoe Area.

As I was pouring water over the breakfast fire one morning, I saw Walt bending over and peering intently at something in the water of the river. When he beckoned to me, there was a queer look on his face. In a quiet pool, tiny, weblike traceries of shore ice were forming."

The boys' physical misery and the looming threat of winter brought on mental anguish, too.

"Slowly, the unending monotony of the forest gloom, the cold, depressing misty half-light in which we travelled and the unceasing discomforts we underwent, began to fray our nerves. Gradually our dispositions gave way under the strain. We became surly and irritable. The slightest mishap set our nerves jumping. A sudden blast of wind against us, the upsetting of a dish of food, the refusal of wood to burn —these little irritants put us into a rage. Impossible as it appears to us now, we began to vent our ugly moods upon each other. . . . Like children, we bickered."

Under the strain, the two boys actually fell to blows. But then their luck changed. They were still uncertain of their whereabouts, still unsure of how much farther they had to go before ice would render the rivers impassable. They thought they were nearing the Shamattawa, a river whose name means "fast-running water" in Cree and that was virtually the last stage on their journey. Then, suddenly, as they rounded a bend, they saw the remains of a still-smouldering campfire. Tense with expectation, they paddled as swiftly as they could and, as they skirted the next bend, saw a small dot—it had to be a canoe—far ahead on the water. Two hours later, they were attempting to talk sign language to a family of Cree Indians.

They kept repeating, "Shamattawa, Shamattawa," and finally the squaw understood. She gestured towards Sevareid's watch pocket. When he took out the watch, it read 5 o'clock. The squaw took it, pointed to 5:30, and said: "Shmattwa". They were only half an hour away from the fast-running water.

Three days later, their food all gone, they rounded a bend in the river Hayes and saw Hudson Bay spread out before them, with a schooner riding at anchor in the river's mouth. It was September 20. They had been paddling for more than three months and had traversed a wilderness under conditions that most people believed were impossible. Sevareid—a Middle Westerner who had never seen the ocean—remembers thinking, at the moment when they first saw the bay: "This is what all rivers come to. All those rivers. This is the sea, where everything ends."

Part of Sevareid's and Port's achievement was paralleled at the time this book was being written by two young men from Coon Rapids, Minnesota, who travelled in two kayaks from the river Red of the North in North Dakota to York Factory. Randy Bauer and Gerry Pedersen had had their full share of adventure when I encountered them on the train going south from Churchill, the same line over which Sevareid and Port returned. Their hands were callused and blackened by weeks of paddling and building campfires: the trip had taken them 61 days. And just a few days before they arrived at York Factory a party of six, in three canoes, had also come in: they too had begun their journey at the river Red of the North.

Bauer and Pedersen kept a journal of their voyage. But the words of a diary written by the light of candles or a campfire are sparse; they can sketch in only the outline of the days and nights spent in a huge wilderness, with stars singing overhead or rain pelting down, and with only a thin-skinned tent for protection against the cold and damp. Out there in the woods the world is an enormous place. Yet the sentiments felt by those who make such journeys are always the same. "Kind and harsh this northland is," wrote Randy Bauer one night in his tent on Windy Lake. "We curse it and love it at the same time." And in 1938 Florence Page Jaques, wife of the north-woods artist Francis Lee Jaques, wrote of a campsite she had come to on her first canoe trip: "It's not our world at all; it's another star."

This sense of being removed, taken right out of one's ordinary life and being transported to a different world, is part and parcel of canoe travel in the north woods. Much of the feeling stems, I think, from the abruptness of the transition: one steps from car or train or aeroplane into this fragile shell of canvas, aluminium or fibreglass, paddles to the first portage, beyond which the outboard-motor boats cannot go, and suddenly the familiar world is gone, and there is nothing but the primitive and the wild all around. There is no way to familiarize oneself gradually with this wilderness; one is simply dropped into it, and there is no continuity of history to soften its hard edges. As Mrs. Jaques wrote: "This country never knew a mediaeval time; it came straight from the primaeval into today."

It is not necessary to travel into the far northern reaches of Canada to find this solitude. It lies everywhere in the canoe country, and the marvel is how little effort is required to enter that world and achieve a sense of harmony with it. I remember a trip I took once, with my brother and my 14-year-old son, into the canoe country along the Canadian border north of Gunflint Lake. There we found an island of genuine enchantment, an island that, as far as we could tell on arrival, had never before been trod by human feet.

We started our trip one August afternoon from a point south of Saganaga Lake, planning a journey of about a week that would take us in a large circle through Saganaga and several other lakes back to our starting point. There were a few cars parked there when we left, indications that other canoe campers had departed into the wilderness before us. Yet in our entire trip we saw another human being only once, and that was from a distance.

Ours was an aluminium canoe, and with two tents, a jungle hammock, sleeping bags, cooking equipment and food for three it was comfortably loaded. We pushed off into a small stream that led through a tiny set of rapids past a point and into Saganaga Lake itself. Within 15 minutes we had left the world we knew.

Overhead a raven croaked, and far above him a hawk sailed in endless circles, rising on a column of warm air. The water was purest blue and crinkled with millions of tiny ripples stirred by a vagrant breeze. Through the days that followed, I paddled in an utterly dreamlike state. My mind revolved around food, campsites and the lake, from which we drank the purest of water whenever we felt thirsty, simply by cupping our hands and dipping it up as we drifted along in the canoe. By 5 or 6 o'clock every afternoon our campsite would appear; we never knew where it might be, but we knew that we would find a place before darkness set in. We landed, pitched our tents, built our fire, cooked our supper, and then we sat around and smoked and talked until, half asleep, we crawled off to bed. And travelling leisurely along in this way we came to the special island.

It was a typical product of the Canadian Shield, this island that was to become uniquely ours: a rounded, shelving, rocky ledge at one end, a clump of pines and soft, mossy ground at the other. There are a thousand variations of this kind of island all through the lake country, shaped aeons ago by glacial action, but we were soon to find certain important differences.

Its rocky end was not only nicely shelved, affording an excellent unloading site, but it also had a troughlike indentation at the water's edge that could have been especially made for a canoe. It was like coming into a slip: we poked our bow in, it came to rest on a rocky incline, and

Nesting in the grass along a lakeshore, a common loon sports its breeding plumage: glossy black head, striped collar and checkered back.

we stepped ashore without so much as wetting the soles of our plim-solls. We could draw the canoe up safely out of reach of evex the stormiest waves. Loading and unloading were as simple as if the canoe were lying alongside a dock, and there was never any fear of carelessly capsizing her as we put our gear ashore.

Just beyond the canoe landing, a little closer to a clump of trees, was another convenience: a level ledge right next to the water that was a perfect place for washing dishes. This is a boon not to be taken lightly, for dishwashing is a chore that must be performed right after a meal, and finding a place where one can comfortably wash the dishes and then stack them without having them slide or roll off into the water is often difficult. Never, in all my subsequent experience, did I find a dishwashing site that came close to that one.

The living quarters on the wooded end of the island were superb. There was level ground at the highest spot where our two small tents and the jungle hammock could be set up secure against wind, and the ground there was springy and soft with brown pine needles. There was no fear of having rain water invade the tent in a storm because the ground sloped off on all sides. A dead tree had fallen precisely where we needed it to sit on; in front of it we built our campfire on a bed of stones we found conveniently at hand.

Finally, we discovered a perfect place for swimming, the best we had ever seen. Across the ledge from the canoe landing, the rock fell steeply down into the lake. The top of this little cliff ranged from five to 10 feet above the water line; it was a natural place on which to stand. And there was no problem of falling on slippery rock when climbing out: the glacier that passed by long ago had obligingly plucked chunks off the rock, leaving a series of rough steps—a natural staircase on which we could comfortably return to land.

What does a person do in a place like that perfect island to pass the time? Actually, the question never arose. I cannot remember a moment in which I was bored, and nor can my brother and my son. For that matter, I cannot remember a moment when I measured time. The first couple of days, I dutifully wound my watch every night. On the third night, I thought to myself: "Why wind it? Why not give it a rest? Why not try to see what it's like to live without measuring time?" And for the balance of the trip that was exactly what we did—we lived like deer or loons, measuring our days by the sun, eating when we were hungry, falling asleep when we were tired, waking up when we had slept long enough. There is no better restorative for a mind and body wearied by the pace of civilized living.

The first thing, every morning, was a plunge in the lake. The lake took care of just about everything that had to do with bodily cleanliness: I washed in it, I brushed my teeth in it, I shaved in it. The water was so clear that we could see the bottom 20 feet below from the cliff on which we stood to dive. There were rocks down there, and the sunlight played on them in beautiful effects of light and shadow filtered through the wavering blue. The water seemed almost a continuation of the air in liquid form; swimming in it was like jumping off a mountainside and gliding, like a gull.

Day after day dawned beautiful and sunny. We would emerge from the lake, shaking the water off our skins like dogs, and build the fire for breakfast. From then until nightfall, the fire never went out; it might sink down to glowing embers, but someone would always put a few branches on in time to keep it going. In the evening, from my sleeping bag, I would see its warm red coals glowing through the entrance of my tent, and I always went to sleep with this vision of man's first primitive warmth and comfort.

What did we eat? One morning we ate three fish that I caught before breakfast—three lovely smallmouth bass, about a pound each. We baked corn muffins, we made pancakes. My brother made bannock, the unleavened bread that has for centuries been a staple of the north woods; it was a skill he had acquired on previous trips. I don't remember the menu that we put together from our stores; I remember only that it was, quite literally, the best food I ever ate because I was hungry for it every day.

We had endless things to do. We fussed with out tents until they were absolutely perfect; we could have lived in them for years. We gathered wood and pine cones for the fire, stacking it neatly, with the cones at one side in a little pile. We washed our clothes and hung them up to dry. When we were sleepy, we took naps. When we woke up, we dived into the lake again.

And one day, down among the rocks on the wooded end of the island, we found a broken paddle. It was a little like Robinson Crusoe's finding Friday's footprint on the sand: suddenly we realized that we were not alone in the world. Where the paddle came from we had not the slightest idea; it could have been an accident that happened 50 weeks before, or 50 years. The paddle was old and silver grey from exposure. Totally by accident, we had found a name for our island: Broken

Paddle Island. We carved the name in the paddle, added our own names and leaned it against a tree.

I have been on many campsites since that magic time on Broken Paddle Island, and I have seen the other side of the coin. Sometimes there simply is no decent place to set up a tent and cook dinner, and on such occasions I have learned to make the best of what there is. There are lakes with marshy banks from which mosquitoes rise in dense stinging clouds as soon as one sets foot ashore; such places are to be tolerated only as long as absolutely necessary, because there is no use trying to fight the insects of the north woods. Get into bed and fall asleep as fast as possible; rise early and flee—that is the only maxim to follow in those situations. The bad nights must be taken with the good, and what one campsite lacks the next will probably have; this is, for me, the best camping country in the world.

Nor should an occasional day of rain spoil the pleasure of a canoe trip. The world takes on a unique beauty when rain is falling on the lakes and forests. Colours are deeper and very pure. The mosses, saturated with water, are rich and full; even the lichens turn thick and spongy and assert their character as living plants rather than just scabs on the rocks. The trees glisten in the soft light, each leaf and needle a resting place for glittering drops of water. The light diffuses softly through and over everything—there are no contrasts, no shadows, only an abiding softness in the shapes and outlines of the landscape that matches the pervading silence. The light reflects dimly off wet roots twisting in the earth, and from wet rocks at the water's edge. It is no hardship to paddle a canoe under these conditions, and the woods may show things that otherwise one might never see.

For example: fog blowing off the hills and through the treetops as though the land were breathing. A distant grove of aspens glowing a pale green among the dark green pines. A duck speeding low over the lake, wings beating a mad tattoo in the quiet air. A deer sticking its nose out of the woods, then advancing to the water unafraid as the canoe glides by.

The water on such a day is the colour of beaten silver. I remember a rainy day on the river Granite when, paddling from one campsite to another, I stopped to study the water as carefully, as reverently, as I might study a work of art. The sound it made as it slipped down among the rocks was a soft gurgling, a quiet talking that reminded me of a child talking to itself as it sits engrossed in play, or the sweet mur-

Mature red and white pines—the reds are oval-crowned and shorter than the whites—dominate the rocky shoreline of Lac La Croix.

murings of lovers. It was a spiritual talking, expressed in tones of marvellous liquidity as the river slowly dimpled its way down through rounded rocks towards the rapids below.

Here the talk became more boisterous. There was conflict now between the water and the rocks, and the river dipped to meet the challenge. Now it rose in a swirl as it met the big rocks, and its talk changed to a continuous protesting and arguing. Waves curled up from the smooth surface, then turned white and foamy as they broke in the rapids. Then, suddenly, as we coursed through this small section of rapids, the water was still again.

It was here on this grey and quiet day that I fished a drowning bee out of the water. I saw it struggling feebly, and as we approached I slid my paddle gently under it and lifted it into the silvery air. The bee was a pitiful sight; it lay there motionless, seemingly unaware that it was out of danger. I held the paddle close to my face to observe it, and I could see the fat black-and yellow thorax pulsing, exactly as if it had been a spent animal fighting for breath after a hard chase. It lay there for a considerable length of time—and then, suddenly, with what was obviously an enormous effort, it staggered to its feet and stood there shakily. Its body heaved, its legs trembled. I could see its wings, all sodden with water, lying flat along its belly. For the time being, it made no effort to raise them.

By this time I was utterly absorbed in watching the struggle for life of this tiny creature. It seemed so courageous, standing there trembling, but still trying to regain control of its water-soaked body. The next move came from its antennae. There was a sudden twitch, then slowly, creakily, the drooping black threads came to life, stiffened, and moved up and forwards. The black antennae turned this way and that, probing the air. Now there was a sudden blur of movement along the bee's belly: the first attempt to use its wings. The effort lasted only a split second; those delicate gossamer members must have felt to the exhausted bee as though they were made of lead. But now the bee raised its yellow hind legs, one after the other, and set about cleaning its wings, stroking them, straightening them, shaking tiny droplets of water off them. And once again it tried to use them—but it was too soon. A blur of movement, and they were still again.

Now the bee began to crawl along the paddle. Its agility was quite surprising. It seemed to be trying to find out where it was. It crawled to the very edge of the paddle, then stopped and seemed to lean out over it. Below, the water was slipping past, smooth, silver and treacherous. Did the bee see it, and remember?

Again it rested, for perhaps half a minute. Then it tried its wings once more. They were still too wet, and so it set about again to clean them. Back and forth the hind legs worked, stroking, smoothing, shaking off the droplets that still held its wings captive. Now it took a few more shaky steps. Now the wings blurred into life once more, and then again. And now the bee rose slowly into the air. For a moment it hovered over the paddle, the wings a blur of silver against the black-and-yellow body; then, with a sudden forward dart, it was gone across the water, back towards the shore.

Such are the rewards of the grey days, when in the soft, damp stillness one can draw close to the essence of the forest and its inhabitants. These are the times of intimate looks, when the forest world seems open and receptive, when its busy work is slowed and strangers may come in. This is a time of sombre beauty in the woods, when the present fades away into the silence.

There are other days, too. I stood one autumn afternoon in a yellow-golden meadow in Manitoba, not far from Sioux Lookout. The air this day was very still, with only the faintest of wandering breezes ruffling the grass and moaning gently in the treetops. The place smelled heavily of mushrooms, damp earth, rotting leaves and pine needles. Birds chirped faintly now and then, but their season was passing and they were few in number. The woods were dark and cold; it was as though here, in this meadow, the essence of summer was still lingering—one last look, one last warm breath before the winter finally closed down.

The Forest's Last Stand

Where the north woods end and the treeless tundra begins there is no sharp line of demarcation. The two environments intermingle in a subarctic zone up to 200 miles wide, and the balance between them shifts gradually, so that a northbound traveller does not get the full impact of the change until he reaches the zone's ragged upper edge. The forest's dramatic last stand is shown here in pictures taken near Churchill, a town on the western shore of Hudson Bay founded by 17th Century English fur traders.

In this bleak landscape, spruces are no longer the giants of the densely wooded terrain to the south; under the savage scourging of the subarctic climate they dwindle to small, scattered clumps. Some trees stand stunted and mis-shapen in sheltered pockets of low-lying muskeg or bog amid stretches of naked or lichen-crusted rock. Other trees, exposed to the powerful prevailing wind, grow aslant with branches only on their leeward side.

The earth itself seems to be working against the trees. Underlaid by permafrost and insulated against the summer sun by a thick mat of tiny plants, the ground thaws out to a depth of only three to five feet. In this thin layer of poor soggy soil, trees must spread their roots wide both to stay upright and to absorb meagre nutriment. Expectably, the trees that dominate this terrain are shallow-rooted, water-tolerant species, chiefly black spruce and tamarack. White spruce, aspen and alder grow on better-drained sites.

The changing of the seasons does little to relieve the trees' ordeal. Spring is ephemeral, and in summer the trees are drenched not only in meltwater but also in 10 inches of rain. September usually brings the first snowfall. Soon afterwards, the Churchill area is once more seized in winter's merciless grip, not to be released for almost eight months.

It would be a triumph if the trees merely held their own in this hostile world. But they may be doing better than just that. Scientists calculate that the ice age glaciers left the Hudson Bay region stripped bare only 7,300 years ago. They consider it a trend that, with the climate warming up in the relatively short span of time since, the plant succession has already created new soil and resettled the area. Thus the mere presence of trees this far north suggests that the forest may still be advancing, invading the tundra's domain.

MARCH: BUFFETED SPRUCE BRANCHES

MARCH: A LONE WHITE SPRUCE FRAMED BY SNOW RIDGES

JUNE: AN ALDER REFLECTED IN MELTWATER

JUNE: A WHITE SPRUCE PIONEERING A ROCKY OUTCROP

JUNE: ROCK AND ICE ALONG HUDSON BAY

OCTOBER: BLACK SPRUCES, TAMARACKS AND LICHENS

OCTOBER: A SPINDLY WHITE SPRUCE AND SUBARCTIC GROUND COVER

OCTOBER: MUSKEG UNDER A FOREBODING SKY

MARCH: WHITE SPRUCES BURDENED BY SNOW

MARCH: A SNOW FORMATION AT THE BAY'S EDGE

Bibliography

*Denotes published in US only.

*Bland, John H., *Forests of Lilliput: The Realm of Mosses and Lichens*. Prentice-Hall Inc., 1971.

*Bolz, J. Arnold, *Portage into the Past*. University of Minnesota Press, 1960.

*Burt, William H., and Richard L. Grossenheider, *A Field Guide to the Mammals*. Houghton Mifflin Company, 1964.

*Cahalane, Victor H., *Mammals of North America*. The Macmillan Company, 1947.

*Cobb, Boughton, *A Field Guide to the Ferns*. Houghton Mifflin Company, 1956.

*Collingwood, G. H. and Warren D. Brush, *Knowing Your Trees*. The American Forestry Association, 1964.

Dewdney, Selwyn, and Kenneth E. Kidd, *Indian Rock Paintings of the Great Lakes*. University of Toronto Press, 1967.

*Douglas, William O., *My Wilderness: East to Katahdin*. Pyramid Books, 1969. (Available only in paperback.)

*Farb, Peter, and the Editors of TIME-LIFE BOOKS, *The Forest*. TIME-LIFE BOOKS, 1963.

Farb, Peter, and the Editors of TIME-LIFE BOOKS, *The Land and Wildlife of North America*. TIME-LIFE BOOKS, 1966.

*Hale, Mason E., *How to Know the Lichens*. Wm. C. Brown Company Publishers, 1969.

*Innis, Harold A., *The Fur Trade in Canada*. University of Toronto Press, 1962.

Jaques, Florence Page, *Canoe Country*. University of Minnesota Press, 1938.

*Kimble, George H. T., and Dorothy Good, eds., *Geography of the Northlands*. The American Geographical Society, 1955.

*Lakela, Olga, *A Flora of Northeastern Minnesota*. University of Minnesota Press, 1966.

Lawrence, R. D., *Wildlife in Canada*. Michael Joseph, 1966.

*MacKay, Douglas, *The Honourable Company*. The Bobbs-Merrill Company, 1936.

*MacLennan, Hugh, *The Rivers of Canada*. Charles Scriber's Sons, 1961.

Mech, David L., *The Wolf: The Ecology and Behaviour of an Endangered Species*. Constable, 1972.

*Meen, V. B., *Quetico Geology*. University of Toronto Press, 1959.

*Moon, Barbara, *The Canadian Shield*. N.S.L. Natural Science of Canada Limited, 1970.

*Morse, Eric W., *Canoe Routes of the Voyageurs*. Minnesota Historical Society, 1962. (Available only in paperback.)

*Morse, Eric W., *Fur Trade Canoe Routes of Canada/Then and Now*. Minnesota Historical Society, 1969.

*Murie, Olaus J., *A Field Guide to Animal Tracks*. Houghton Mifflin Company, 1954.

*Nelson, Bruce, *Land of the Dacotahs*. University of Minnesota Press, 1946.

*Nute, Grace Lee, *Rainy River Country*. Minnesota Historical Society, 1950. (Available only in paperback.)

*Nute, Grace Lee, *The Voyageur*. Minnesota Historical Society, 1955.

*Nute, Grace Lee, *The Voyageur's Highway*. Minnesota Historical Society, 1965.

*Olson, Sigurd F., *Listening Point*. Alfred A. Knopf, 1970.

*Olson, Sigurd F., *The Lonely Land*. Alfred A. Knopf, 1961.

*Olson, Sigurd F., *The Singing Wilderness*. Alfred A. Knopf, 1957.

*Olson, Sigurd F., and Les Blacklock, *The Hidden Forest*. Viking Press, 1969.

*O'Meara, Walter, *The Savage Country*. Houghton Mifflin Company, 1960.

*Orr, Robert T., *Mammals of North America*. Doubleday and Company, 1971.

*Petrides, George A., *A Field Guide to Trees and Shrubs*. Houghton Mifflin Company, 1958.

Pruitt, William O., *Animals of the North*. Harper and Row, 1967.

*Robbins, Chandler S., Bertel Bruun and Herbert S. Zim, *Birds of North America*. Golden Press, 1966.

*Rue, Leonard Lee III, *The World of the Beaver*. J. B. Lippincott Company, 1964.

*Rutter, Russell J., and Douglas H. Pimlott, *The World of the Wolf*. J. B. Lippincott Company, 1968.

*Seton, Ernest Thompson, *Life Histories of Northern Animals, Vol. I*. Charles Scribner's Sons, 1909.

*Sevareid, Eric, *Canoeing with the Cree*. Minnesota Historical Society, 1968.

Silvics of the Forest Trees of the United States. U.S. Department of Agriculture, Forest Service, 1965.

Smith, Alexander Hanchett, *Mushroom Hunter's Field Guide*. University of Michigan Press, 1963.

*Spears, Borden, ed., *Wilderness Canada*. Clarke, Irwin and Company, Limited, 1970.

Steinhacker, Charles, *Superior: Portrait of a Living Lake*. Harper and Row, 1971.

*Taverner, P. A., *Birds of Canada*. National Museum of Canada, Canada Department of Mines, 1934.

*Warren, Edward Royal, *The Beaver, Its Work and Its Ways*. The Williams and Wilkins Company, 1927.

Wilsson, Lars, *My Beaver Colony*. Souvenir Press, 1969, also Pan Books, 1970.

Acknowledgements

The author and editors of this book are particularly indebted to William O. Pruitt Jr., Professor of Zoology, University of Manitoba, Winnipeg. They also wish to thank: Donald F. Bruning, Assistant Curator of Ornithology, New York Zoological Park, New York City; Selwyn Dewdney, London, Ontario; Harold S. Feinberg, Department of Living Invertebrates, The American Museum of Natural History, New York City; Dorothy Gimmestad, Minnesota Historical Society, St. Paul; Miron L. Heinselman, Principal Plant Ecologist, North Central Forest Experiment Station, U.S. Forest Service, Ely, Minnesota; Douglas Hornby, Director, Peace-Athabasca Delta Project, Edmonton, Alberta; Sidney S. Horenstein, Department of Invertebrate Paleontology, The American Museum of Natural History, New York City; John W. Miller, New York City; Eric W. Morse, Tenaga, Quebec; Charles W. Myers, Department of Herpetology, The American Museum of Natural History, New York City; John Pallister, Department of Entomology, The American Museum of Natural History, New York City; Larry Pardue, The New York Botanical Garden, New York City; Douglas Pimlott, Professor of Animal Ecology and Wildlife Biology, University of Toronto, Ontario; Russell J. Rutter, Huntsville, Ontario; Alexander Smith, Professor of Botany and Director, University Herbarium, University of Michigan, Ann Arbor; Frederick Ward, Professor of Zoology, University of Manitoba, Winnipeg.

The translation of the song "Quand un Chrétien Se Détermine à Voyager," pages 72-73, is from *The Voyageur*, pages 151-154, by Grace Lee Nute, Minnesota Historical Society, 1955 (© 1931 D. Appleton & Co.).

Quotations, pages 152, 154, are from *Canoeing with the Cree*, pages 161-166, by Eric Sevareid, Minnesota Historical Society, 1968 (© 1968 Eric Sevareid).

Picture Credits

Sources for pictures in this book are shown below. Credits for pictures from left to right are separated by commas, from top to bottom by dashes.

Cover—Gerald R. Brimacombe. Front end papers 2, 3—Gerald R. Brimacombe. Front end paper 4, page 1—Jim Brandenburg. 2, 3—Paul Jensen. 4, 5—Les Blacklock. 6, 7—Harald Sund. 8 to 11—Charles Steinhacker. 12, 13—Paul Jensen. 18, 19—Map by R. R. Donnelley Cartographic Services. 24—Paul Jensen. 29—Barbara K. Deans, John Kohout from Root Resources—Dr. E. R. Degginger. 30—Larry West—Dr. W. A. Crich—G. J. Harris, Dr. E. R. Degginger. 31—Dr. E. R. Degginger—Barbara K. Deans, Dr. W. A. Crich (2). 37—*The Minneapolis Tribune.* 38 to 41—Gerald R. Brimacombe. 42, 43—Gerald R. Brimacombe, Les Blacklock. 44—Paul Jensen. 45, 46, 47—Les Blacklock. 50, 51—G. J. Harris. 54—Gerald R. Brimacombe. 56, 57—Gerald R. Brimacombe. 59—Bruce Litteljohn. 64—from *Harper's Weekly*, Feb. 1, 1890. 68, 69—Jim Brandenburg. 75—Paulus Leeser courtesy Public Archives of Canada. 76, 77—Glenbow-Alberta Institute. 78 to 81—Paulus Leeser courtesy Public Archives of Canada. 84—T. W. Hall. 87—Les Blacklock. 90—Jim Brandenburg. 91—Lynn L. Rogers. 95—David Cavagnaro. 96, 97—Kenneth W. Fink, David Cavagnaro—Craig Blacklock. 98 to 105—David Cavagnaro. 106, 107—Kenneth W. Fink. 112, 113—Les Blacklock. 117—D. Mohrhardt from the National Audubon Society—W. Victor Crich, Jim Brandenburg (2). 121, 122, 123—Harald Sund. 124, 125—Ed Cesar from The National Audubon Society. 126—Les Blacklock. 127—Les Blacklock (2)—L. David Mech, Gilbert F. Staender. 128, 129—Harald Sund. 134, 135—Robert Walch. 136—Les Blacklock. 140 to 149—Robert Walch. 152, 153—Jim Brandenburg. 157—James H. Bellingham. 160, 161—Gerald R. Brimacombe. 165, 166, 167—Harald Sund. 168, 169—Gerald R. Brimacombe. 170, 171—Norman R. Lightfoot. 172 to 175—Paul Jensen. 176 to 179—Harald Sund.

Index

Numerals in italics indicate a photograph or drawing of the subject mentioned.

Filmsetting by C. E. Dawkins (Typesetters) Ltd., London, SE1 1UN.
Printed and bound in Belgium by Brepols S.A.—Turnhout. **XXX**

JESUS: THE EVIDENCE

JESUS: THE EVIDENCE

THE LATEST RESEARCH AND
DISCOVERIES INVESTIGATED BY

IAN WILSON

REGNERY PUBLISHING, INC.
Washington, DC

Library of Congress Cataloguing-in-Publication Data

ISBN 0-89526-239-8

Published in the United States by
Regnery Publishing, Inc.
An Eagle Publishing Company
One Massachusetts Avenue, NW
Washington, DC 20001
www.regnery.com

Distributed to the trade by
National Book Network
4720-A Boston Way
Lanham, MD 20706

Printed on acid-free paper
Manufactured in the United States of America

10 9 8 7 6 5 4 3 2 1

Books are available in quantity for promotional or
premium use. Write to Director of Special Sales, Regnery
Publishing, Inc., One Massachusetts Avenue, NW,
Washington, DC 2001, for information on discounts and
terms or call (202) 216-0600

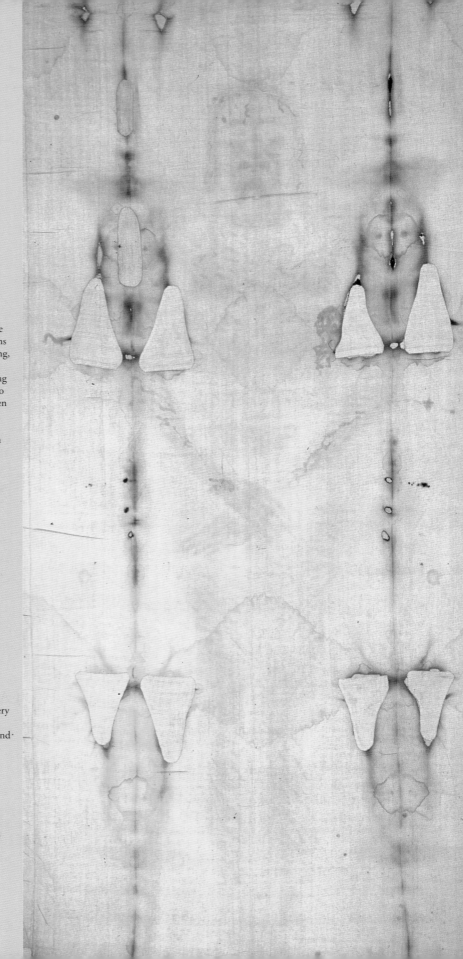

CONTENTS

AUTHOR'S PREFACE

When the first edition of this book was written back in 1984, it was as an accompaniment to London Weekend Television's subsequently notorious three-part television series of the same name. In the course of my working together with the series' makers it became apparent that they had some quite different ideas from my own regarding what constituted a properly objective approach to the historical Jesus. Although we agreed to differ in a variety of ways, even so it was necessary for me partly at least to incorporate elements which they regarded as necessary and topical, but which I would have preferred to omit.

Happily the book has remained continuously in print, and it has been a particular delight to be asked by Michael Dover of Weidenfeld to write a major update of its text, now free of any of the constraints of the former television partnership. One of the benefits of this update, besides the release from such fetters, has been the chance to incorporate the considerable number of discoveries relating to Jesus that there have been since 1984, such as the discovery of a fishing boat of his time; of the bones of the high priest Caiaphas; and of what may be the oldest known fragments of a gospel text. Another of the benefits has been to give the book a whole new look with totally fresh, high-quality photographs specially chosen to bring life, and equally importantly colour, to the world in which Jesus moved.

For much of this fresh material, both textual and visual, I am indebted to an invaluable re-visit to Israel with my wife in 1994, and to one very special publication, *Biblical Archaeology Review* of Washington DC. It was BAR's founding editor, Hershel Shanks, who campaigned relentlessly and ultimately successfully for the recent opening up of the Dead Dea Scrolls to general scholarship. In his superbly illustrated journal, which appears six times a year, Shanks manages that rare feat of providing authoritative up-to-the-minute articles in which both Jews and Christians can find common interest, and his publication deserves much greater acceptance by the world's university libraries than it currently receives. Many of the fine photographs and reconstructions included in this new edition are ones that I first came across in the pages of *Biblical Archaeology Review*, and I am particularly grateful to BAR for introducing them to me.

Overall, this new edition has been designed as a careful meld of both the old and the new, with the joins made as invisibly as possible. As in the first edition, I have almost invariably used the Jerusalem Bible translation of the Old and New Testaments for its clear, modern English. While much of the old framework has been retained, the original book's chapter on the time of Constantine the Great is one that has been dropped on the grounds that it unnecessarily highlighted the divisions between Christians, when the emphasis should be on what they have in common. In several other ways my pro-Christian bias may be rather more to the fore in this than in the earlier edition, but wherever possible I have tried to maintain historical objectivity – even if some purists may frown at my continued usage of the traditional 'BC' and 'AD' rather than the now more politically correct 'BCE' and 'CE'.

For coping admirably with an author now living ten thousand miles distant from them in Australia, my warmest congratulations and thanks to Anthony Cheetham, Michael Dover, Clare Currie and Ariane Bankes of Weidenfeld/Orion of London, together with picture researcher Joanne King, designer Mark Roberts and proofreader Antony Wood. Also, as ever, my thanks go to my wife, Judith, who was by my side throughout our 1994 tour of the land of Jesus, and who, amidst all the chores of moving continents, single-handedly scanned the original *Jesus: The Evidence* text onto my word-processor, saving me much unnecessary re-typing.

Ian Wilson,
Bellbowrie,
Queensland,
November 1995

INTRODUCTION

Short of some unforeseen catastrophe, the great majority of the umpteen million people alive today will live to experience the year 2000 AD, theoretically the two-thousandth birthday of a Galilean Jew named Jesus of Nazareth. For many of those millions, many who even without thinking about it count their years from his birthday, Jesus is a figure of supreme irrelevance. A mere name to use for abuse. Just some Jew who died two millennia ago and who has absolutely no place in today's scientific, material-minded world. For others, however, Jesus is someone very special, a seemingly flesh-and-blood man whose life was preordained and whose death, the most public and degrading imaginable, demonstrated that death is *not* the end.

The issues could therefore not be more clearcut. Have those who believed that Jesus was special wasted the last two thousand years on worthless make-believe? Have they been victims of the biggest hoax in history? Or could those who have consistently chosen to ignore Jesus and his message be the ultimate, very long-term losers?

At the heart of these questions are what should *anyone*, of whatever background, religious or non-religious, believe about Jesus? That he was born of a virgin? That his birthday was on 25 December, 0 AD? That he could heal the sick and walk on water? That he married Mary Magdalen? That he died on a cross, and then resuscitated two days later? That he wanted his followers to dress up in funny clothes and call themselves popes and cardinals, archbishops and bishops, priests and nuns? That he is the second person of a divine Trinity?

The need for straight answers to these questions, reverent and irreverent, has become all the more necessary in recent years with the decline of formal Christian religious instruction in schools, as a result of which a generation is growing up, certainly in the UK, who have never been taught what my own preceding generation learned as basics.

Accordingly, the object of this book is to weed out all that is unworthy, of which there has been a great deal in recent years, and to look at what may be considered truly valid of the human Jesus of Nazareth as deducible from every possible source: the oldest surviving scraps of the gospels; extracts from early historical documents; comments from early opponents of Christianity; the most recent Israeli archaeological finds; the latest insights of theologians; and much more.

Fascinatingly, even in the decade since the first edition of this book was published some significant new discoveries have been made, particularly on the part of Israeli archaeologists, belonging as they do to a people who for twenty centuries have so firmly rejected Jesus. Although this author would be failing the reader if he did not make clear that he has been a practising Christian for more than two decades, and can therefore hardly avoid some bias, he is also a trained historian, and there will be absolutely no attempt to fudge the issues where doctrine and a fair-minded approach to the evidence part company.

For, as even the most hardened sceptic must be bound to admit, the still obscure Galilean Jew who forms the subject of this book, who died a seeming failure, executed as a criminal and abandoned by his followers, is probably the most influential individual there has ever been in all history. And this is not least of the reasons why whatever is written about him should be honest and true to the best of each individual writer's ability, whether that writer is the author of an original gospel, or anyone approaching him afresh at the present time.

1

GETTING BACK TO THE BASICS

In an ideal world we would obviously want to examine the original manuscripts of the gospels as first written by Matthew, Mark, Luke and John. We might want those authors to have signed and dated them. We might even feel that they should have been accompanied by some sort of curriculum vitae setting out how well each author knew Jesus and/or his disciples. All this should be some form of assurance for us that what they related about Jesus was based on hard fact.

Now, given that there has come down to us no original manuscript even of a single one of William Shakespeare's thirty-seven plays – despite the fact that they were mostly written less than four hundred years ago – it might seem even more unlikely that there should survive the originals of four gospels written about Jesus after a span of two thousand years. Yet in some ways Jesus is better documented than Shakespeare. And as few realize, much of the oldest documentation about him has only come to light within the last century, and is continuing to do so.

The urge to find such early documentation is nothing new. When at the beginning of the sixteenth century the great Dutch scholar Erasmus compiled the first-ever printed edition of the New Testament in its original Greek, he was well aware that the biblical manuscripts he was using derived

Opposite *St Catherine's Monastery, Sinai, seen from the north-east, set at the base of the Jebel Musa, the mountain on which Moses reputedly received the Ten Commandments. Because of its remoteness, St Catherine's has never been pillaged throughout fourteen centuries. As a result, some of its earliest manuscripts have survived to modern times, among these the famous Codex Sinaiticus discovered by the German scholar Constantin Tischendorf in 1844. Reaching this monastery once required an arduous journey by camel, but now there is a proper road, and it has been opened to regular tourism.*

from successions of copyists over many centuries. Inevitably errors and mis-readings had crept in, discrepancies that logically had to be less the further back in time the manuscript had originated.

Erasmus therefore did his best to use only the earliest available manu-scripts, but as a pioneer he had little to guide him on how to date such material. Only after his time did it become realized that the minuscule, or upper and lower case Greek lettering of the manuscripts he had mostly consulted meant that they could not have been written before the ninth century AD. Before then handwriting was in uncials, that is all in capitals, or upper case Greek letters only.

As this became recognized, so better-informed travellers began to look for manuscripts with such writing, particularly when visiting remote monasteries where there was the chance that such documents might have lain undisturbed over the centuries. The ignorance and lack of historical concern of many of those in charge of such treasures quickly became apparent. In 1677, after visiting Mount Athos in Greece, British Ambassador Dr John Covel reported seeing there 'vast heaps … all covered with dust and dirt, many of them rotted and spoiled'. In the 1830s, also at Athos, British aristocrat Robert Curzon came across a page in uncial hand-writing lying discarded in an obviously neglected room, and asked if he might take it. When the abbot, momentarily suspicious that the page might be valuable, asked Curzon the reason for his request, he quick-wittedly concocted the excuse: 'My servant suggested that it might be useful to cover some jampots or vases or preserves which I have at home'. His suspicions allayed, the abbot not only handed the page over, but also generously cut off an inch-think wad of some other early manuscript pages as a gift to his honoured guest.

However it was to be a German specialist in ancient languages, Constantin Tischendorf, a contemporary of Curzon's, who would pioneer an altogether more professional approach to seeking out the very earliest documents attesting to Jesus. As had already become recognized in Tischendorf's time, mediaeval scribes had sometimes re-used the expensive vellum on which ancient manuscripts had been written. They would scrape away the ink of the original writing, then copy some other text on top of this – creating what manuscript specialists call a palimpsest. Sometimes the earlier writing could still be read, but a fifth-century uncial scriptural text beneath one such palimpsest, the *Codex Ephraemi* in Paris, had long been thought irretrievable until the arrival of Tischendorf. He managed the task in two years, using such methods as holding the pages up to the light. In order to familiarize himself further with materials written in uncials, he also travelled to Rome in the hope of examining there the Vatican's *Codex Vaticanus*, dating back to the fourth century. However, although Pope Gregory XVI received him kindly, the cardinal directly in charge of the manuscript was less forthcoming, denying him access for any longer than six hours.

Undaunted, in 1844 Tischendorf set off on what would be his most famous quest: to the monastery of St Catherine in the scorching wilderness of the Sinai Desert. There he hoped that he might find as yet unknown New Testament manuscripts that had been protected from the outside world by the monastery's remoteness. Dating from the sixth century, St Catherine's is spectacularly set at the foot of the granite cliffs on which Moses reputedly received the Ten Commandments, and while today the tourist can arrive there in the comfort of an air-conditioned coach, Tischendorf's only option was a gruelling twelve-day trek by camel.

Furthermore, even when he and his party arrived at the monastery's four-storey-high walls, which seemed to have no gate, their shouts were at first met only by a stony silence, as if the monastery had been abandoned. Then from some internal hoist a rope basket was lowered for Tischendorf's letters of introduction. This was whirled aloft, to be followed, after an unnerving delay obviously for the scrutinizing of the credentials, by the lowering of a second basket for Tischendorf himself. Bumped unceremoniously upwards and over the walls (later he would learn that there was a secret door for true VIPs), he found himself in a world that time seemed to have abandoned long before.

In fact the black-robed Orthodox monks of St Catherine's received their German visitor with characteristic warmth and hospitality, and in the course of the ensuing days they allowed him unrestricted access to their three libraries. Initially he found these somewhat disappointing, suggesting his long journeying might have been for nothing. But then, in his own words:

> I perceived in the middle of the great hall a large and wide basket full of old parchments; and the librarian, who was a man of information, told me that two heaps of papers like these, mouldered by time, had already been committed to the flames. What was my surprise to find amid this heap of papers a considerable number of sheets of a copy of the Old Testament in Greek, which seemed to me to be one of the most ancient that I had ever seen. The authorities of the monastery allowed me to possess myself of a third of these parchments, or about forty-three sheets, all the more readily as they were destined for the fire. But I could not get them to yield up possession of the remainder. The too lively satisfaction I displayed aroused their suspicions as to the value of this manuscript.

Directly as a result of Tischendorf insufficiently concealing his interest in the material, the monks denied the very existence of the parchments on his next visit to St Catherine's, and it was to take another fifteen years, and only then with the leverage of credentials provided by Tsar Alexander II of Russia, before he was allowed to visit the monastery again. This time the monks received him with renewed warmth, their steward even inviting the visitor to his cell to enjoy a glass of home-brewed date liqueur. And it was on this particular occasion that, with the words 'And I too have read a Septuagint' (a Greek translation of the Old Testament), the steward suddenly took down a cloth-wrapped bundle from a shelf, and laid it before Tischendorf. As Tischendorf subsequently related, upon the cloth's removal, he instantly recognized:

> ... not only those very leaves which, fifteen years before, I had taken out of the basket, but also other parts of the Old Testament, the New Testament complete, and in addition the 'Epistle of Barnabas', and a part of the 'Shepherd of Hermas'. Full of joy, which this time I had self-commanded to conceal from the steward and the rest of the community, I asked, as if in a careless way, for permission to take the manuscript into my sleeping chamber to look over it more at leisure. There by myself I could give way to the transport of joy which I felt. I knew that I held in my hand the most precious biblical treasure in existence – a document whose age and importance exceeded that of all the manuscripts which I had ever examined during twenty years' study of the subject.

The manuscript which Tischendorf so emotionally leafed through that night, there and then transcribing the 'Epistle of Barnabas' and 'Shepherd of Hermas', is today known throughout the world as the *Codex Sinaiticus*. The monks allowed Tischendorf to borrow it, and although he is often unfairly accused of having stolen it from them, the truth seems to be that he simply acted as intermediary for Tsar Alexander to buy it for the Russian imperial collection. In 1933, by which time ownership had passed to the then impecunious Soviet revolutionaries, it was purchased by London's British Museum for £100,000, at that time by far the largest amount ever paid for any ancient manuscript.

Today the *Codex Sinaiticus* is displayed with little science and even less art in an old-fashioned showcase on the British Museum's ground floor. But as recognized by a consensus of modern scholarship it is a sister manuscript to the much-prized *Codex Vaticanus* that the Vatican cardinal had so obdurately prevented Tischendorf from properly studying. Exemplifying the discrepancies that have occurred as a result of scribal copying, both *Sinaiticus* and *Vaticanus* lack the last eleven verses of the Mark gospel, suggesting this may have been a late addition. They also do not have the John gospel story of the woman taken in adultery. Both have been reliably dated to approximately the mid-fourth century, and they remain the oldest near-complete texts of the Old and New Testaments in existence. Written on expensive vellum – *Sinaiticus* alone required the skins of 360 young sheep and goats – they were most likely created as a result of Christianity winning official status in the Roman Empire following the conversion of the Roman Emperor Constantine the Great.

A page of the Codex Sinaiticus. From characteristics of the uncial handwriting, scholars date the composition of Sinaiticus to the mid-fourth century and, with the Codex Vaticanus, it remains the earliest near-complete biblical text. Most importantly, its New Testament text is virtually entire. All the 346 pages of the manuscript as found by Tischendorf are today housed in London's British Museum, but more came to light as recently as 1975, when workmen at St Catherine's, Sinai opened up a hitherto unknown room in the monastery's north wall, revealing a cache of more than 3,000 manuscripts, icons and other items. The page reproduced, among the latest finds, is part of the 'Shepherd of Hermas', an early Christian apocalyptic work which the compilers of Sinaiticus clearly considered should be included in the Bible.

Thanks both to modern archaeology and to the enterprise of some sharp-eyed Moslem peasants, since Tischendorf's time significant quantities of other even earlier documentation relating to Jesus have been found – albeit in often very fragmentary form. How such material can be accurately dated is a fascinating topic in its own right, for contrary to popular supposition, radiocarbon dating, as used so famously for the Turin Shroud, is rarely the best method. Altogether more reliable are the guidelines set by the changes in fashion in handwriting, punctuation and spacing that have occurred century by century, changes sufficiently well catalogued to have become developed into a near-science (see table, pp.16-17). By noting such variations as they appear on documents that can be internally dated, i.e. by their references to the year of an emperor's reign, etc., scholars can with quite reasonable reliability date documents that do not have such clues.

Unfortunately, the fact that most early Christian documentation seems to have been written on cheap papyrus paper – somewhat inevitable in the years when Christianity was the religion of the poor and oppressed – has reduced the chances of such material's survival virtually to zero in most European countries. However Egypt, with its dry climate, is a happy exception, although many examples probably perished even there beneath workmen's picks during the years when archaeologists' main ambition was to find pharaonic gold. It was only in 1883, when the great Egyptologist Flinders Petrie, tripping over some rubbish, fleetingly recognized a fragment of what he called the 'finest Greek writing' that it became realized

HOW A CHRISTIAN SCRIPTURAL MANUSCRIPT CAN BE DATED

AD	HANDWRITING		OTHER CHARACTERISTIC FEATURES	
1600 –	ERA OF PRINTING			ERA OF PAPER
1500 –			1557 division into numbered verses by Robert Stephanus	
1400 –				
1300 –	irregular, variegated lettering	PERIOD OF MINUSCULE * WRITING		
1200 –			c. 1200 division into present-day chapters by Stephen Langton	
1100 –				
1000 –	precise, upright lettering		breathing marks more regularly used	PERIOD OF VELLUM (animal skin) CODICES
900 –		upright exaggerated lettering	introduction of the comma	
800 –		marked slope to right		
700 –				
600 –		letters ЄΘΟC upright ovals		
500 –	PERIOD OF UNCIAL † WRITING	vertical strokes thicken	5th c. introduction of dated colophons †† (initially in Syriac mss)	
400 –				PERIOD OF PAPYRUS CODICES ** (bound books)
300 –		Simple, dignified lettering	c. 300 nut-gall and iron sulphate inks replace soot-based variety	early 4th c. New Testament books consistently titled and divided into sections; Eusebian cross-reference system introduced
200 –				PERIOD OF PAPYRUS ROLLS **
100 –		letters ЄΘΟC circular		✧

*   Greek upper and lower case letters, eg. Πυρίοισ

†   Greek capital letters, eg. ΤΑϹЄ

††   a colophon is a paragraph, usually found at the end of a manuscript, giving information about authorship, sources, etc.

SURVIVING CHRISTIAN MANUSCRIPTS AND WHEN THEY WERE WRITTEN

CANONICAL			NON-CANONICAL	AD
LATIN	**GREEK**	**OTHER**		− 1600
	1516 Erasmus' first printed edition			− 1500
1445 Gutenberg's first printed Vulgate				
	c. 4000 SURVIVING MINUSCULE MSS (but few of complete Bible)			− 1400
				− 1300
				− 1200
ERA OF THE LATIN VULGATE				− 1100
				− 1000
			COPYING OF NUMEROUS APOCRYPHAL MSS (begun at very early date)	− 900
	835 first surviving dated minuscule of gospels	**897** earliest Georgian mss of gospels **887** earliest Armenian mss of gospels		− 800
716 earliest extant Vulgate of complete Bible	**c. 270 SURVIVING UNCIAL MSS** (but few complete)			− 700
				− 600
541-6 Codex Fuldensis **late 5th c.** Codex Sangallensis of gospels		**5th/6th c.** earliest Gothic mss of gospels **5th c.** Coptic gospels of Mark & Luke (Barcelona)		− 500
	early 5th c. Codex Ephraemi **4th c.** Codex Vaticanus; Codex Sinaiticus	**4th c.** Coptic Deuteronomy, Jonah & Acts	**4th c.** Achmim 'Gospel of Peter': Nag Hammadi Gnostic hoard and 'Thomas' gospel	− 400
	3rd c. Chester Beatty papyri of most New Testament books; Bodmer papyrus fragments from Luke and John gospels		**3rd c.** Dura fragment of Tatian harmony of canonical gospels	− 300
	early 2nd c. Rylands fragment of John gospel		**mid-2nd c.** Egerton papyrus of unknown gospel; Oxyrhynchus fragment of 'Thomas' gospel	− 200
	late 1st c.(?) Magdalen College fragment of Matthew gospel			− 100

** vellum was in use at this period, but is unknown for surviving Christian documents, no doubt because of expense (although 3rd-c. epistle of Hebrews is written on the back of a vellum roll)

✧ the period of papyrus rolls lasted until the sixth century for literary works, as distinct from scriptural material

that such material could sometimes be preserved.

As a result, Egyptian workmen, suitably alerted with promises of reward, soon began turning up odd papyrus fragments, prompting Britain's Egypt Exploration Fund in 1895 to send a young Oxford graduate, Bernard Pyne Grenfell, and his friend Arthur Surridge Hunt specifically to look for such material in a proper scientific manner. Although this partnership's first season in the Fayum was unrewarding, the next year they decided to investigate the apparently totally unprepossessing Futuh el Bahnasa, site of the former Hellenistic settlement of Oxyrhynchus, where in antiquity there had been a long-abandoned complex of early Christian monasteries and churches. Since no papyrus finds had ever been heard of from Oxyrhynchus, Grenfell suspected that it might have escaped the plundering that occurred elsewhere.

Deciding against excavating Oxyrhynchus' early church buildings, which he anticipated would long since have been cleared of anything of interest, Grenfell opted instead for the seventy-foot-high ancient rubbish heaps that lay on the site's outskirts. Recognizing that to investigate these properly demanded using local labour, who would need the most eagle-eyed supervision, he hired a seventy-strong workforce to cut into the most promising looking mound. As he subsequently recalled of the task's more unpleasant aspects, it meant:

> …standing all day to be half-choked and blinded by the peculiarly pungent dust of ancient rubbish, blended most days with the not less irritating sand of the desert; probably drinking water which not even the East London waterworks would have ventured to supply to its consumers, and keeping incessant watch over men who, however much you may flatter yourself to the contrary, will steal if they get the chance and think it worth their while doing so.

In the event, the work soon began to produce encouraging results, as papyrus scraps of considerable variety and quantity began to emerge. Many were private letters, contracts and other legal or official documents, most helpfully illuminating the everyday life of antiquity, though of no special relevance to Christian origins. Also represented, however, were occasional fragments in the characteristic handwriting styles of early religious and literary texts. And it was Hunt who would make the first significant find among these.

Only two days after he had begun preliminary sorting, as he was carefully smoothing out a scrap that seemed to have come from a numbered, paged book (quite different, therefore, from the long scrolls on which early Jewish and pagan religious literature was written), Hunt's eye fell on the word *karphos*. This he recognized as the Greek word which is translated as 'mote' in the familiar King James Bible text:

And why beholdest thou the mote that is in thy brother's eye, but considerest not the beam that is in thine own eye? (Matthew 7: 3; also Luke 6: 41)

As he deciphered further, Hunt recognized the fragment in his hand as being a version of the same well-known saying:

… then you will clearly see to cast the mote from your brother's eye.

The oddity, however, was that the form of words was significantly different from those in the known gospels. From this he quickly realized that the scrap could not be from one of them. Yet it included no less than seven sayings, each clearly preceded by the words 'Says Jesus'. Although three had no obvious counterpart in the known gospels, they still sounded as if they could well have come from the mouth of the gospel Jesus. What is more, the style of uncials in which the sayings were written dated them to about 200 AD. So could this be from a gospel written before what we now know as the canonical gospels?

As Grenfell and Hunt continued their excavations, other fragments of this same unknown gospel came to light. But it was not until nearly fifty years later that its full text was found – totally unexpectedly. Four hundred miles south of Oxyrhynchus, in a cave-dotted mountainside near the Upper Egyptian town of Nag Hammadi, a group of Arab peasants were digging for natural fertilizer beneath a boulder when they came across a large, sealed earthenware jar. Hoping for gold, one of the group eagerly smashed this open with his mattock, but to their disappointment, all that tumbled out was a collection of thirteen leather-bound papyrus books and some loose papyri, mostly written in Coptic, the language of Egypt after that spoken during the time of the pharaohs. When, following various adventures, these reached scholarly scrutiny, they turned out to be mostly apocryphal works of the fourth century – an 'Apocalypse of Paul', a 'Letter of Peter to Philip', an 'Apocalypse of Peter', a 'Secret Book of James', etc. – thought to have been part of the library of one of the fringe Gnostic groups which proliferated during Christianity's earliest centuries.

However, one work beginning 'These are the secret sayings which the living Jesus spoke, and which Didymos Judas Thomas wrote down', was qualitatively different. It seemed nothing spectacular, simply comprising some 114 sayings attributed to Jesus, and without any account of his crucifixion and resurrection. But several of these sayings were so similar to those that Grenfell and Hunt had found at Oxyrhynchus that there could be no doubt that the Nag Hammadi text was a later and altogether more complete Coptic version of the earlier Greek text as found at Oxyrhynchus. This 'Gospel of Thomas', as it became labelled, could therefore be dated as a whole back to the late second century AD, bringing it to within a century and a half of the lifetime of Jesus.

Fragments of the Egerton Papyrus 2, the handwriting of which suggests a date around 150 AD. Part of the text reads: '[...they urged] the crowd to [pick up] stones and stone him. And the leading men would have arrested him to [hand him over] to the crowd, but no-one could take him because the time of his betrayal had not yet come. So he, the Lord, that is, slipped away through their midst. A leper now came up and said "Master Jesus, through travelling with lepers and eating with them at the inn I myself likewise became a leper. If you want to, you can cure me." The Lord then said to him, "Of course I want to: be cured!" And his leprosy was cured at once...' Elements are clearly familiar from the canonical gospels, as for example the attempt to stone Jesus (John 7 and 8) and the healing of the leper (Matthew 8: 2-3; Mark 1: 40-2; Luke 5: 12-13). But differences in wording and sequence show that this cannot be from any canonical gospel, and it is probably the oldest non-canonical text yet discovered.

Now we should not be surprised at the turning up of gospels previously unknown to us, for the canonical gospel writer Luke mentions (1: 1, 2) 'many' other gospels in existence in his time, most of which have clearly been lost. The writings of the early Church fathers provide clues to the existence of a few: a 'Gospel of the Hebrews', evidently of a strongly Jewish character, mentioned by Origen and Jerome; a 'Gospel according to the Egyptians', apparently somewhat ascetic and favoured by Gentile Christians in Egypt, mentioned by Origen and Clement of Alexandria; and a 'Gospel of the Ebionites', apparently strongly opposed to the writings of the apostle Paul, mentioned in a condemnation of heresies by the fourth-century writer Epiphanius. Of the non-canonical material of this kind actually found, besides the 'Gospel of Thomas', the British Museum has two imperfect leaves and a scrap of papyrus, known by scholars as Egerton Papyrus 2, that appear to derive from a narrative work unlike the canonical gospels but with material closely based on theirs. Recognizable from these fragments are a near-identical version of the Matthew, Mark and Luke accounts of the healing of a leper (Matthew 8: 2-3; Mark 1: 40-2; Luke 5: 12-13) together with a description of Jesus escaping stoning, similar to that in John 8: 59. Originally part of a papyrus book, the Egerton fragments, like the Oxyrhynchus and Nag Hammadi materials, had again been found in Egypt, the handwriting identifying them as certainly not later than 150 AD.

Now it might be unsettling if non-canonical, though scarcely heretical, gospels such as 'Thomas' and 'Egerton' were the earliest to have come down to us. But in fact other similarly early-dated canonical discoveries have redressed the balance. Thus in the 1920s and 1930s the American mining millionaire Alfred Chester Beatty managed to acquire, via Egypt's still notorious antiquities black market, fragmentary papyrus texts of most of the recognized books of the New Testament, datable, like the Oxyrhynchus Thomas, to around the late second century. Mostly now in the Chester Beatty Collection in Dublin (though some are in Michigan and Princeton

University libraries and in the Austrian National Library, Vienna), these include parts of the Matthew and John gospels, a little more of the Mark and Luke gospels, half of Acts, a third of Revelation, and some 86 pages from what had once been a 104-page booklet of Paul's epistles. Likewise, a Swiss collector, Martin Bodmer, managed during the 1950s to acquire substantial portions of a late second-century papyrus codex of the John and Luke gospels, again via the sort of semi-shady under-cover deals employed by Chester Beatty.

From such material it is possible to deduce that written copies of gospels as carried among Jesus' earliest followers mostly took the form of codices or booklets, with relatively small, numbered pages. As such they would have been much cheaper and easier to carry around than any scroll. The extent to which each example contains variations compared to others as a result of copying has also enabled specialist scholars to trace back whole families of texts, to which they have given labels such as Caesarean, Byzantine, Western, Alexandrian, etc. The texts can thus also mutually support each other's authority – the Bodmer papyri, *Vaticanus* and *Sinaiticus*, all, for instance, were found to belong to the same Alexandrian text family.

But from the point of view of our aim to get back to the real basics, exactly how old is the oldest scrap of a gospel yet found? Until recently the essentially undisputed claimant to this title was an ostensibly insignificant-looking two-and-a-half inch by three-and-a-half inch papyrus fragment preserved in the John Rylands Library of Manchester University. Consisting simply of verses from the 18th chapter of the John gospel, this was purchased by Bernard Grenfell back in the early 1920s via the same sort of Egyptian antiquities traders that Chester Beatty and Martin Bodmer had cultivated. However, ill-health prevented Grenfell from ever studying it thoroughly, as a result of which no-one appreciated its full significance until 1934, when it was examined by a young Oxford University graduate called Colin Roberts. From Roberts' careful study of the handwriting, he was able to date it to between 100 and 125 AD, i.e. well within a century of Jesus' lifetime. As Princeton University manuscript specialist Bruce Metzger has remarked of it:

> Although the extent of the verses preserved is so slight, in one respect this tiny scrap of papyrus possesses as much evidential value as would the complete codex. As Robinson Crusoe, seeing but a single footprint in the sand, concluded that another human being, with two feet, was present on the island with him, so 𝔓⁵² [the Rylands fragment's international code name] proves the existence and use of the Fourth Gospel in a little provincial town along the Nile far from its traditional place of composition (Ephesus in Asia Minor), during the first half of the Second Century.

But if this Rylands Library find might seem important enough in getting

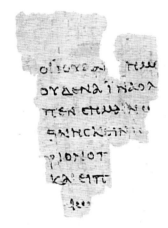

Papyrus fragment of the gospel of John, preserved in Manchester University's John Rylands Library. Analysis of the handwriting indicates that it was written between 100 and 125 AD, i.e. within a century of Jesus' death. On the front (above) is the Greek text of John 18: 31-4; on its back is John 18: 37-8. Because parts of the margins have been preserved, the original page can be calculated to have measured 21.5 x 20 cm and would have formed part of a 130-page codex, or primitive book. Found in Egypt, hundreds of miles from Ephesus in Turkey, where the John gospel is believed to have been composed, this is the earliest known surviving fragment of any gospel, canonical or non-canonical - with the possible exception of the still-contested Matthew gospel fragments at Magdalen College, Oxford.

us back to the earliest documentation for Jesus, it has been potentially eclipsed by claims recently made for another possibly even earlier example preserved at Magdalen College, Oxford. Between 1893 and 1901, and therefore at much the same time that Grenfell and Hunt were working at Oxyrhynchus, the Reverend Charles Bousfield Huleatt spent each winter at Luxor, Egypt, working as missionary chaplain of the English church there on behalf of the Colonial and Continental Church Society. In 1901 he and his family were transferred from Egypt to continue their work in Messina, Sicily, and there they perished during the great Sicilian earthquake of 28 December 1908.

However, just after Huleatt left Egypt, he bequeathed a souvenir of his sojourn there to his old college, Magdalen, Oxford, where he had studied classics. This souvenir, subsequently catalogued as Magdalen's MS.Gr.17,

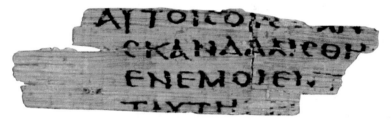

simply consisted of three tiny papyrus fragments that Huleatt had presumably acquired from some antiquities trader. Although the fragments bear on their front and reverse sides just a few words in Greek uncial characters, these are quite sufficient to identify them as belonging to the 26th chapter of the gospel of Matthew, essentially just as we have it today. On one side is part of the story of a woman anointing Jesus' head with costly ointment while he was eating at the house of Simon the leper. On the other are extracts from Jesus' words during the Last Supper. From the fall of the words it is again possible to reconstruct the front and back of the whole page on which they would have appeared, and thereby the whole original papyrus booklet.

But when was this booklet written? When the fragments were first examined at Magdalen back in 1901, they were tentatively assigned to between the third and fourth centuries AD. In 1953 Colin Roberts suggested the late second century and became supported by other acknowledged experts, such as T.C. Skeat and Sir Harold Bell. Although this dating became that of orthodoxy, it still made the fragments comparatively late compared to the Rylands, so much so that they were inconspicuously stored in a college library display cabinet along with Magdalen alumni trifles such as Oscar Wilde's ring and Addison's shoebuckle. Even though an undergraduate at Magdalen between 1960 and 1963, I for one remained unaware even of their existence.

But then in February 1994 the papyrologist Dr Carsten Thiede, Director of the Institute for Basic Epistemological Research, Paderborn, Germany, happened to visit Oxford for a family celebration, and decided to use the opportunity to make a routine call at Magdalen just to make a first-hand assessment of Huleatt's fragments. When courteously shown them by the college's assistant librarian, Sally Speirs, Thiede was astonished to note that the writing was strikingly similar to that of texts from Pompeii, Herculaneum and Qumran, ones with which he had already gained a specialist familiarity, and which had not been available to those who had last examined the Magdalen fragments back in 1953. Crucially, these dated to no later than the third quarter of the first century AD, Pompeii and Herculaneum having been destroyed in 79 AD and Qumran – the site of the Dead Sea Scrolls – closed down in 70 AD.

His interest thoroughly roused, Thiede has subjected the Magdalen fragments to the most intensive scrutiny and concluded that they are in a handwriting that had been common back in the first century BC but which was already petering out as early as the mid-first century AD. He would date them to around 70 AD. If he is right, the latest they are likely to date is within fifty years of Jesus' death, making them even older than the Rylands papyrus. As one Magdalen fellow has put it, this 'means that the people in the story must have been around when this [the Matthew gospel] was being written. It means they were there.'

Now it would be quite wrong to conclude that Dr Thiede has anything like proven the dating he claims. While some leading scholars have tentatively voiced their support, others, such as the formidable Graham Stanton, Professor of New Testament Studies at King's College, London, have been more than vociferous in their opposition. On the issue of whether Magdalen's Matthew papyrus genuinely dates from within a generation or so of Jesus' lifetime, the jury has to be considered still out.

But even without the Magdalen papyrus the discoveries of Jesus-related documents during the last hundred years have been impressive to say the least. As few realize, whereas we have just a single manuscript, copied around the twelfth century, for Tacitus' history of the early Roman emperors, of canonical material alone attesting to Jesus' existence there are some 274 vellum manuscripts, brothers and sisters of *Sinaiticus*, dating from between the fourth and the eleventh centuries, and 88 papyrus fragments datable to between the second and the fourth centuries (among these latter, of course, the Rylands and Magdalen examples). Additionally, as we have already seen, there is an intriguing variety of non-canonical material.

Papyrus fragments of the gospel of Matthew, preserved in the library at Magdalen College, Oxford. Like the Rylands papyrus, these were found in Egypt and derive from a codex once bound in the manner of a book. According to papyrologist Dr Carsten Thiede they date to around 70 AD.

We can therefore be sure that the gospel texts were genuinely early. From the relatively minor text differences to be found even in the earliest versions, we can also be confident that those who copied them one from another did so mostly reasonably accurately. But what of the actual origination of the gospels? Who wrote them? And when? Even more crucially, how much can we trust them? For the answers to these questions we need to look to another specialist discipline, the work of New Testament theologians.

2

HOW MUCH CAN THE GOSPELS BE TRUSTED?

Few, if any, pieces of writing can have received greater scrutiny than the traditional, canonical gospel stories of Jesus. Printed copies of them, translated into almost every language, are to be found in hundreds of millions of homes across the world. Thousands of professional theologians are paid salaries to study them, and to teach and write about them. Many thousands more are paid, as vicars, chaplains and priests, to read and review a passage from them each week for the purposes of conducting a Christian service and preaching a sermon.

It can therefore come as quite a shock to discover that no-one can even be sure who wrote the gospels. Despite the versions printed in our Bibles long having borne the names Matthew, Mark, Luke and John, these names are mere attributions, and even as such are rather less reliable than attributions given to unsigned works of art. Many of the earliest writers to refer to the gospels notably failed to mention the authors' names. Each gospel, whether among the canonical 'big four', or among those that failed to gain general acceptance, seems to have been designed as the teaching about Jesus for an early Christian community, with whoever wrote it seeming relatively unimportant. And only gradually did the canon of the 'big four' drift into general usage, each gospel at the

Opposite *Caves of the Scrolls. In 1947 a Bedouin goatherd's chance exploration of these caves overlooking the Dead Sea brought to light Jewish documents from close to the time of Jesus, the famous Dead Sea Scrolls. The caves are here viewed from the adjoining first-century AD Jewish settlement of Qumran, where the scrolls are thought to have been written.*

same time becoming linked with specific names from Christianity's earliest years.

It also needs bearing in mind that the earliest texts had none of the easy reading and reference features that they bear now. Without exception, everything was written in capital letters, the uncials referred to in the last chapter. There were neither headings, nor chapter divisions, nor verse divisions. Refinements such as these did not appear until the Middle Ages. Adding further to the difficulties both for people of the earliest years and for specialist scholars of today, there was practically no punctuation or space between words.

Given such a background, it may come as little surprise, particularly for sceptics, to discover that there can be inconsistencies between one gospel and another. While according to the Mark and Luke gospels Jesus stayed in Peter's house, and only afterwards healed the leper (Mark 1: 29-45; Luke 4: 38 ff.; Luke 5: 12 ff.), according to the Matthew gospel (8: 1-4 and 14ff.) Jesus healed the leper first. While according to Matthew the Capernaum centurion spoke man-to-man with Jesus (Matthew 8: 5 ff.), according to Luke (7: 1 ff.) he sent some Jewish elders and friends to speak on his behalf. Whereas according to Matthew (5: 1) Jesus delivered his Beatitudes on a hill (hence the Sermon on the Mount), according to Luke (6: 17) he gave what seems to have been the same discourse after he had come 'down with them and stopped at a level piece of ground'. Although according to Acts Judas Iscariot died from an accidental fall after betraying Jesus (Acts 1: 18), according to Matthew he went and hanged himself (Matthew 27: 5).

There are also differences in the reporting of Jesus' sayings, even in respect of some of the most central of these. Thus while Matthew's 'Our Father' prayer (6: 9-13) has seven petitions and begins 'Our Father in heaven' Luke's (11: 2-4) begins simply 'Father' and has only five. With regard to Jesus' institution of the Eucharist, Matthew has Jesus say 'Take it and eat, this is my body', while Mark has 'Take it, this is my body', and Luke 'This is my body'.

Of course the reasonable and fair-minded approach to such discrepancies is to regard them as no worse than the minor reporting errors which occur daily even in our more respected modern newspapers. But over the last couple of centuries New Testament criticism has gone much deeper, and in some quarters there is a fashion for each new critic to try to outdo his predecessors in casting doubt on the gospels' authenticity.

The first such forays into trying to get back to the true facts behind the gospels began harmlessly enough. Many incidents concerning Jesus are related in two or more of the gospels, and an early research method, still extremely valuable, was to study the corresponding passages side by side, the so-called 'parallel passage' technique. This is very useful for showing up which episodes are common to all gospels, which are peculiar to a single gospel, the variation of interest or emphasis between one writer and another and so on. And to anyone who tries it, immediately obvious is the fact that

THE PARALLEL PASSAGE TECHNIQUE

MARK 16: 2–5

... very early in the morning on the first day of the week they went to the tomb just as the sun was rising. They had been saying to one another 'Who will roll away the stone for us from the entrance to the tomb? But when they looked they could see that the stone - which was very big - had already been rolled back. On entering the tomb they saw a young man in a white robe seated at the right-hand side.

LUKE 24: 1–4

On the first day of the week, at the first sign of dawn, they went to the tomb with the spices they had prepared. They found that the stone had been rolled away from the tomb, but on entering discovered that the body of the Lord Jesus was not there. As they stood there not knowing what to think, two men in brilliant clothes suddenly appeared at their side ...

MATTHEW 28: 1–4

... towards dawn on the first day of the week Mary of Magdala and the other Mary went to visit the sepulchre. And all at once there was a violent earthquake, for the angel of the Lord, descending from heaven, came and rolled away the stone and sat on it. His face was like lightning, his robe white as snow ...

the Matthew, Mark and Luke gospels are the three that have most in common with each other. They report the same 'miracles'. They quote the same sayings. Essentially they share a common narrative framework, and in about 1774 the pioneering German scholar Johann Griesbach coined the word 'synoptic' for them, from the Greek for 'seen together'.

The John gospel, on the other hand, often referred to as the Fourth Gospel, seems to be some sort of maverick. With the exception of the events surrounding Jesus' death, it mostly describes quite different incidents of Jesus' life. Much of it is taken up with lengthy, apparently verbatim speeches that seem quite unlike Jesus' pithy utterances reported elsewhere. It is as if its author has chosen to present a side of Jesus that is different from that of the three synoptics, and the gospel has thereby mostly been regarded as having been written later than the other three.

The seeming flaws in the trustworthiness of the gospels began to emerge as critics, particularly in Germany, started to develop and apply more and more rigorous analysis techniques in order to get back to the original gospel writers and their closeness or otherwise to the events they reported. During the eighteenth century a faltering start on such techniques was made by Hamburg University oriental languages professor Hermann Samuel Reimarus. Working in secret, Reimarus wrote *On the Aims of Jesus and his Disciples*, arguing that Jesus was merely a failed Jewish revolutionary, and that after his death his disciples cunningly stole his body from the tomb in order to concoct the whole story of his resurrection. So concerned was Reimarus to avoid recriminations that he would only allow the book to be published after his death.

Following in this controversial tradition, in the years 1835-6 Tübingen University tutor David Friedrich Strauss launched his two-volume *Life of*

Careful comparison of the three gospel passages above reveals a fundamental common grond - the time of the morning, the day of the week, the rolling away of the stone, the visit to the tomb by women. But it also discloses some equally fundamental differences which serve to tell us something about the gospel writers. The Mark author, for instance, speaks merely of 'a young man in a white robe', with no suggestion that this individual was anything other than an ordinary human being. In the Luke version we find 'two men in brilliant clothes' who appear 'suddenly'. Although not absolutely explicit, there is already a strong hint of the supernatural. But for the Matthew writer all restraints are abandoned. A violent earthquake has been introduced into the story; Mark's mere 'young man' has become a dazzling 'angel of the Lord... from heaven'; and this explicitly extra-terrestrial visitor is accredited with the rolling away of the stone. Such comparisons provide important insights into the gospel writers' differing personalities and interests.

Jesus Critically Examined, making particularly penetrating use of the parallel passage technique. Because of the discrepancies he found, he cogently argued that none of the gospels could have been by eyewitnesses. Instead they must have been the work of writers of a much later generation who freely constructed their material from probably garbled traditions about Jesus in circulation in the early Church. Inspired by the materialistic rationalism of the philosophers Kant and Hegel – 'the real is the rational and the rational is the real' – Strauss uncompromisingly dismissed the gospel miracle stories as mere myths invented to give Jesus greater importance. For such findings Strauss was dismissed from his tutorship at Tübingen, and later failed, for the same reason, to gain an important professorship at Zurich.

But such sanctions merely served to intensify the efforts of those, particularly Protestants, who felt that they had some sort of mission to strip the gospel accounts of Jesus back to what they considered, in their theological judgment, to have been the original facts. Under the professorship of the redoubtable Ferdinand Christian Baur, a prodigiously productive theologian who was at his desk by 4 o'clock each morning, Tübingen University in particular acquired a reputation for a ruthlessly iconoclastic approach, one which spread not only throughout Germany, but also into the universities of other predominantly Protestant countries.

Some of this iconoclasm was undeniably useful and valid. The Matthew gospel, for instance, had long been considered as the earliest of the four New Testament gospels and to have been composed by none other than Matthew, the tax-collector disciple of Jesus. Then in 1835 Berlin philologist Karl Lachmann showed that the Matthew and Luke gospels, which each contained material (mostly sayings) that Mark's did not have, agreed in their order only when they followed Mark's. Only three years later the theologian Christian Wilke drew from this and similar deductions the firm conclusion that the Mark gospel had to have been written first among the three synoptics.

Now from both internal and external clues, the Mark gospel, simpler and more primitive than the other two, was almost certainly written in Rome. Among the three synoptics it ostensibly has the least claim to eyewitness reporting, for even according to tradition, the best said about its authorship is that Mark was some sort of secretary or interpreter for Peter. And even if this were so, at best Peter can hardly have carefully supervised the gospel's writing, for it shows some serious ignorance of the geography of Jesus' haunts. In the 7th chapter, for instance, Jesus is reported going through Sidon on his way to Tyre and to the Sea of Galilee. Not only is Sidon in the opposite direction, but there was no road from Sidon to the Sea of Galilee in the first century AD, only one from Tyre. Similarly the 5th chapter refers to the Sea of Galilee's eastern shore as the country of the Gerasenes. Yet Gerasa, today's Jerash in Jordan, is more than thirty miles to the south-east, too far away for a story which, in any case, requires the setting of a city not far from a steep slope down to the sea. Aside from geography, Mark represents Jesus as saying: 'If a woman divorces her husband and marries another she is guilty of adultery' (Mark 10: 12). Such a precept would have been meaningless for Jesus' Jewish world, where women had no rights of divorce, so whoever wrote the Mark gospel, addressing a Gentile readership, seemingly put into Jesus' mouth what he might have said on this issue.

The interesting question that now arises is where all this leaves the Matthew gospel. Since it can be seen that Matthew's author drew a substantial amount of his material from the Mark gospel, it is difficult to see how he can have been Jesus' original tax-collector disciple Matthew. For would this Matthew, a man represented as having known Jesus personally, and had travelled with him, have based his gospel on the work of someone who had no such firsthand knowledge and who made errors of basic fact? For such reasons theological opinion has largely, though not entirely, rejected the idea that the original disciple Matthew could have written the gospel that bears the same name. Whoever did so must have brought it out after the Mark gospel had already appeared, and this led the German theologians increasingly to date the composition of all three synoptic gospels to well into the second century AD.

Then the John gospel, in its turn, came under close scrutiny. The long speeches that its writer put into the mouth of Jesus, all quoted in fluent Greek, seemed Hellenistic in character, corresponding to the gospel's traditional place of authorship, the Hellenistic city of Ephesus in Asia Minor. Since even Church tradition acknowledged the John gospel to have been written later than the rest, the Germans concluded that it must date from close to the end of the second century.

Even one of the Mark gospel's more convincing features, its air of primitive 'matter-of-factness', became weakened with the publication, in 1901, of Breslau professor Wilhelm Wrede's *The Secret of the Messiahship*. In this Wrede argued powerfully that whoever wrote Mark tried to represent Jesus as making a secret that he was the Messiah while he was alive, so much so that even most of his disciples failed to recognize this until after his death. While not necessarily giving this idea their full endorsement, most modern scholars accept that Wrede may well have been right in regarding Mark's author as more concerned with putting over theology than with writing straight history. Five years after Wrede's publication, in a closely written treatise *From Reimarus to Wrede*, translated into English as *The Quest for the Historical Jesus*, Albert Schweitzer, later to become the world-famous Lambarene missionary, summarized the work of his fellow Germans in these terms:

There is nothing more negative than the result of the critical study of the life of Jesus. The Jesus of Nazareth who came forward publicly as the Messiah, who preached the ethic of the Kingdom of God, who

founded the Kingdom of Heaven upon earth, and died to give his work
its final consecration, never had any existence...This image has not
been destroyed from without, it has fallen to pieces, cleft and dis-
integrated by the concrete historical problems which came to the
surface one after another...

As if this were not damage enough, onto the scene stepped Rudolf
Bultmann of Germany's Marburg University with a new and yet more devastating weapon, *Formgeschichte* or 'form criticism'. Before Bultmann, the
German pastor Karl Ludwig Schmidt had noted that in all the gospels, but
in Mark's gospel in particular, there were link passages that seemed to have
been invented to give an impression of continuity between one episode or
saying and the next. So Bultmann set his sights on determining what if
anything might be authentic about the links, looking at each of the elements in each gospel – birth stories, miracle stories, ethical sayings, etc. –
from the point of view of whether they might be original, or borrowed
from the Old Testament, or from contemporary Jewish thought, or merely
invented to suit some particular theological line which early Christian
preachers wanted to promulgate.

  Nothing if not Procrustean, Bultmann firmly discarded anything that
savoured of the miraculous – the gospels' nativity stories, references to
angels, accounts of wondrous cures of the sick, and the like – on the
grounds that these were simply the gospel writers' attempts to make Jesus
seem divine. Anything that appeared to him to fulfil an Old Testament
prophecy – Jesus' birth in Bethlehem, his entry into Jerusalem on a donkey,
his betrayal, and much else – he threw out as a mere attempt to represent
Jesus' life as fulfilling such prophecies. Any of what Jesus reportedly said
that could be traced to the general Jewish thinking of his time, Bultmann
rejected likewise. For instance, Jesus' reported saying '...always treat others
as you would like them to treat you; that is the meaning of the Law and the
Prophets' (Matthew 7: 12) Bultmann ruled as inadmissible because it is
mirrored almost exactly in a saying of the great first-century BC Jewish
Rabbi Hillel: 'Whatever is hateful to you, do not do to your fellow-man.
This is the whole Law [Torah] ...'

Another example, from Mark's gospel, concerns the incident in which
Jesus reportedly told a paralytic: 'Your sins are forgiven' (Mark 2: 5),
causing the Jewish scribes to quibble that only God could forgive sins, and
prompting Jesus to go ahead and cure the man anyway. In Bultmann's
logic, early Christians probably invented this incident in order to bolster
their own claim to be able to forgive sins. By a series of deductions of this
kind he concluded that much of what appears in the gospels was not what
Jesus had actually said and done, but what Christians at least two generations removed had invented about him, or had inferred from what early
preachers had told them. Not surprisingly, the approach left intact all too
little that might have derived from the original Jesus – not much more than

the parables, Jesus' baptism, his Galilean and Judaean ministries and his crucifixion. Recognizing this himself, Bultmann condemned as useless further attempts to try to reconstruct the Jesus of history:

> I do indeed think that we can now know almost nothing concerning the life and personality of Jesus, since the early Christian sources show no interest in either, are moreover fragmentary and often legendary.

Somewhat ludicrously, all this damage was done by men who counted themselves good Protestant Christians, Bultmann, for instance, defending his destruction of so much that had been considered historical about Jesus on the grounds that still intact was his own Lutheran Christ of faith. As the leading Jewish scholar Dr Geza Vermes has most aptly remarked of the German theologians' position, it was like having 'their feet off the ground of history and their heads in the clouds of faith'.

Even so, when Bultmann died in 1976, at the age of ninety-two, he left behind a whole generation of mostly still active New Testament scholars – his Marburg successor Werner Kümmel, Bristol University's Dennis Nineham, Harvard University's Helmut Koester, and others – almost all of whom acknowledge him as the twentieth century's most influential theological thinker. But did he and his fellow-German predecessors go too far? Have their attitudes been too Teutonically rigid and unshakeable?

Throughout, there have been other scholars, often less fashionable, who have certainly felt this, acknowledging that while each gospel per se may have been written at second hand, they nonetheless contain substantial underlying elements of genuine first-hand reporting.

Thus not long after Bultmann had begun his professorship at Marburg, across the Channel at Queen's College, Oxford, a shy and retiring Englishman, Canon Burnett Streeter, quietly put the finishing touches to *The Four Gospels – A Study in Origins*. Thanks to both British and German theological research, it had already become recognized that the authors of Matthew and Luke, in addition to drawing on the gospel of Mark, must have used a second Greek source, long lost, but familiarly referred to by scholars as 'Q' (from the German *Quelle*, meaning source). Something of Q's original text was even reconstructible from some two hundred verses of the Matthew and Luke gospels, mostly relating to the teachings of Jesus, which bear a close resemblance to each other, but are absent from Mark, thereby suggesting a common written source. Supporting this thinking, Streeter went further to postulate at least two additional lost sources: 'M', which had provided material peculiar to the Matthew gospel, and 'L' which had furnished passages exclusive to that attributed to Luke. To clarify his arguments Streeter produced a chart showing the synoptic gospels' apparent relationship to these lost sources, and suggested that 'M' and 'L' may well have been written in Aramaic, the spoken language of Jesus and his disciples.

Streeter died in 1937, but his line of thought was continued by other

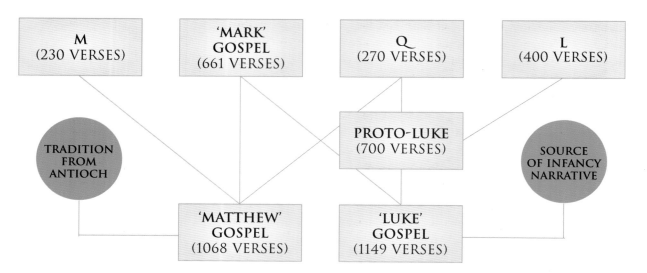

Sources of influence on the synoptic gospels as deduced by Canon Burnett Streeter. 'Proto Luke' is a theoretical early gospel, comprising Q plus the special Luke source L, which Streeter believed to have been a prototype for the so-called 'Luke' gospel.

major British theological scholars, among them Professor Charles Dodd, who went on to make his own special contribution to an understanding of the John gospel. To this day the broad outlines of Streeter's hypothesis remain the basis for much synoptic literary criticism, and the clues to underlying Aramaic sources are indeed there. In the Luke gospel, for instance, which includes 'exclusives' such as the parables of the Good Samaritan and the Prodigal Son, there occurs the following saying:

> Oh, you Pharisees! You clean the outside of cup and plate, while inside yourselves you are filled with extortion and wickedness... Instead *give alms* from what you have and then indeed everything will be clean for you. (Luke 11: 39-41)

Although 'give alms' appears to make no sense, it occurs in the very earliest available Greek texts, thereby showing that any error in transcription has to have occurred at a very early stage. All then becomes clear when we discover that the Aramaic *zakkau* (to give alms) looks very similar to *dakkau* (to cleanse). That the original saying genuinely did refer to 'cleansing' rather than 'giving alms' can be checked because Matthew includes a parallel passage in what we may now judge to have been the correct form: 'Blind Pharisee! Clean the inside of cup and dish first so that the outside may become clean as well...' (Matthew 23: 26). As has been remarked by Cambridge theologian Don Cupitt, this conveys more clearly than any amount of Bultmannesque theology that whoever wrote Luke in its 'original' Greek did not compose his material out of nothing, but had struggled with an earlier Aramaic *written* source that he was obviously determined to follow even if he did not fully understand it.

A similar misunderstanding is detectable in the Matthew gospel, notable for its remarkable 'Sermon on the Mount' passages. When translated from Greek into Aramaic, some of these passages take on such a distinctive verse form that Aramaic must have been the language in which they were first framed, rather as happens when the ostensibly dull-sounding words 'On the bridge at Avignon' are translated back into their original French. According to the Dutch Roman Catholic scholar Edward Schillebeeckx, the lost 'Q' also seems to have had an original Aramaic text, then, as in the case of the synoptic gospels, becoming translated into Greek and adapted for Gentile consumption.

Surprisingly, despite having been dismissed by the Germans as very late and very Greek, the gospel which would seem, in part at least, to have the most authentic underlying Aramaic flavour of all is that of John. The first shock to the Germans, with their so dismissive attitudes towards this gospel, came with the papyrologist Colin Roberts' publication of the Rylands fragment, and his closely argued insistence on its early date. For if a copy of the John gospel had reached as far as provincial Egypt by between 100 and 125 AD, then its original, if it were composed at Ephesus (and at least no-one has suggested it was written in Egypt), could only have been written significantly earlier, probably at least a decade before 100 AD, and thereby a century before the sort of late dating the Germans had been suggesting.

A second shock to the Germans came with the discovery of the much publicized Dead Sea Scrolls that had been stored in caves in the hillside surrounding Qumran on the Dead Sea. Despite many sensationalist claims, fuelled by several decades in which much of their content remained unpublished, the Scrolls can now be determined to contain absolutely no readily recognizable mention of Jesus (see fragment on p.35), even though there is general agreement that they date from very close to his time. But the intriguing feature of the Scrolls is that their authors, generally thought to have been the community which lived at Qumran in a settlement dating no later than 70 AD (often but by no means conclusively identified with a Jewish sect called the Essenes), were using already in Jesus' time precisely the same type of language and imagery that had previously been dismissed as late and 'Hellenistic' in John. As is well known, the John gospel prologue speaks of a conflict between light and darkness, and the whole gospel is replete with phrases such as 'the spirit of truth', 'the light of life', 'walking in the darkness', 'children of light', and 'eternal life'. A welter of such phrases and imagery occur in the Dead Sea Scrolls' Manual of Discipline. For instance the John gospel's prologue,

> He was with God in the beginning.
> Through him all things came to be,
> Not one thing had its being but through him.
>
> (John I: 2-3)

is strikingly close to the Manual of Discipline's

Steps to the Qumran community's cistern, showing fault from earthquake damage. Although the community who lived at Qumran, and were therefore most likely responsible for the Dead Sea Scrolls, are generally believed to have been monastic Essenes, in recent years there have been a variety of alternative theories for the settlement's main purpose, from luxury villa to guerrilla fortress. The cistern steps were repaired following a devastating earthquake of 31 BC which toppled the community's main building, and left the terrace's eastern half (seen at left), two feet lower than before. The community repaired their buildings after the damage, but were subsequently snuffed out by the Romans shortly before 70 AD.

All things come to pass by his knowledge,
He establishes all things by his design
And without him nothing is done.

(Manual 11: 11)

This is but one example of a striking similarity of cadence and choice of words obvious to anyone reading gospel and Manual side by side.

Even before such discoveries the Oxford scholar C.F. Burney and ancient historian A.T. Olmstead had begun arguing forcibly that the John gospel's narrative element at least must originally have been composed in Aramaic, probably not much later than 40 AD. One ingenious researcher, Dr Aileen Guilding, has shown in *The Fourth Gospel and Jewish Worship* that the gospel's whole construction is based on the Jewish cycle of feasts, and the practice of completing the reading of the Law, or Torah, in a three-year cycle. That the gospel's author incorporated accounts provided by close eyewitnesses to the events described is further indicated by detailed and accurate references to geographical features of Jerusalem and its environs before the city and its Temple were destroyed by the Romans in 70 AD, following their suppression of the Jewish Revolt which had broken out four years earlier. It is John who mentions a Pool of Siloam (John 9: 7), the remains of which are thought to have been discovered in Jerusalem, also a 'Gabbatha' or pavement, where Pilate is said to have sat in judgment over Jesus (John 19: 13), generally identified as a substantial area of Roman

paving now in the crypt of the Convent of the Sisters of Our Lady of Sion in Jerusalem.

From the historical point of view, therefore, while some elements in the gospels are undeniably clumsily handled and suggest that their authors were far removed in time and distance from the events they are describing, others have such a strikingly original and authentic ring that it is as if a second generation has come along and adulterated genuine first-hand material. In the case of the Matthew gospel at least this idea is certainly supported by a cryptic remark by the early Bishop Papias (c. 60-130 AD):

Matthew compiled the Sayings in the Aramaic language, and everyone translated them as well as he could.

As some have interpreted this, the disciple Matthew himself may have genuinely set down in his native Aramaic those sayings of Jesus that he had heard at first hand (perhaps in a form very like the 'Thomas' sayings discovered at Nag Hammadi), then others translated them and adapted them for their own literary purposes. This would readily explain the Matthew gospel's traditional attribution to Matthew without its having been written by him, at least in the form it has come down to us. The crunch question, though, is why this situation should have come about. Why should original eyewitness material, emanating from genuine original Jewish followers of Jesus, have been editorially adulterated and

Reference to Jesus in a Dead Sea Scroll fragment? According to Californian Robert Eisenman, this fragment refers to a Jesus-like 'pierced messiah', the 4th and 5th lines reading, in his translation: 'and they put to death [shall put to death?] the leader of the community, the Bran[ch of David] ... with wounds [stripes? piercings?], and the Priest [the High Priest] shall order...' But according to Oxford University's Dr Geza Vermes this particular messiah appears to do the piercing, Vermes' translation reading: 'and the Prince of the Congregation, the Bran[ch of David] will kill him by [stroke]s and by wounds. And a Priest [of renown?] will command...' Scholarly consensus seems to be on the side of Vermes, and the Scrolls therefore seem to contain no readily recognizable mention of Jesus.

Carved for posterity on Titus' triumphal arch in Rome, the Roman army that crushed the Jews processes through Rome's streets carrying spoils from the Jerusalem Temple, among these the great menorah or seven-branched candelabrum, the gold table, and musical instruments. This representation of the menorah may not be exact, as it is thought to have been three-footed, rather than with the six-sided stand represented by the Roman artist.

swamped by interference from Gentile writers of a later time?

The answer almost certainly lies in one event, the Jewish Revolt of 66 AD, which had its culmination four years later in the sacking of Jerusalem, the burning and subsequent total razing to the ground of its Temple and the widespread extermination and humiliation of the Jewish people. As is historically well attested, in 70 AD the Roman general Titus returned in triumph to Rome, parading through the streets such Jewish treasures as the *menorah* (the huge seven-branched candelabrum of the Temple), and enacting tableaux demonstrating how he and his armies had overcome savage, ill-advised resistance from this renegade group of the Empire's subjects, many of whom they had had to crucify wholesale. At the height of the celebrations the captured Jewish leader, Simon bar Giora, was dragged to the Forum, abused and executed. In Titus' honour Rome's mints issued commemorative sestertii coins with the inscriptions 'JUDAEA DEVICTA' and 'JUDAEA CAPTA', and within a few years a magnificent commemorative arch was erected next to the Temple of Venus.

Intimately linked to this episode, according to at least one British authority, the late Professor S. G. F. Brandon, was the writing of the key canonical gospel of Mark. Generally recognized as having been written in Rome, according to most present-day thinking it was composed around the time of the Revolt and Titus' triumph, and it certainly displays one overwhelming characteristic, a denigration of Jews and whitewashing of Romans. Whoever wrote 'Mark' portrays Jesus' Jewish disciples as a dull, quarrelsome lot, always jockeying for position, failing to understand Jesus, denying him when they are in trouble (as in the case of Peter) and finally deserting him at the time of his arrest. The entire Jewish establishment, Pharisees, Sadducees, chief priests and scribes, is represented as being out to kill Jesus. Even his own family think him 'out of his mind' and want 'to take charge of him'. By contrast Pilate, the Roman, is portrayed as positively pleading for Jesus' life: 'What harm has he done?' (Mark 15: 14). At the very moment when Jesus, amid Jewish taunts, breathes his last it is a Roman centurion, standing at the foot of the cross, who is represented as the first man in history to recognize Jesus as divine: 'In truth this man was a Son of God' (Mark 15: 39).

Given the background of the Jewish Revolt and the Roman triumph, it is not too difficult to understand why someone writing the Mark gospel in Rome might choose to bias his story in this way. For the Rome community of Gentile Christians, who would have been still reeling from the atrocities that the Emperor Nero reportedly inflicted upon them in 64 AD, it could only have been acutely embarrassing that the very founder of their religion had been a member of this accursed Jewish people, crucified at Roman hands like so many of the recent rebels. How could one hope to win more converts in such a situation? Arguably, for whoever wrote 'Mark', and for those who followed him, there could be only one answer: to de-Judaize Jesus by representing him as a reject of, and utterly divorced from, his own people. In like vein, the Luke gospel even avoids representing Roman soldiers as crucifying Jesus, while that of Matthew quotes what seems to be the Jewish people directly assuming responsibility for Jesus' death with the words: 'His blood be on us and on our children' (Matthew 27: 25). There is also a strikingly anti-Jewish character to the speeches attributed to Jesus in the John gospel, where Jesus is recorded as condemning 'the Jews' in the most vituperative way, using the words 'your Law', when referring to the Torah, as if this were no part of his own beliefs, and telling them that they are uncompromisingly evil, with the devil as their father (John 8: 43-7).

The Jewish Revolt therefore needs to be seen as a possibly important key to an understanding of how and when the canonical gospels came to be written. Trying to reconcile Bultmann's thinking with the papyrologists' early datings of some of the gospel scraps, the influential New Testament

Roman coin of the Emperor Vespasian (69-96 AD), commemorating the Roman crushing of the Jewish revolt, 70 AD. Inscribed 'JUDAEA CAPTA' on its reverse, the coin features Judaea as a grieving female figure seated beneath a palm tree, while to the left of the tree a Jewish captive stands with his hands tied behind his back.

DATINGS FOR THE WRITING OF THE CANONICAL GOSPELS

Earliest to latest dates for the writing of the canonical gospels, according to the late Dr John Robinson

Earliest to latest dates for the writing of the canonical gospels, according to Werner Kümmel

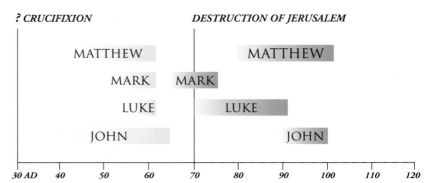

scholar Werner Kümmel has set widely accepted datings for each of the gospels (see above), based largely on the idea that Jesus' apparent prophecies of the fall of Jerusalem and destruction of the Temple (Matthew 24: 1-3; Mark 13: 1-4; Luke 21: 5-7) were 'written in' by the gospel writers after the event.

But such are the uncertainties that this dating peg cannot be regarded as assured. As came to be asked by the late Dr John Robinson of Trinity College, Cambridge, famed for his controversial *Honest to God*, what if Jesus' prophecies of Jerusalem's destruction were real prophecies – ones uttered a whole generation before the event actually happened? In his *Redating the New Testament*, published in 1976, Dr Robinson pointed out that if the gospels were not written until after Jerusalem's fall, it was surely surprising that the writers should not have capitalized on this amazing piece of fulfilment. Yet the Revolt and destruction as past events go entirely unmentioned. Among other indications of the gospels' origins before 70 AD, Robinson noted the Matthew gospel's reference to the Jews' obligation to pay the Temple tax (Matthew 17: 24-7), a burden which disappeared after the Temple's destruction. Similarly, if the gospels were written after 70 AD, why should their writers have represented Jesus as predicting his return 'before this generation has passed away' (Matthew 24: 34-6; Mark 13: 30-2; Luke 21: 32-3), surely already somewhat late for anyone living in the generation after the Jewish Revolt? Accordingly, and in the teeth of Kümmel's chronology, John Robinson drew up a radical 'new' scheme of dating showing the writing of all the gospels to have been completed by around 65 AD (see chart). Although there remain many of today's New Testament scholars who would reject this, and who continue to prefer Kümmel's scheme, even before John Robinson the distinguished biblical archaeologist William Albright had remarked on the basis of his quite independent archaeological insights:

We can already say emphatically that there is no longer any solid basis for dating any book of the New Testament after about AD 80, two full generations before the date between 130 and 150 given by the more radical New Testament critics of today.

Accordingly, while the canonical gospels may not be quite the one hundred per cent contemporary eyewitness descriptions that sceptics demand, neither are they the tissue of late second-century fabrications that Strauss and other German theologians once tried hard to promulgate. Ironically, it has not been theologians but outsiders, such as scholars of ancient history, well used to imperfections in the works of the pagan writers of antiquity, who have been most prepared to recognize the gospels' strong underlying vein of genuine history. E.M. Blaiklock, Professor of Classics at Auckland University, has argued:

> I claim to be an historian. My approach to the Classics is historical. And I tell you that the evidence for the life, the death, and the resurrection of Christ is better authenticated than most of the facts of ancient history.

Likewise Nicholas Sherwin-White, writing in *Roman Society and Roman Law in the New Testament*:

> ... it can be maintained that those who had a passionate interest in the story of Christ, even if their interest in events was parabolical and didactic rather than historical, would not be led by that very fact to pervert and utterly destroy the historical kernel of their material.

Not least, the Oxford English don C.S. Lewis, speaking particularly of the John gospel, expressed it particularly beautifully:

> I have been reading poems, romances, vision literature, legends, myths all my life. I know what they are like. I know that none of them is like this. Of this text there are only two possible views. Either this is reportage – though it may no doubt contain errors – pretty close to the facts; nearly as close as Boswell. Or else, some unknown writer in the second century, without known predecessors or successors, suddenly anticipated the whole technique of modern, novelistic, realistic narrative. If it is untrue, it must be narrative of that kind. The reader who doesn't see this simply has not learned to read.

Overall, then, there is a good case for more than a little trust of the canonical gospels – particularly that, whoever were their actual authors in the form we now have them, they were written genuinely close to the time of the events they describe and were founded on the recollections of individuals who had directly known the living Jesus.

Even so, do they carry the authority of the sort of historical biography that we would expect of, say, a modern-day public figure? At the most basic level of information, do they tell us even when Jesus was born? And are they reliable about the circumstances surrounding this?

3

CAN WE BE SURE OF ANYTHING ABOUT JESUS' BIRTH?

We have seen that the surviving documentation for Jesus is surprisingly early and plentiful. We have also noted good grounds for believing that much of this is based on earlier, first-hand witnesses. Even so, some refuse to take for granted even that Jesus ever existed as a human being. In the former Soviet Union it used to be a basic part of Communist education that Jesus was invented in the second century AD as the hero of an early proletarian communist movement. In 1970 Manchester University oriental studies specialist John Allegro argued in all seriousness in his *The Sacred Mushroom and the Cross* that Christianity began as a secret cult of the sacred mushroom, and that the name 'Jesus' was a code word for this. During the late 1970s and early 1980s championship of the 'Jesus did not exist' school was taken over by G.A.Wells, professor of German at Birkbeck College, London, author of no less than three scholarly-looking books on the theme.

With regard to Wells's arguments, their linchpin is the writings of the apostle Paul, an individual whom Wells does admit to have existed, and to have authored at least some of the New Testament letters attributed to him.

Opposite *Adoration of the Magi: detail of fresco of the first half of the third century in the Capella Graeca, cemetery of Priscilla, Rome. The early date of this fresco is one attestation of how the Matthew gospel story of Jesus' birth had become well established within less than two hundred years of Jesus' death.*

But because Paul's letters are generally agreed to have been written before the canonical gospels (at least as based on Kümmel's chronology), for Wells their interest lies in their apparent ignorance of any detail of Jesus' earthly life. As he has pointed out, Paul does not name Jesus' parents, does not say where he was born, where he lived, even when he lived. Although his writings comprise a substantial proportion of the New Testament, they contain no mention of Jesus' parables or 'miracles'. They make no reference to his trial before Pilate, nor of Jerusalem as the place of his execution.

No-one can seriously deny any of this, for Paul freely admitted that he had never known Jesus in his lifetime, his conversion having come about sometime afterwards as a result of a claimed vision of Jesus in his resurrected form. It is therefore hardly to be expected that he would be full of chapter and verse on Jesus' biography. Nevertheless for Wells the inescapable deduction to be drawn was that Jesus was a mere figment of Paul's imagination who, when people began to believe in him, had to be made to seem a real-life historical individual. The writing of convincing-sounding pseudo-biographies thereupon became the task of the gospel writers, who drew upon all sorts of Old Testament material to give flesh to these, crowning them with the similarly invented story of the fictional hero being executed during the Roman governorship of Pontius Pilate.

Whatever view may be taken on Wells, few but the most die-hard of Christians can deny that some of the seemingly most essential facts concerning Jesus and his life are remarkably difficult to come by. At first sight this appears to be borne out by the lack of references to Jesus outside the gospels. For instance, although the great Roman historian Tacitus is often quoted as having mentioned Jesus, close scrutiny of the original reference reveals this to speak merely of certain Christians, barbarically put to death on Nero's orders, whose 'originator, Christ, had been executed in Tiberius' reign by the governor of Judaea, Pontius Pilate'.

For Professor Wells and like detractors Tacitus' vagueness and his undoubted distance from events in the Jewish world is sufficient to argue that a totally illusory belief in Jesus as a historical figure might have grown up by the second century in which he lived. For instance he referred to Jesus as 'Christ', as if this were his proper name, in apparent ignorance that it is a Greek form of the Hebrew *Māshiāh* (Messiah), or 'anointed one'. Nor does Tacitus' near contemporary Suetonius seem to have been better informed, referring merely to some Jews of Rome who, during the reign of Claudius (41-54 AD), rebelled at the instigation of one 'Chrestus'. The only other early classical reference is that of Pliny the Younger, who, as a rather fussy governor of Bithynia, wrote to Trajan in 112 AD reporting Christians to be an apparently harmless people who met at daybreak and sang hymns in which they appealed to their 'Christus' as God. Pliny commented of them, 'I found only a depraved superstition carried to extreme lengths'.

In all this, therefore, there might seem precious little to compel a belief that Jesus ever existed. But where we meet evidence of an altogether different order is in the writings of the Jewish historian Josephus. Born in 37 or 38 AD, the son of a Judaean priest, Josephus was educated as a Pharisee. In 66 AD he helped defend Galilee against the Romans during the Jewish Revolt, but when he was captured he took the realistic, though bitterly resented step of defecting to the Romans, subsequently pleading with his countrymen that further resistance was useless. In 70 AD, after acting as interpreter to Titus who besieged Jerusalem, he moved to Rome, and was there well looked after by successive Roman emperors, enjoying the leisure to write *The Jewish War*, which he completed around 77 or 78 AD, followed about fifteen years later by his monumental *The Antiquities of the Jews*. Both these works, packed with contemporary detail that is often confirmed by modern-day archaeological discoveries, have survived via later copies, and they represent our prime sources of information on the history of the Jewish people during the very period that Jesus, if indeed he existed, lived and breathed in what we now call the Holy Land.

If therefore we look at Josephus for some mention of a historical Jesus and his followers – which we might expect, since his interest in religious matters is evident from his having spent three of his early years living in the desert with a hermit called Bannos – we are certainly not disappointed. In the surviving text of the *Antiquities* there appears this passage:

> At about this time lived Jesus, a wise man, if indeed one might call him a man. For he was one who accomplished surprising feats and was a teacher of such people as are eager for novelties. He won over many of the Jews and many of the Greeks. He was the Messiah. When Pilate, upon an indictment brought by the principal men among us, condemned him to the cross, those who had loved him from the very first did not cease to be attached to him. On the third day he appeared to them restored to life, for the holy prophets had foretold this and myriads of other marvels concerning him. And the tribe of the Christians, so called after him, has to this day still not disappeared.

Now since the rest of Josephus' writings make it quite clear that he was not a Christian, there can be no doubt that some copyist of his manuscript must either have interpolated this passage or adulterated it, very clumsily, in a pro-Christian way. And this inevitably gives the likes of Professor Wells ready excuse to discount it altogether. But later in *Antiquities* Josephus includes a lengthy reference to the unjust execution in Jerusalem in 62 AD of James, whom he describes as 'the brother of Jesus called the Christ'. Of course this too might be dismissed as an interpolation, except that it does not sound like one, because it refers to Jesus merely as 'called the Christ', inconsistent with the earlier passage, and just the sort of remark that Josephus might well have made, given his non-Christian standpoint. Furthermore, we can be quite sure that this particular passage existed in a

Roman bust in the Ny Carlsberg Glypotek, Copenhagen, thought to represent Flavius Josephus (c.37-100 AD), whose prolific writings provide the main source of information on Jewish history of the first century AD. Josephus' reference to Jesus, although unmistakably adulterated by later Christian copyists, provides important attestation of Jesus' existence independent and supplementary to that of the Christian gospels.

very early version of his text, together with some separate passage casting doubt on Jesus' Messiahship, since in the third century the Christian writer Origen expressed his astonishment that Josephus, while disbelieving that Jesus was the Messiah, should have spoken so warmly about his brother. This information effectively therefore confirms that Josephus did make a reference to Jesus, albeit without regarding him as Messiah, before any Christian copyist had a chance to make alterations.

So with this established, is it still possible to reconstruct what Josephus may originally have said about Jesus in the first *Antiquities* passage, before it was tampered with? Encouragement for this is provided by the opening description of Jesus as 'a wise man', a comment that we would not expect from any Christian writer, but that was definitely characteristic of Josephus. This has encouraged completely uncommitted scholars such as the Jewish Dr Geza Vermes to try removing all pro-Christian elements from the passage, resulting in what has become accepted as a close approximation, though not necessarily complete, of what Josephus originally wrote:

> At about this time lived Jesus, a wise man ... He performed astonishing feats (and was a teacher of such people as are eager for novelties?). He attracted many Jews and many of the Greeks ... Upon an indictment brought by leading members of our society, Pilate sentenced him to the cross, but those who had loved him from the very first did not cease to be attached to him ... The brotherhood of the Christians, named after him, is still in existence ...

There is excellent justification for such a restoration, for the words 'astonishing feats', or more literally 'paradoxical deeds', are precisely the same as those used by Josephus to describe the healings of Elisha. The reconstructed text corresponds closely with a possibly unadulterated version preserved in the writings of the tenth-century Arabic Christian Agapius, which also includes the following:

> his disciples ... reported that he had appeared to them three days after his crucifixion and that he was alive; accordingly he was perhaps the Messiah, concerning whom the prophets have recounted wonders.

If Josephus originally wrote something approximating to these words – and as we have seen, Jewish as well as Christian scholars have been prepared to affirm that he did – then we have positive and authoritative corroboration of Jesus' existence from very nearly the best possible independent source, a man who actually lived in Galilee well within the lifetimes of individuals who would have known Jesus at first hand.

Other early Jewish sources too, while similarly saying nothing very favourable about Jesus, also at least tacitly acknowledge that he existed. Among both Christians and Jews these references are all too little known because, as a result of Christian persecution, Jewish religious books came under repeated attack during the Middle Ages, and references of all kinds were censored and not restored. But the last two generations of Jewish scholars, anxious to discover who Jesus was, have done much to retrieve them. As they have recognized, the name by which Jesus would have been known by his own Jewish contemporaries was not 'Jesus' – which is merely an adaptation for Graeco-Roman usage – but 'Yeshu'. Meaning 'God Saves', this was a common enough name in the first-century Jewish world, being found among several of the individuals referred to in Josephus' *Antiquities*, including no less than four of the Jerusalem Temple's line of twenty-eight high priests.

But specifically thought to refer to the Christians' 'Jesus' are at least five references to a 'Yeshu' in the *Baraitha* and *Tosefta*, supplements to the *Mishnah*, the great collection of Jewish religious literature compiled after what Christians know as the Old Testament, and mostly before 200 AD. The following are examples:

1. It has been taught: On the eve of Passover they hanged Yeshu...because he practised sorcery and enticed and led Israel astray.
2. Our rabbis taught: Yeshu had five disciples – Mattai, Nakkai, Netzer, Buni and Todah.
3. It happened with Rabbi Elazar ben Damah, whom a serpent bit, that Jacob, a man of Kefar Soma, came to heal him in the name of Yeshu[a] ben Pantera; but Rabbi Ishmael did not let him. He said 'You are not permitted, Ben Damah'. He answered, 'I will bring you proof that he may heal me.' But he had no opportunity to bring proof, for he died.
4. Once I was walking on the upper street of Sepphoris [capital of Galilee] and found one of the disciples of Yeshu the Nazarene, by the name of Jacob, a man of Kefar Sechanya. He said to me: 'It is written in your Torah: "Thou shalt not bring the hire of a harlot, etc." How about making with it a privy for the high priest?' But I did not answer him at all. He told me 'Thus did Yeshu the Nazarene teach me: "For the hire of a harlot hath she gathered them, And unto the hire of a harlot shall they return, from the place of filth they come, and unto the place of filth they shall go." And the utterance pleased me...'

Clearly the references do not sound particularly warm towards 'Yeshu', and the quoted number and names of his disciples are somewhat astray with what we learn from the gospels. But the other details, such as his 'hanging' on the eve of the Passover, the specific appellation 'Yeshu the Nazarene', his association with Galilee, and his accrediting with healings and 'sorcery' (another word for miracles), all indicate beyond reasonable doubt that the Yeshu of the *Mishnah* supplements was one and the same as the Jesus of the gospels. Arguably, therefore, there is sufficient acknowledgement of Jesus' existence from very early non-Christian sources for his one-time presence on earth to be beyond all reasonable doubt.

But what about our knowledge of how and when he was born? Because of the Western world's commercialization of Christmas, images of Jesus' birth in a stable, with visiting kings and shepherds, are among the most popularly known aspects of his life, readily familiar even to the many non-Christians who observe the festival, albeit in the old pagan way. Even many practising Christians, however, all too rarely appreciate that two of the gospels, those of Mark and John, carry absolutely no information about the human circumstances of Jesus' birth, while the other two, Matthew and Luke, contradict each other in several important particulars.

Historian and writer Marina Warner, in her highly acclaimed study *Alone of all her Sex – the Myth and Cult of the Virgin Mary*, has produced an excellent, yet inevitably disquieting summary of the main discrepancies. For instance, according to Matthew's gospel, the news of Jesus' impending birth is conveyed to Mary's husband, Joseph, in a dream, while according to Luke it is conveyed directly to Mary by the 'Angel Gabriel'. According to Luke, Jesus' parents had to travel from their home in Nazareth to Bethlehem for the Roman census, while according to Matthew they lived in Bethlehem already, and were only obliged to leave when King Herod began killing off the children. Although in Luke Jesus is represented as God's son by Mary, his ancestry is illogically traced back to King David via his human father Joseph. While Matthew's gospel similarly gives Jesus' genealogy via the male line, it provides a list of antecedents so different from those in Luke that even Joseph's father appears with a different name – Jacob instead of Heli.

Nor are these the greatest of the Matthew and Luke nativity stories' weaknesses. For instance, Matthew tries to justify Jesus' apparent divine parentage from Isaiah's famous prophecy: 'The virgin will conceive and give birth to a son' (Isaiah 7: 14).

Unfortunately this all too clearly reveals that whoever wrote at least this part of Matthew's gospel was no true Jew. In the original Hebrew text of Isaiah the crucial word *'almah* is used, which simply means 'young woman'. While it carries a general connotation of eligibility for marriage, this does not necessarily mean virginity. Only when, in the third century BC, the Hebrew scriptures were translated into Greek, to become the Septuagint – the bible of those Jews so absorbed into Greek-speaking communities that they had lost much of their Hebrew – was the Greek word *parthenos* inaccurately used as a translation of *'almah*, carrying with it a strong implication of untouched virginity absent from the original Hebrew. To this day, no true Jew expects the Messiah of Isaiah's prophecy, whoever he may be, and whenever he may appear, to be conceived by anything other than normal means, and it is to be noted that the writers of the Mark and John gospels show no awareness of anything unusual about Jesus' human parentage, and neither does Paul. Similarly, Mary's famous words of the *Magnificat* in the Luke gospel (Luke 1: 46-55) seem rather too close for comfort to the sentiments of the song of Hannah in I Samuel 2: 1-10.

What confidence can we have that we know the year when Jesus was born? Every day of their lives, everyone in the Western world organizes themselves according to a calendar that is ultimately based on the supposed year of Jesus' birth, and although it is often supposed that this must have been 0 AD, or 'the year dot', in fact our calendar system as devised by a sixth-century Byzantine monk, Dionysius Exiguus, has Jesus born in 1 AD, a year immediately succeeding 1 BC. But with regard to whether this was the true year of Jesus' birth, when we turn to the Matthew and Luke gospels, we find this is immediately contradicted, since Matthew, for one, very firmly sets Jesus' birth in the reign of Herod the Great, who died in 4 BC, while Luke likewise has the births of both Jesus and John the Baptist announced in Herod's reign (Luke 1: 5). Complicating Luke's information on the date, however, he then ruins any seeming point of agreement with Matthew by relating an apparent impressive historical detail:

> Now at this time Caesar Augustus issued a decree for a census of the whole world to be taken. This census – the first – took place while Quirinius was governor of Syria, and everyone went to his home town to be registered … (Luke 2: 1-3).

The problem here is that while the first-ever census among Jews did indeed take place during Quirinius' governorship, this did not happen until at least 6 AD, the first year that Judaea came under direct Roman rule. This was reliably reported by Josephus as an unprecedented event of that year. There is an unavoidable inference, therefore, that the Luke gospel's author may have been trying to make it appear that he knew more about Jesus' birth than he actually did.

Roman Census Order. According to the Luke gospel, Jesus was born at the time of a census (apographes) of the Roman world ordered by the Emperor Augustus (27 BC-14 AD). Such a census is known to have been called in 6 AD, but for an actual surviving census decree the example shown here dates from 104 AD, the time of Trajan. Found in Egypt, it is an order from the Prefect Gaius Vibius Maximus requiring all those in his terrritory to return to their homes to be counted, a situation clearly analogous to that described in the Luke gospel.

As for the actual day of Jesus' birth, both the Matthew and Luke gospels tell us absolutely nothing, but quite undeniably today's annual festivities focused on 25 December have their basis not in any early Christian tradition, but in the Roman festival of the Saturnalia, which celebrated the (re)birth of the sun. According to the Romans' Julian calendar the winter solstice, or shortest day of the year, was 25 December, after which days began to lengthen and become warmer, leading towards summer. December 25 was therefore regarded as the sun's birthday, a time for celebration, the exchange of gifts, and the decoration of temples with greenery, and because the festival was as popular in Roman times as 'Christmas' is today, when the Roman Empire went over to Christianity, it was shrewdly decided to assimilate it by celebrating Jesus' birth on the same day. This could of course have been justified then because of the concept of Jesus as the 'light of the world', though there are no known grounds for arguing that such justification actually took place.

The best we have then is that if there is any historical truth at all in the Matthew and Luke nativity stories, Jesus was born in the reign of Herod the Great, requiring us to look to a year sometime before 4 BC. With a view to pinpointing this, even possibly to the day, the Matthew gospel's references to the unusual star which hung over Bethlehem (Matthew 2: 2-11) have been a subject of intense interest on the part of the more astronomically minded. As long ago as 1603 the astronomer John Kepler, observing a striking conjunction of the planets Saturn and Jupiter in the constellation Pisces on 17 December of that year, calculated that a very similar conjunction must have occurred in 7 BC. Accordingly he speculated that this might have been the true year of Jesus' birth, even finding support in a Jewish rabbinical reference to the Messiah appearing when Saturn and Jupiter were in conjunction in the constellation of Pisces. When seventy-nine years later English astronomer Edmund Halley discovered the comet that now bears his name, it was calculated that one of its periodic fly-pasts must have occurred in 12 BC. It too was suggested as the star of Bethlehem, while much more recently three British astronomers, David Clark of the Royal Greenwich Observatory, John Parkinson of Dorking's Mullard Space Science Laboratory and Richard Stephenson of Newcastle University, have offered yet another theory – that the star of Bethlehem was a nova, or exploding star, which Chinese astronomers of the Han dynasty observed 'for more than seventy days' in 5 BC.

While any or all of such speculations are possible – and each of them of course has an important bearing on the age of Jesus at the time of his death – the hard reality is that neither the Matthew nor the Luke nativity stories offers sufficient historicity (and the story of the wise men and the star appears only in Matthew) for anyone to be confident that there was a star at all. And this lack of confidence extends to aspects such as Matthew's story that King Herod was so anxious to kill the infant Jesus that he ordered the slaughter of all recently born children in the hope of eliminating Jesus. Certainly the historical record as we have it from authorities such as Josephus makes clear that Herod the Great was no paragon of virtue. A wily Idumaean politician appointed by the Romans to rule the Jews on their behalf, Herod was loathed by his subjects from the first, and with good reason. While, as we shall see, he initiated some daringly ambitious and innovative building projects, not least the rebuilding of Jerusalem's Temple, he also surrounded himself with a shadowy network of informers and secret police with whose aid he systematically liquidated all whom he considered potentially dangerous to him, including his own wife and two of his sons. There is no difficulty, therefore, in thinking him

Adoration of the Magi, Capella Graeca, cemetery of Priscilla, Rome.

capable of ordering the wholesale murder of infants, particularly if he felt the personal gain would outweigh the inevitable public antipathy. But whether he actually did so is very much more debatable. Josephus, who never shrank from cataloguing Herod's crimes, has no mention of such an atrocity, yet had anything like it actually occurred it would surely have rated among the best-remembered of Herod's misdeeds.

These by no means exhaust the uncertainties relating to the Matthew and Luke nativity stories. According to Luke, Jesus was circumcised in accordance with Jewish custom eight days after his birth (Luke 2: 21), after which he was presented in the Jerusalem temple on the fortieth. Only after these observances of the Jewish religion did Jesus' parents make a seemingly leisurely and peaceful return with him 'to their own town of Nazareth' (Luke 2: 39), in Galilee. Yet according to Matthew this was the very time that the trio fled to Egypt from what had been their home in Bethlehem to escape Herod's massacre of the new-born, remaining there for an unspecified period until the news reached them that Herod had died, whereupon they returned, settling not in Bethlehem as it was still too dangerous, but in Galilean Nazareth instead (Matthew 2: 22-3).

Of the circumstances surrounding Jesus' birth, therefore, the two gospel narratives that give us any information on this lack adequate assurance that they are based on reliable eyewitness reporting, even at second or third hand. The very fact that the two nativity stories sit somewhat uncomfortably in their gospels' opening chapters, and are never referred to again, adds to a genuine cause for disquiet. But it has to be remembered that if Jesus lived to, say, his mid-thirties (assuming he was born before 4 BC), then any memories from around the time of what may have seemed an unremarkable birth would have worn distinctly thin by the time of his death, and even thinner with every decade later than this that the gospels became committed to writing. Any inadequacies in the credibility of the Matthew and Luke nativity stories may therefore be accounted but a minor blip in relation to the content of the four gospels as a whole.

4

WHAT OF JESUS' UPBRINGING?

Even aside from our lack of reliable information on Jesus' birth, of the rest of his life Canon Streeter once calculated that aside from the forty days and nights in the wilderness (of which in any case we are told all too little), virtually everything described in the gospels could be compressed into a time scale of just three weeks, leaving by far the greater part of Jesus' life unrecorded.

That there is far too much we do not know is undeniable. For instance, not one of the four gospel writers seems to have given a thought to setting down even the tiniest morsel of information about what the adult Jesus looked like – whether he was tall or short, bearded or clean shaven, handsome or ugly. Because the Hebrew scriptures expressly forbade portraiture (Exodus 20: 4), the earliest surviving artistic depictions of him are Gentile works dating from the third century onwards, and such are the variations among these – in some of them vaguely he appears bearded (see p.172), but most depict him as beardless (whereas as a Jew, he would almost certainly have worn a beard) – that it is clear that even early on any reliable idea of what he looked like had already been lost.

Similarly, aside from readily predictable details, such as that as required by the Jewish Law he was circumcised on the eighth day after his birth

Opposite *Caesarea seen from the air, showing the sites of several of Herod the Great's ever-ambitious engineering projects. To the north is the harbour, one of the largest in the Mediterranean of Jesus' time, formed, according to Josephus, by a Herodian breakwater comprising huge blocks 50 feet long, 18 feet wide and 10 feet high, much of which later came to be destroyed in an earthquake. To the south an irregular landmass jutting into the sea marks the site of Herod's Promontory Palace, the dining room of which faced a large pool. The fine 4,000-seat theatre in the foreground is also of Herodian origin.*

(Luke 2: 21), the gospels tell us almost nothing about Jesus' upbringing, inevitably giving rise to some way-out theories. For instance, often put about is the idea that he spent his formative years in India, Tibet or China. According to one such argument, when he was two years old the 'three wise men' journeyed from India to identify him as a Dalai Lama-like high incarnation, whereupon, when he was thirteen years old, he followed the Silk Road to India, studied Buddhism, and thereby learnt his trade as a spiritual master. In reality such theories are extremely thin on substance, not least because Jesus is never recorded alluding to any life experience outside his own immediate Judaeo-Galilean environs, and nor do his highly individual teachings have their foundation in any religion other than that of his own characteristically Jewish roots.

With regard to even those roots, however, it is prudent not to take too literally the two gospel versions of Jesus' ancestry, the first as given in the Matthew nativity story (Matthew 1: 1-17) and the second as given in the Luke gospel associated with Jesus' baptism (Luke 3: 23-38). The Matthew gospel, for instance, makes some serious omissions from its Old Testament sources in order to have the magic number of exactly fourteen generations from Abraham to King David, from King David to the time of the Jewish exile and from the exile to Jesus. Furthermore, this descent from King David, so very important for Jesus' subsequent Messiahship claim, is somewhat incongruously given as via Joseph – whom the same gospel insists had not been responsible for Jesus' paternity.

On this issue of paternity it may be remembered from the documentary references in the Jewish *Mishnah* to the 'Yeshu' identified with Jesus, that he was given the patronymic 'ben Pantera' or 'son of Pantera' in one of the references (see p.45). Scurrilous Jewish stories about Jesus from the later Tannaitic period in fact claim that Jesus was the illegitimate son of a union between his mother Miriam or Mary and a Roman soldier variously called Pandera, Pantera or Panthera. That a rumour of this kind was early is confirmed by the Christian writer Origen who mentioned that he had heard it from the second-century philosopher Celsus, suggesting that it was already circulating before 150 AD. Equally undeniable is that at Bingerbrück in Germany there came to light the tombstone of one Tiberius Julius Abdes Pantera, the inscription on which shows that its owner was a Roman soldier from Sidon whose cohort of archers is historically known to have been posted to the Rhine in 9 AD. It is therefore just conceivable that this Pantera could have been Jesus' true father.

In fact, once this rumour and the gospel writers' somewhat flaky genealogies are set aside, there is much to suggest that Jesus was genuinely descended from King David, son of Jesse, as prophets such as Isaiah and Jeremiah had specifically predicted of the Messiah whose coming they promised (Isaiah 11: 1-10; Jeremiah 33: 15-22). Notably Jesus would later, on his entry to Jerusalem, be specifically hailed as 'Son of David' (e.g. Matthew 21: 9). St Paul, despite the little he seemed to know about the human Jesus, insisted that he was descended from David (Romans 1: 3). And perhaps most tellingly of all, the very scholarly and reputable church historian Eusebius, writing in the fourth century, quoted from the second-century church historian Hegesippus (whose works are now lost) how even in the reign of the Emperor Domitian (81-96 AD) close relations of Jesus were arrested specifically because they were known descendants of King David, then released because they seemed no more than harmless peasants.

If we rule out exotic Tibet or India, where was it that Jesus had his upbringing? Traditionally Jesus' family has long been associated with Nazareth (Luke 2: 4-5) , which is set on a hill overlooking what is today called the Bet Netofa Valley, though it is important to stress that this association is by no means as firm as the present-day town's tourist trade and modern New Testament translations' repeated reference to 'Jesus of Nazareth' might imply. This is partly because 'Jesus the Nazarene' is the more common form of the words in the original Greek, while in the Jewish record it is 'Hanotzri' – not particularly meaningful even for Jews. As Rabbi Morris Goldstein has commented:

> It might refer to *netzer*, as in Isaiah 11: 1, to mean 'a branch', used in Christian tradition with a messianic connotation. It might allude to Jesus as the source of the Nazarene sect. It might be a derivation from *noter*, which would describe those who keep the [new] Law of Jesus. It might mean, as is generally understood, 'of Nazareth'.

Another problem is that, as earlier noted, although the Luke gospel insists that Nazareth was Jesus' parents' home town, the second chapter of the Matthew gospel strongly suggests that Bethlehem was their original place of residence, and that they only settled in Nazareth following their return from Egypt. There has even been a suggestion that Nazareth may not even have existed in the first century; Josephus, in his listing of what appear to be all Galilee's main towns and villages (and he was the region's commander during the Jewish revolt), fails even to give it any mention throughout his writings, and the earliest Jewish literary reference (in a poem) does not occur until about the seventh century AD.

However, such negative thinking has been decisively changed by excavations carried out at Nazareth in the 1950s by the Franciscan Bellarmino

Was Jesus' father a Roman archer? According to one widespread early Jewish story, Jesus was the illegitimate son of a Roman soldier called Pantera or Panthera. The name is an unusal one, and was thought to be an invention until this first-century tombstone came to light at Bingerbrück, Germany. The inscription reads: 'Tiberius Julius Abdes Pantera of Sidon, aged 62, a soldier of 40 years' service, of the 1st cohort of archers, lies here.'

Bagatti. Digging both beneath and in the environs of the town's Church of the Annunciation – built above much older Crusader and Byzantine shrines reputedly marking where Jesus' mother Mary was told of the son she was to bear (Luke 1: 26-38) – Bagatti found wells, granaries and olive presses that seemed to date from around the first-century period. But these also clearly denoted that early Nazareth's economy was essentially rustic, and that at best it was a very small and insignificant place.

Readily corroborating Jesus' upbringing in precisely such environs is the easy familiarity with country life that he displays throughout the sayings that the gospels attribute to him. Within just a single chapter of the Luke gospel (Luke 13) he is depicted as knowing how to revive a barren fig tree (vv. 6-9), as being sensitive to farm animals' need for watering (v. 15), as being aware of the remarkable growth propensity of mustard seed (v. 19), being well informed on the amount of yeast needed to leaven dough (v. 21) and as keenly observant of the characteristic manner in which a hen gathers

The shores of the Sea of Galilee (also referred to in Luke 5: 1 as the 'Lake of Gennesaret'), the setting for most of what is known of Jesus' early life. The Sea of Galilee abounds in fish, and the historian Josephus, who lived just a generation after Jesus, described its environs as 'excellent for crops or cattle and rich in forests of every kind ... every inch has been cultivated by the inhabitants'.

her brood under her wings (v. 34). In the Matthew gospel he is the first man to go on record as interpreting a red sky at night as a portent for good weather the following day (Matthew 16: 1-3). Furthermore, we know from Josephus that almost the whole of Galilee, in which Nazareth was set, was a prolifically agricultural region – in Josephus' words:

> … excellent for crops or cattle and rich in forests of every kind, so that by its adaptability it invites even those least inclined to work on the land. Consequently every inch has been cultivated by the inhabitants and not a corner goes to waste.

If, therefore, as we have good reason to believe, Jesus grew up in such a rustic environment, then we can count it as also very likely that he spoke with the notorious Galilean accent. From sources quite independent of the New Testament it is known that certainly some of his fellow-Galileans greatly amused the snobbish southerners of Jerusalem by their characteristic sloppiness in pronouncing Aramaic, as, but one example, dropping their aitches, or more accurately, their alephs. As noted by the Jewish scholar Dr Geza Vermes, the Talmud features a typical Galilean being ridiculed in the Jerusalem market-place for trying to buy what he called *amar*. He was chided: 'You stupid Galilean, do you want something to ride on [*hamár*: a donkey]? Or something to drink [*hamár*: wine]? Or something for clothing [*'amar*: wool]? Or something for a sacrifice [*immar*: a lamb]?' The Matthew gospel mentions that Jesus' disciple Peter was specifically remarked upon in Jerusalem because of his accent: 'You are one of them for sure! Why your accent gives you away' (Matthew 26: 73).

This Galilean flavour is even conveyed by the gospels' references to two different individuals called Lazarus, one the poor man of Luke 16: 19-31, the other the man raised from the dead, John 11: 1-44. As various surviving funerary inscriptions make clear, in Jerusalem the name took the form 'Eleazar' or 'Elazar', with the initial aleph, but in Galilee this same name is found as 'Lazar' or 'Laze', just like the Lazarus of the gospels. Despite the gospels being written in Greek, therefore, they carry clear indications of Jesus' Galilean roots.

But to limit Jesus' background to that of just some Galilean rustic would be quite inadequate. Today, visible as little more than a pine-clad hillock four miles from Nazareth, is the site of ancient Sepphoris, which according to one Christian tradition was where Jesus' mother Mary was born. All too few Christians have even heard of Sepphoris, which is hardly surprising, since it goes entirely unmentioned in the gospels. But it was mentioned, it may be recalled, in one of the earlier quoted Mishnaic references to 'Yeshu'/Jesus, viz: 'I was walking on the upper street of Sepphoris and found one of the disciples of Yeshu the Nazarene, by the name of Jacob [i.e. James]' (see p.45). And while scholars have long known from Josephus and others that Sepphoris was the administrative capital of the Galilee

Nazareth as it looks today, a busy provincial town, with, visible in the background at three miles' distance, the green hillock with lone Crusader tower marking the site of Sepphoris. In Jesus' time the rôles were reversed, with Nazareth the rustic Galilean village and Sepphoris (traditionally the birthplace of Jesus' mother, Mary) the sophisticated Graeco-Roman administrative capital of the Galilee and Perea regions, complete with theatre and classically designed public buildings.

region, only very recently, and thanks to American-led archaeological excavations carried out since the early 1980s, have they appreciated the cultural timbre which went with that status.

For under the trowels of South Florida University's James Strange and Duke University's Eric and Carol Meyers have been steadily coming to light the remains of a one-time substantial Roman provincial capital of very considerable style and sophistication. Although the work is being painstak-

ingly conducted, and much remains to be uncovered, it is already evident
that the Sepphoris of Jesus' time sported an acropolis; a colonnaded east-
west main street, bordered by shops and public buildings, leading to a
forum; pools; fountains; public baths; community ritual baths; a royal
palace; and by no means least, a 4,000-seat theatre – a capacity vying with
those among London or New York's largest.

All this just four miles from Jesus' Nazareth, yet without the slightest mention from a single gospel writer? As has been remarked by Dr Geza Vermes, the omission can hardly have been accidental. So who was responsible for initiating Sepphoris' hilltop magnificence and urban affluence? And how would this have been viewed by those, such as the young Jesus and his family, who lived less than an hour's walk away in rustic Nazareth?

For this we need to be aware of the Jewish people's long and often extremely painful struggle to preserve their religious and cultural identity in the face of what was, to them, the often offensive paganism of the surrounding peoples with whom they came into contact and too often conflict. Even when, as their tradition told, Moses had led them out of Egypt, some of their number had wanted to worship a golden calf in the manner of the Canaanites. Then, after the all too brief heyday of their independent kingdom under David and Solomon, the Babylonians had swept in, destroyed the beautiful Jerusalem Temple that Solomon had built, and deported all but the lowest-born to Babylonian exile. Not long after the Persians had released them, along came Alexander the Great, whose generals now brought in all the refinements of Hellenistic culture, such as bronze statues, public baths and gymnasia where athletes sported themselves stark

Offensive to Jews, Greek athletes exercising totally naked, from a Greek vase painting. Such nudity, the expected norm for the male athletics events and public bathing widely enjoyed in the Graeco-Roman world, embarrassed Jews observant of the Mosaic Law.

naked. Such a lifestyle was anathema to the Jews, whose Law forbade depictions of the human face and form, and whose practice of male circumcision could only make them conspicuous in any all-nude sporting event.

To make matters even worse, in 167 BC the Seleucid King Antiochus IV Epiphanes went to the lengths of specifically prohibiting circumcisions, abolishing the Sabbath as a day of rest, erecting Zeus' statue in the restored Jerusalem Temple, and sacrificing pigs on its altars – all more than enough to provoke the Jews to revolt. In the event they were successful in this, the Maccabee family who led it founding the Hasmonean dynasty which preserved a fragile independence for just over a century. But in 63 BC in burst the Romans – quite literally, with the inquisitive general Pompey, having captured Jerusalem, striding into the Temple's Holy of Holies.

Finding to his disappointment that this was no more than a small, empty room, without even a window, Pompey had the prudence to withdraw, and in conformity with Roman toleration, leave the Temple intact. But by 40 BC the Romans brought in Herod the Great, an Idumaean who had wormed his way into the Hasmonean dynasty, as their local client-king to rule the Jews. And although Herod provoked much hatred among those he ruled, he managed remarkably cleverly to preserve at least the appearance of traditional Jewish religion, while bringing in every refinement of the Rome-sponsored Graeco-Roman culture.

In the latter, there can be absolutely no doubt that Herod excelled to the point of genius. Besides his spectacular remodelling of the Jerusalem Temple, which we will look at in a later chapter, at Caesarea he built a complete port with accompanying Graeco-Roman installations (see p.50), including a theatre and a superbly appointed palace for himself, which incorporated a large fresh-water swimming pool almost completely surrounded by the sea (see overleaf). On Masada, high in the desert overlooking the Dead Sea, he taxed Roman engineering to its limits by again insisting on the installation of a 60-foot swimming pool. As for his Jerusalem palace, according to Josephus this was

baffling all description: indeed in extravagance and equipment no building surpassed it. It was completely enclosed with a wall thirty cubits high, broken at equal distances by ornamental towers, and contained immense banqueting halls and bedchambers for a hundred guests. The interior fittings are indescribable – the variety of the stones (for species rare in every other country were here collected in abundance), ceilings wonderful both for the length of the beams and the splendour of their surface decoration, the host of apartments with their infinite varieties of design, all amply furnished, while most objects in each of them were of silver and gold ... There were groves of various trees intersected by long walks, which were bordered by deep canals, and ponds everywhere studded with bronze figures, through which the water was discharged ...

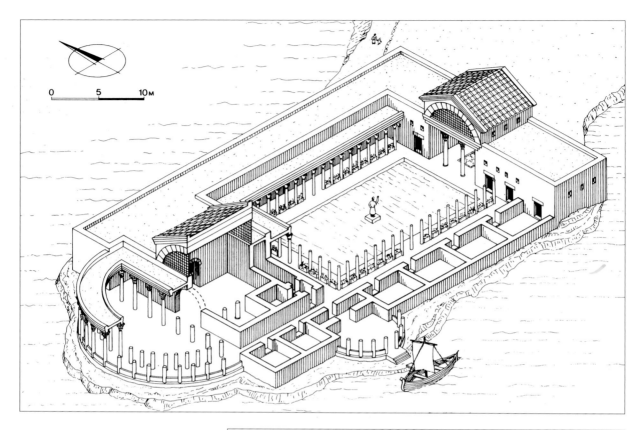

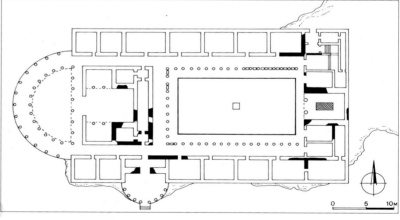

Reconstruction of Herod the Great's Promontory Palace at Caesarea, in an artist's rendition (above) and in plan form (right). With typical Herodian flamboyance, the palace was surrounded on three sides by the sea and had a special landing stage for visitors to arrive by water. Dominating the palace's interior was a near Olympic-sized swimming pool, 115 feet long, 59 feet wide and at least 8 feet deep, which some excavators think may have been filled with fresh water piped from the mainland.

Testimony to Herod's political grip while initiating such splendour (albeit aided by the power of Rome) is the fact that only when he died – after a 36-year-long reign – did pockets of rebellion break out, particularly strongly in Galilee where Sepphoris, which had an arsenal of weapons the rebels captured, became a major centre of resistance. With characteristic efficiency the Romans ruthlessly crushed this revolt, reducing Sepphoris to a smouldering ruin. And it was Herod's son, Antipas, whom they appointed to restore political order, and who decided to rebuild Sepphoris as his new capital with much the same enthusiasm for Graeco-Roman style and opulence as exhibited by his father. The magnificent city currently being revealed by the American archaeological excavations led by James Strange was therefore largely built at Herod Antipas' instigation. Like his father, he enjoyed a long life, his reign, and thereby his Sepphoris building projects, extending to 39 AD, and thereby throughout and beyond the entire known lifetime of Jesus.

So we now know that just four miles from Jesus' Nazareth there lived in considerable splendour a king over the Galileans whose thirst for stylish edifices in his new capital would have demanded the labour of many a skilled construction worker for miles around – including of course Nazareth, where there lived just such workers in the persons of Joseph and (probably) his son Jesus. Although the Matthew and Mark texts which refer to Jesus' family's mode of business leave it unclear whether Jesus was himself a carpenter (Mark 6: 3), or merely a carpenter's son (Matthew 13: 55; Mark 6: 3 variant texts), whichever was the case the word in the original Greek meant something closer to our 'builder' or 'construction worker' than the rather more limited word 'carpenter' by which it is now so often translated.

And in this regard, just as we noted how the imagery of a countryman is present in Jesus' sayings, so too is that of a carpenter, and/or construction worker. Hence in Luke's gospel alone there is reference to the planning needed by a man building a tower (14: 28-30); the parable of a house built on rock (6: 47-9); and allusion to Psalm 118, 'It was the stone rejected by the builders that became the keystone' (20: 17 and also in other gospels). Also, if we still prefer to see Jesus' father and/or Jesus as just carpenters in the more traditional sense, there is the saying: 'Why do you observe the splinter in your brother's eye and never notice the plank in your own' (6: 41, also Matthew 7: 3-5).

Accordingly, Shirley Jackson Case, Professor of New Testament studies at the University of Chicago, has noted that Sepphoris' proximity to Nazareth makes it 'no very daring flight of the imagination' that Jesus, and probably Joseph as well, may have played some part in Antipas' construction schemes there. For Jesus to have worked in a cosmopolitan city would also make sense, for instance, of the way, in the parables with which he later illustrated his teaching, he displayed easy familiarity with a keenly observed cast of characters far removed from any to be found in rustic Nazareth: kings, tax-collectors, unscrupulous judges, crafty stewards, virtuous Pharisees and many more. Likewise, in the Matthew gospel, when he is represented as addressing John the Baptist's disciples, he asks them what manner of man they had sought in the desert: 'A man wearing fine clothes? Oh no, those who wear fine clothes are to be found in palaces' (Matthew 11: 8). When Jesus spoke those words, it is not unreasonable to suppose that he had in mind the people in fine clothes that he had seen while working in Herod Antipas' palace at Sepphoris.

In this regard, a particular Sepphoris location where the archaeologist

James Strange has suggested Jesus and/or his father may have worked is the city's theatre. Although in their excavations of it Strange and his fellow archaeologists found the original stage's front and back walls, they did not find any part of its floor, suggesting that this had probably been of wood. So might Joseph and/or his son have crafted some of the planking? Speculative as this might seem, one fascinating indication of Jesus' apparent familiarity with Graeco-Roman theatre, and also of the possibility that he may well have been able to speak rather more than just the local Galilean version of Aramaic, derives from the notable frequency in the gospels in which he is represented as using the word 'hypocrite'. This occurs no less than seventeen times in sayings of his throughout the synoptic gospels, most frequently appearing as an expression of disapproval directed either towards the Pharisees (Matthew 6: 2, 5, 16; 7: 5; 15: 7; 22: 18; 23: 13, 14, 15; Mark 7: 6; Luke 6: 42; 13: 15), or, as in two instances in the Luke gospel, towards 'the crowds' (6: 17; 12: 56). Because the word derives from Greek, English New Testament translations almost invariably give it unchanged from this. But what this fails to convey is that in Jesus' time the image it carried was that of a play-actor, one who spoke behind a dramatic mask, and thereby a pretender. So Jesus seems to have been using specifically theatrical imagery – and pejoratively. Equally important, modern scholars have pointed out that 'hypocrite' has no equivalent in either Hebrew or Aramaic. So Jesus had either to be bringing in a specifically Greek word to make his point – or actually to have been fully speaking Greek at the time.

This raises the interesting point as to whether Jesus' upbringing included the learning of Greek. As has recently been argued by Joseph A. Fitzmyer, Jesuit Professor of Biblical Studies at the Catholic University of America, Washington DC, this is looking increasingly probable. Because of the powerful impact of Graeco-Roman culture, even many of Lower Galilee's funerary inscriptions of Jews of around Jesus' time were written in Greek, and when later in the gospels Jesus is represented as conversing, apparently easily, both with a Roman centurion and with Pontius Pilate, it seems very much more likely that these exchanges would have been in Greek rather than Aramaic. This does not mean to say that when Jesus used the term 'hypocrite' he did not simply introduce it among words spoken in Aramaic, just as Parisians blithely use English words such as 'football' and 'weekend' when speaking French. But there are certainly signs that Jesus had experienced the Graeco-Roman culture at close hand. There are also signs that he pointedly distanced himself from those Jews who embraced this rather too warmly at the expense of their own culturo-religious heritage.

Amidst the new importance that must now be attached to Sepphoris as a formative influence on Jesus's life, we might ask whatever happened to his father, Joseph? Once we set the nativity stories aside, Joseph effectively disappears from the gospels, suggesting that by the time that Jesus emerged to commence the rôle he felt he was destined for, Joseph was by then already dead. At this point it would seem to have been Jesus, as the eldest of four brothers and at least two sisters (Matthew 13: 55-6; Mark 6: 3–see family tree p.159), who became head of the family, for there are several instances in the gospels in which his family seem to look to him for leadership (e.g. Mark 3: 31-5), and these indications of an apparent family line of succession are important, because they effectively give the lie to the later Jewish stories of Jesus being the son of a Roman soldier. Had Jesus genuinely been known to have been born illegitimate, the eldest legitimate brother would have taken charge after Joseph's death, which certainly does not appear to have been the case.

None of this, however, answers one most fundamental question: just how did a construction worker's son from tiny Nazareth, even if he had the blood of King David running through his veins, acquire the sense of mission to give up the family trade and begin attracting ordinary men and women to follow him and his teaching?

5

HOW DID HE ACQUIRE HIS SENSE OF MISSION?

As we have already seen, the authors of both the Mark and the John gospels chose not to commence their accounts of Jesus with the story of any seemingly miraculous nativity. Instead, aside from the John gospel's remarkable proiogue they begin with the wild man John the Baptist proclaiming the coming of 'someone more powerful than I am'. Immediately following this, both gospels tell of the apparently adult Jesus' arrival (from Nazareth, according to Mark), on the banks of the Jordan, a Jesus who to all appearances wants to be baptized by John, just as many others had been, for the forgiveness of sins.

Now there can be no doubt that John the Baptist's one-time existence is historically very well attested. Throughout early Christian literature he was referred to as a man of whom everyone had heard, and according to the New Testament book of Acts his disciples carried his teachings as far afield as Alexandria and Ephesus (Acts 18: 25; 19: 2). All four gospel authors referred to him at some length, and although naturally their prime focus was on Jesus (and there are hints of even a little rivalry between John's disciples and those of Jesus), they freely acknowledged that great crowds had flocked to John from 'Jerusalem and all Judaea and the whole Jordan

Opposite *Jesus' baptism by John the Baptist, from a fifth-century mosaic in Santa Maria in Cosmedin, Ravenna. John the Baptist's existence is independently attested by Josephus and others. Note Jesus' nudity and the 'spirit of God' descending in the form of a bird.*

district' (Matthew 3: 5). Furthermore, from quite outside the Christian milieu, the first-century historian Josephus mentioned John the Baptist in a passage that scholars generally agree is not a copyist's interpolation:

> He [John] was a good man, and exhorted the Jews to lead righteous lives, practise justice towards one another and piety towards God, and so to join in baptism. In his view this was a necessary preliminary if baptism was to be acceptable to God. They must not use it to gain pardon for whatever sins they committed, but as a consecration of the body, implying that the soul was thoroughly purified beforehand by right behaviour.

As has been argued by Dr Martin Purbrook of Maynooth, Ireland, and others, the full extent of John the Baptist's influence on Jesus has probably been played down in the gospels, particularly by the synoptic authors. But besides John's baptism of Jesus being the first event on which all four gospels are in agreement, one reason for confidence that this baptism actually happened lies in the fact that there was no advantage to be gained by the gospel writers from inventing it. Rather the reverse, as it implied that Jesus had past sins that needed washing away. A hint even of early Christian sensitivity on this matter is to be found in the Matthew gospel, which represents John the Baptist as saying to Jesus: 'It is I who need baptism from you', and Jesus replying, 'Leave it like this for the time being...' (Matthew 3: 15).

So if John's baptism of Jesus actually occurred, what sort of event was it? The John gospel remarks that one of the settings in which John the Baptist conducted his work was 'Aenon, near Salim, where there was plenty of water' (John 3: 23), and as was pointed out half a century ago by the noted American archaeologist Professor W. F. Albright, this particular spot can almost certainly still be identified:

> ... Salim cannot be separated from the well-known ancient town of that name, south-east of Nablus, nor can it be quite accidental that there is an 'Ainun in the immediate vicinity. The nearby sources of the Wadi Far'ah are extremely well provided with water.

In fact, the gospels are fairly explicit that the specific baptism of Jesus was somewhere else along the Jordan, rather than at 'Ainun, but an obvious deduction to be drawn is that an open-air location and a plentiful supply of fresh water were required, the intention, clearly, being total immersion. John or one of his disciples appears to have needed to officiate, and for each recipient the event appears to have been a unique, once in a lifetime ritual, there being no accounts of anyone returning for a second baptism.

It is important to notice that in each of these respects the John baptism seems to have distinctively differed from the routine, self-administered ritual ablutions long commonplace for religious purification among Jews of all denominations. Directly challenging the Jerusalem Temple's claimed monopoly on the cleansing of sins, it seems to have been a form of consecration or initiation by which, after repentance, an individual could feel purified from his past sins in preparation for a better life thereafter.

Of John's baptism of Jesus, the gospels tell us enough to be able to envisage something of the scene, the hairy John in his camel-skins and Jesus himself most likely naked, for according to early churchman Hippolytus, and references to 'complete stripping' by Paul (I Colossians 2: 11), that is how the earliest Christian baptisms seem to have been conducted. Since no source specifically describes witnesses at John's baptisms, some degree of privacy may have been managed, thereby adding to the ceremony's element of mystery.

The very popularity of John's baptisms suggests that they had a powerful impact on those who received them and, we may assume, on no-one more so than on Jesus, for we are told that as he surfaced after immersion he seemed to receive a vision in the form of a dove, accompanied by a heavenly voice announcing: 'You are my son...' (Mark 1: 11). While sceptics might dismiss this as an obvious piece of Christian deification of Jesus, it cannot be tossed aside altogether lightly, for in the traditional Jewish royal ritual a perfectly human King of the Jews became 'Son of God' at the time of his anointing as Messiah. And an especially intriguing feature of Jesus' baptism, to be found in all four canonical gospels (also in non-canonical ones such as the Gospel of the Ebionites), is the association of a bird with his reported vision. As pointed out by an American scholar, the late Dr Morton Smith, the vision of a bird also occurs in early mystery religion initiations, as in one Greek magical papyrus description in which an initiate, after lying naked in a sheet and repeating a prescribed chant, is told to expect to see 'a sea-hawk flying down' as a sign that union with the deity had been achieved.

Accordingly, it would not be at all unreasonable to interpret Jesus' baptism, his first real appearance on the stage of history, as hugely life-changing. According to the Mark gospel, it was immediately after this that he spent his forty days in the wilderness. The John gospel even seems to suggest that initially he became one of the Baptist's disciples, spreading his work into other areas (John 3: 22-4), and becoming even more successful at it (John 4 : 1), although we are somewhat contradictorily told 'in fact it was his [Jesus'] disciples who baptised, not Jesus himself' (John 4: 2).

Whatever may have been the exact relationship between John the Baptist and Jesus, circumstances were to be dramatically changed by John's arrest and subsequent execution. It is the Mark gospel that very matter-of-factly gives us the fullest account, in which, in very unsavoury and tragic circumstances, we renew our acquaintance with the now familiar Herod Antipas:

Now… Herod [Antipas]… had sent to have John arrested, and had him chained up in prison because of Herodias, his brother Philip's wife whom he had married. For John had told Herod, 'It is against the Law for you to have your brother's wife'. As for Herodias, she was furious with him and wanted to kill him, but she was not able to, because Herod was afraid of John, knowing him to be a good and holy man, and gave him his protection. When he had heard him speak, he was greatly perplexed, and yet he liked to listen to him.

An opportunity came on Herod's birthday when he gave a banquet for the nobles of his court, for his army officers and for the leading figures in Galilee. When the daughter of this same Herodias came in and danced, she delighted Herod and his guests, so the king said to the girl, 'Ask me anything you like and I will give it to you'. And he swore her an oath, 'I will give you anything you ask, even half my kingdom'. She went out and said to her mother, 'What shall I ask for?' She replied, 'The head of John the Baptist'. The girl hurried straight back to the king and made her request, 'I want you to give me John the Baptist's head, here and now, on a dish.' The king was deeply distressed but, thinking of the oaths he had sworn, and of his guests, he was reluctant to break his word to her. So the king at once sent one of his bodyguard with orders to bring John's head. The man went off and beheaded him in prison; then he brought the head on a dish and gave it to the girl, and the girl gave it to her mother. When John's disciples heard about this, they came and took his body, and laid it in a tomb. (Mark 6: 17-29)

Now the basic facts are firmly historical. Josephus, for instance, supplemented the gospels by even providing the name of Herodias' daughter, Salome, also the information that the location was Machaerus, Herod Antipas' palace-fortress near the Dead Sea. Overall also quite clear is that John the Baptist had taken upon himself the rôle of one of the Jewish people's 'prophets' – men and women referred to rather more accurately in Hebrew as *nabi'im*, literally 'mouthpieces of God', to interpret the Law of Moses as it applied to everyday life problems. Unlike the Temple's priests, who were mere functionaries, essentially supervisors of animal sacrifices, *nabi'im* were individuals who could step from any background and fearlessly speak as if for God before the highest and mightiest in the land. One such had been Nathan, who openly denounced King David's duplicity over his adultery with an officer's wife; another the goatskin-clad Elijah the Tishbite, who similarly condemned Israel's ninth-century King Ahab and his flagrantly pagan Queen Jezebel. Such encounters always ran high risks of blood being spilt, and for John the Baptist this particular confrontation with Herod Antipas and his Herodias ended with the ultimate penalty, death. Not without good reason was it widely put about after John's death that he had been Elijah born again (Matthew 17: 12), for if he had been Elijah, then according to some schools of thought, this meant that the whole purpose of his return would have been to recognize and anoint the promised new Messiah – an individual who may not even have known his identity himself.

At the very least, therefore, Jesus would have been deeply moved and affected by the news of John's so unjust execution. Despite the Mark gospel's detailed account of how John died, its seemingly Rome-based author characteristically avoided stating anything too overtly political. Only in the Luke gospel are we told of Jesus' attitude to Antipas as expressed in just two words: 'that fox…' (Luke 13: 32). However what Mark's author did describe, in very next breath, was a large crowd 'like sheep without a shepherd' who, with scant thought for provisions, immediately journeyed to a 'lonely place' to seek out Jesus. There were five thousand of them, and Dr John Robinson pointed out that the original Greek makes clear that they were all men (Mark 6: 44). Although exactly what happened on this occasion has been somewhat obscured in the gospels by the accompanying 'miracle' – the feeding of the five thousand – the story's origins are undoubtedly early, for it can be seen that Mark drew on no less than two previous accounts of the happening, one referring to five thousand people, the other to four thousand. And the strong inference is that the popular following which John the Baptist had stirred up had turned to Jesus, both as John's natural successor, and as the potential Messiah so badly needed to free the Jewish people from the yoke of Rome and from self-seeking Roman-collaborator lackeys like Herod Antipas.

But what would Jesus do with this following? We are told that in common with John the Baptist before him he called upon them to repent, and proclaimed the closeness of what he called the Kingdom of God (Mark 1: 15). He also quite evidently impressed them, hence the story of the feeding miracle, whatever kind of explanation may be attributed to this (see chapter 7). But if those who had sought Jesus out expected him, as they surely did, to lead them in some sort of armed insurrection, then they were in for dis-

'They collected twelve basketfuls of scraps of bread and pieces of fish' (Mark 6: 43). Remarkably modern in appearance, this Jewish basket, dating from within a century of Jesus' lifetime, was found in caves in which rebels hid from the Romans during the Second Jewish Revolt. It vividly evokes the baskets described as being used during Jesus' feeding 'miracle'.

appointment. According to the John gospel, immediately after the food left over from the feeding miracle had been gathered up in baskets, 'Jesus could see they were about to come and take him by force and make him king' (John 6: 15) – whereupon his response was to make a swift diplomatic exit to the hills.

And in this lies one of the most explicit indications of Jesus' purpose. Had he been a mere guerrilla leader, undoubtedly he would have seized upon the wave of popular support, and there and then drawn up plans for a blood-letting rebellion. But whatever the effect of John's baptism upon him, what he was about was not of this order. A succession of post-war writers, among them Manchester University's Professor S.G.F. Brandon and Jewish scholars Hyam Maccoby and Joel Carmichael, have all tried to represent Jesus as an ardent Jewish nationalist whom the gospel writers deliberately misrepresented as a pacifist in order to make him more accept-able to Gentiles. If this were so, Jesus' pacifism would stand out as a glaring inconsistency with the rest of his message. Instead it seems all of a piece with everything else that he was about.

For if we try to define the essence of Jesus as at his succession to the mantle left by John the Baptist, it was his claim of the nearness of what he called the 'Kingdom of God'. And very clear in his mind was that this 'Kingdom' was not anything pertaining to the world of fancy palaces and fine clothes that (as we have suggested) he had seen displayed in Herod Antipas' Sepphoris. As related in the Mark gospel when the five thousand sought Jesus out in the 'lonely place', he 'set himself to teach them at some length' (Mark 6: 34), and although there is no record of his exact message on that occasion, it may readily be deduced from such texts as the Matthew 'Sermon on the Mount':

> Do not store up treasures for yourself on earth, where moths and wood-worm destroy them and thieves can break in and steal … You cannot be the slave both of God and money. That is why I am telling you not to worry about your life and what you are to eat, nor about your body and how you are to clothe it. Surely life means more than food and the body more than clothing? Look at the birds in the sky. They do not sow or reap or gather into barns; yet your heavenly Father feeds them. Are you not worth much more than they are? Can any of you, for all his worry-ing, add one single cubit to his span of life? And why worry about clothing? Think of the flowers in the fields, they never have to work or spin; yet I assure you that not even Solomon in all his regalia was robed like one of these. (Matthew 6: 19-29)

This so striking and compelling message, at once both so simple to preach and so extraordinarily difficult to put into practice, has never appealed to any vainglorious power-seeker, whether a Louis XIV or a Herod Antipas. Even in conventional Christianity it has too often been neglected, not least

Aerial view of the Judaean wilderness. Despite its apparent remoteness, this 'wilderness' is located only a few miles south of Jerusalem, and is in similar close proximity to the Dead Sea Scrolls community at Qumran. After John the Baptist's death, Jesus was sought out by a reputed five thousand male Jews at a place such as this.

by Renaissance popes. But from time to time it has been taken to heart by men and women from as variegated backgrounds as St Francis of Assisi, William Blake, Tolstoy, Mother Teresa of Calcutta and Mahatma Gandhi. And ultimately it may be distilled into a simple attitude of mind: self-abnegation, shedding the earthly bonds of property, clothes, family ties and the like, and dwelling in a heaven of the mind. Almost everything that Jesus would say and do can be related to this utterly simple and consistent way of thought, including the counselling of extreme pacifism by which he spurned the sentiments of those who wanted him to overthrow the Romans by force: 'offer the wicked man no resistance. On the contrary, if anyone hits you on the right cheek, offer him the other also' (Matthew 5: 39).

Fired by their evangelical fervour, Christian writers have sometimes tried to claim that Jesus introduced such doctrines as total novelties into a world that had heard nothing like them before. But this needs some rather careful qualification. For instance, the New Testament book of Acts has a description of how Jesus' followers lived in Jerusalem after his death: '…all lived together and owned everything in common; they sold their goods and possessions and shared out the proceeds among themselves according to what each one needed' (Acts 2 : 45). This is effectively little different from what we are told of the Essenes by Josephus: 'each man's possessions go into the pool', and as with brothers their entire property belongs to them all. Similarly, just as Jesus sent his disciples on their missions 'with no haversack for the journey or spare tunic or footwear' (Matthew 10: 10), so we are told of the Essenes, '…when they travel they carry no baggage at all, but only weapons to keep off bandits … Neither garments nor shoes are changed till they are dropping to pieces or worn out with age'.

But although such parallels might seem to detract from Jesus' originality, reducing his ideas to ones simply typical of the Jewish spiritual thought of his time, also clear is that time and again Jesus did give such existing ideas a new twist, and not always in the same direction. While John the Baptist asked for the man with two tunics to give away the one he did not need – 'If anyone has two tunics he must share with the man who has none', Jesus asked him, if called upon, to give away both: 'If a man … would have your tunic, let him have your cloak as well' (Matthew 5: 41). Likewise, whereas the book of Leviticus ruled: 'You must love your neighbour as yourself' (Leviticus 19: 18), Jesus urged, 'Love your enemies, and pray for those who persecute you' (Matthew 5: 44). Precepts such as these, so far as can be ascertained, were utterly new, and exclusive to the gospel Jesus. They have no obvious counterparts in the teachings of either the Pharisees or the Essenes. Humane and inspired as the old Mosaic code was, Jesus' code went far beyond it.

But there was a further element. As we have already noted, John the Baptist had seen himself as being in the tradition of the Old Testament *nabi'im*, men and women who felt that God spoke through them on fundamental issues. Quite clearly Jesus too felt he could and did speak for God, but even more intensely. The gospels notably include a scattering of his utterances left in their original Aramaic, ones that because of this, even the Bultmann school of thought has recognized as having the greatest claim to authenticity. Among these undoubtedly one of the most striking is his apparent addressing God as 'Abba', 'Father'. This has caused more than a little controversy because, while some commentators have claimed that as a mode of address to God this carried a sense of familiarity virtually equivalent to 'Daddy', others have seen this as somewhat exaggerated, 'Abba' as a way of addressing God, for instance, certainly being used a century before by the grandson of a Jewish holy man, Honi the Circle Drawer.

This qualification aside, however, there can be little doubt about the contrast between this apparent intimacy and the normal Jewish tradition. Traditionally for Jews the name of God carried such awe and mystique that no ordinary man could either utter it, or set it in writing. Thus the earliest manuscript copies of the books of the Old Testament feature God's name in the form of the 'Tetragrammaton', four Hebrew letters, the equivalents of YHWH , or Yahweh with the vowels omitted, and usually written in a more archaic form than the rest of the text, the custom being that when readers in the synagogue came to these letters they would automatically substitute Adonai, Hebrew for Lord.

And that Jesus did see himself as very special, sufficient to cause deep offence even to those with whom he had grown up in Nazareth, is quite evident from the Luke gospel's account of him reading in his local Nazareth synagogue a passage from Jewish scripture as if it pertained to himself. Whatever may survive of Nazareth's synagogue as it existed in Jesus' time has not yet been located, and indeed in all Galilee the only first-century synagogue remains for the tourist to see are at Gamla, on the slopes of the Golan with distant views of the Sea of Galilee. However, the Gamla remains show that early synagogue designs differed comparatively little from those known from later centuries, and by way of further background Professor Alan Millard of Liverpool University has painted the following vivid picture of the typical Sabbath day scene as Jesus would have known it at Nazareth:

> Entering, they [the congregation] climbed the steps and walked along to find a place to sit. Men and women may have had separate sections; that is not clear. They sat in rows along the steps, leaving the central area empty. The floor there was probably covered with rugs, giving a splash of colour. Men wore shawls, white, some with long fringes (Matthew 23: 5). When everyone was seated, the leader could begin the service. An important moment was the reading of the Bible lessons. The Scrolls of the Law and the Prophets would be brought respectfully from their ark or cupboard, carried through the congregation and laid on the reading desk in the centre.

Thanks to the discovery of the Dead Sea Scrolls, the visitor to Jerusalem

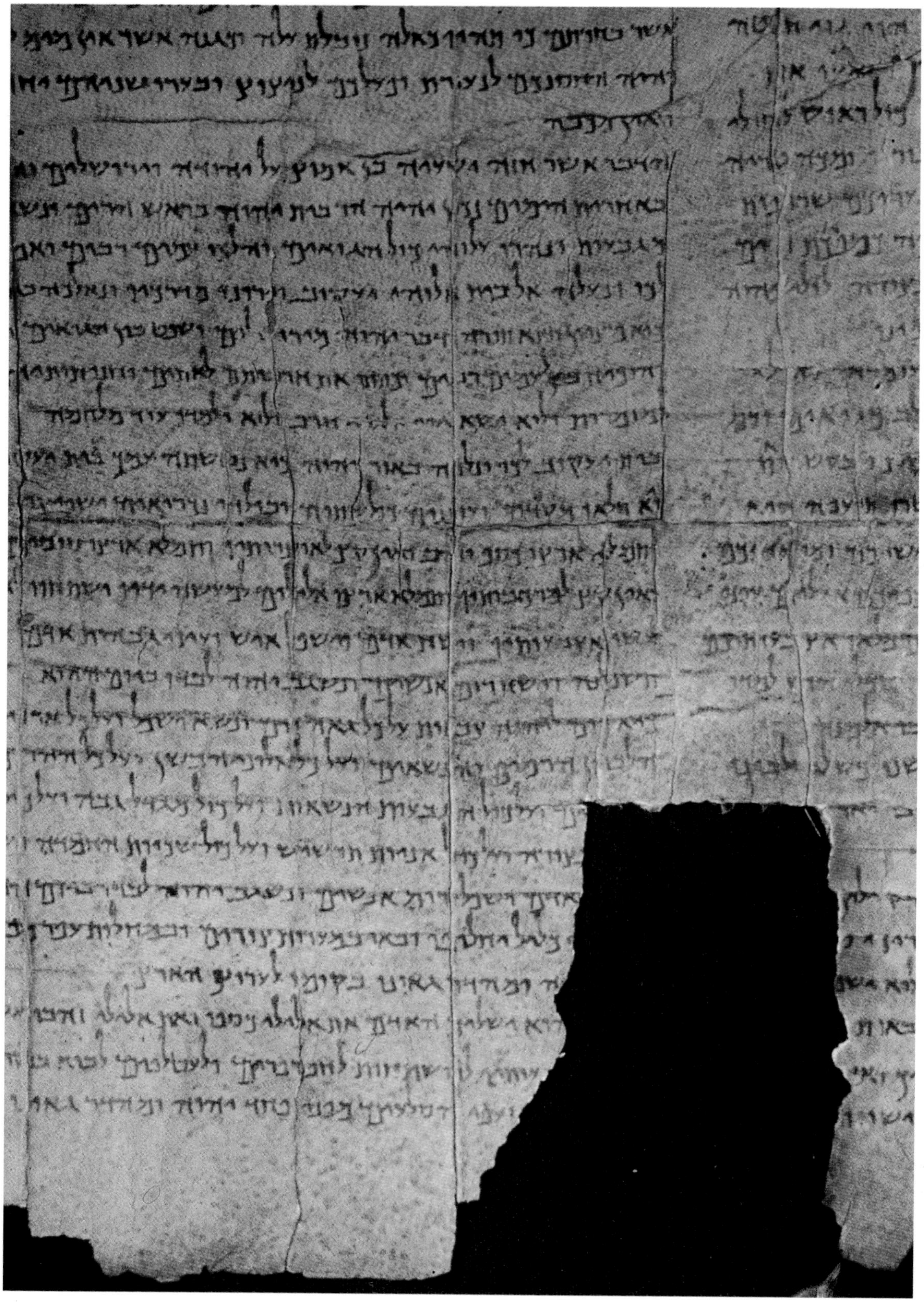

can today examine, rolled around a great drum in the centre of the city's Shrine of the Book, at least a facsimile of a scroll of the prophet Isaiah of the kind that would have been read in synagogues around Jesus' time. Sadly, the original developed cracks from having been forced into the very reverse of the way that it had been rolled up for nearly two thousand years, but it would have been from just such a scroll that, as described by the Luke author, Jesus read to fellow-Nazarenes Isaiah's long familiar passage relating to the promised Messiah:

> The spirit of the Lord has been given to me,
> for he has anointed me.
> He has sent me to bring the good news to the poor,
> to proclaim liberty to captives
> and to the blind new sight,
> to set the downtrodden free,
> to proclaim the Lord's year of favour.
>
> (Isaiah 61: 1-2)

According to the Luke author Jesus then rolled up the scroll, gave it back to the assistant, sat down and told his audience: 'This text is being fulfilled today even as you listen'. Although whatever happened next has almost certainly been somewhat fudged by the gospel writers, it can hardly have been anything less than ugly, for after first learning that Jesus 'won the approval of all', we are next told of the Nazarenes muttering 'This is Joseph's son, surely?' None too diplomatically, Jesus reportedly pointed out to them the persistence with which the Jews rejected their *nabi'im*, whereupon in the Luke author's words:

> Everyone in the synagogue was enraged. They sprang to their feet and hustled him out of the town; and they took him up to the brow of the hill their town was built on, intending to throw him down the cliff, but he slipped through the crowd and walked away. (Luke 4: 28-30)

Readily apparent from this, even though it derives from one of the two gospels that have a nativity story, is the conviction that in his home-town of Nazareth Jesus enjoyed nothing of any protective cocoon of stories of his miraculous birth accompanied by visitations of angels. In rude country fashion Jesus' fellow-Nazarenes saw one of their own number, 'Joseph's son', affecting to be a far more important and indeed sacred person than they knew him to be, and their reaction was the thoroughly understandable one of disbelief. Yet as we are about to see, others, from outside Nazareth, would react to him altogether differently.

The Isaiah Scroll, from the Dead Sea Scrolls. From such a scroll Jesus read out the text that (because he identified it with himself) led to his forcible expulsion from the Nazareth synagogue. A thousand years older than any previously known biblical text in Hebrew, this and the other biblical scrolls found at Qumran show that the Old Testament 'Bible' was faithfully transmitted from Jesus' time to our own.

6

FISHER OF MEN–AND WOMEN

Howevernegative may have been the
impact that Jesus made upon those with
whom he grew up in Nazareth, the
gospels convey that he had no difficulty
drawing followers from elsewhere. In the
Mark author's very first chapter he is
described seemingly casually strolling
'along by the sea of Galilee' and coming
across two different pairs of fishermen brothers, Simon (Peter) and Andrew,
and James and John, apparently easily persuading them to join him.

We are given no clear explanation for how Jesus exerted so instant an
attraction upon these fishermen, nor upon the other eight male disciples
whom he similarly gathered. Nor it is at all obvious even how and where
Jesus was living at this point. According to the John gospel the two pairs of
fishermen brothers came from Bethsaida (John 1: 44), which may or may
not be the Bethsaida on the east bank of the River Jordan, where it enters
the Sea of Galilee. But, when in the synoptic gospels Jesus is described as
beginning his active ministry, both he and these same disciples seem to be
living in Capernaum. The Matthew and Mark gospels both indicate that it
was at Capernaum, and specifically Simon Peter and Andrew's house there,
that Jesus healed Simon Peter's mother-in-law of a fever (Matthew 8: 14-

Opposite *Remains of New Testament-
period Capernaum seen from the air,
looking towards the Sea of Galilee. The
octagonal-shaped foundations closest to
the tree-lined lakeside are those of the
Byzantine church marking what has
come to be called 'St Peter's house'. The
large edifice on the lighter-coloured
ground is the fourth-century synagogue,
thought to be the successor to the one in
which Jesus taught (Mark 1: 21).
Other remains found at Capernaum
indicate that the town was the base for
a Roman garrison, arguably that
commanded by the very centurion
whose servant was reportedly cured by
Jesus (Matthew 8: 5-13 et al.).*

15; Mark 1: 29-31). Earlier the Matthew version relates that Jesus had gone to live in Capernaum after leaving Nazareth (Matthew 4: 13). The John gospel describes Jesus and his disciples, after the feeding of the five thousand, rowing across the Sea of Galilee to Capernaum as if they were returning home (John 6: 15). The Mark gospel suggests that Jesus somehow owned a Capernaum house sufficiently large to accommodate quite a gathering of disciples, tax-collectors and sinners (Mark 2: 15). Again according to Mark, Jesus taught in the Capernaum synagogue, reportedly sustaining a rather more favourable impression than he had in Nazareth (Mark 1: 21). Furthermore, this Capernaum synagogue appears to have been built by a locally based Roman centurion or royal official whose servant Jesus reportedly cured of his sickness in an intriguing incident that is described in no less than three of the gospels (Matthew 8: 5-13; Luke 7: 2-29; John 4: 46-53).

So where in present-day Israel was this Capernaum with so many close associations with Jesus? After many centuries in which its whereabouts remained unknown, in 1866 the British engineer and biblical enthusiast Captain Charles Wilson identified it with a site the local Arabs called Tel-Hum on the shores of the Sea of Galilee. An important clue lay in the Arab name, preserving the original Hebrew *Kfar Nahum* or 'village of Nahum' (in Greek, Capernaum), and the accuracy of Wilson's identification has been readily demonstrated by more recent archaeological excavations.

For instance, although the well-preserved Capernaum synagogue that today's tourists flock to see dates only to the fourth century, beneath this archaeologists have found the traces of an earlier, circa first-century version that is arguably the very one built by the Roman centurion whose servant Jesus healed. The presence of Roman occupants of Capernaum is further indicated by the remains of a 64-foot long bath-house of unmistakably Roman, rather than Jewish design. Although this dated from the second or third centuries, beneath it were again found indications of a similar building from the first century. The inference is that there was a substantial Roman presence – and thereby very likely a garrison commanded by a centurion – stationed at the Capernaum of Jesus' time, almost certainly as support troops to the Herod Antipas regime.

Yet more pertinently, within the last two decades archaeologists digging below the foundations of Capernaum's long-gone fifth-century Byzantine octagonal church came across the remains of a large and yet more ancient private house that the church had clearly been intended to honour. This was found to date to the first century, thereby to around the time of Jesus, and to have been specially rebuilt, even at that early date, to transform it into a large meeting place whose early Christian function was clearly indicated by unmistakably Christian inscriptions (such as 'Lord Jesus Christ help your servant ...' and 'Christ have mercy'), some in Aramaic, Syriac and Hebrew, scratched into what remained of its walls. A key question therefore arises as to what made this dwelling so special for it to have been transformed into such a 'house-church' at so early a period? One possibility is that it belonged to Jesus' disciple, Simon Peter, who as we have already noted, seems to have had a house in Capernaum, and for tourism purposes the house is indeed popularly dubbed 'St Peter's house'. Another possibility – and no less credible – is that it was the very house in which Jesus himself lived while in Capernaum, and in which he held the gatherings of the tax-collectors and sinners already noted from the Mark gospel.

But these possibilities aside, why among his fellow-Jews did Jesus choose Galilean fishermen to be the most prominent occupational group among his disciples? A leading classical historian has recently pointed out that in antiquity fishermen were regarded as socially very much the bottom of the scale, and Jesus' selection of them may have been part of his policy of seeking out such social outcasts. But the particular fishermen with whom Jesus associated may not necessarily have been quite as humble as they have sometimes been painted. In January 1986 an unusually severe drought lowered the level of the Sea of Galilee, whereupon the outlines of a clearly long-buried boat became revealed in the mud just five miles east of Capernaum. A quick expert appraisal revealed that it had been made in the ancient manner, the planks of the hull being edge-joined with 'mortise-and-tenon' joints held in place by wooden pegs. Not least because it was the first ancient boat ever known to have been found in the Sea of Galilee, immediate steps were taken to get it to shore for proper conservation and study before rains could restore the Sea's usual level.

This proved no small problem for the appointed Israeli government archaeologist, Shelley Wachsmann, and his hastily assembled team of

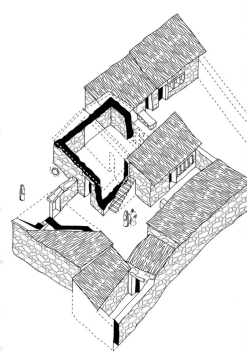

Artist's reconstruction of the original appearance of a first-century house as found beneath the foundations of Capernaum's octagonal Byzantine church (as seen below left). According to the archaeological findings, Judaeo-Christians remodelled this house sometime in the first century, removing some walls (shown by dotted lines) to convert it into a domus ecclesia, or very early house-church. Indicative of this early Judaeo-Christian usage were symbols and inscriptions found on the walls. In the fourth century, the time of the first Christian Emperor Constantine the Great, the building was substantially altered. Then in the first half of the fifth century almost all the previous structure was demolished in favour of the octagonal-shaped church.

Left: *Close-up of the excavated foundations of the fifth-century octagonal Byzantine church found at Capernaum. At that time the octagonal shape denoted a particularly holy site.*

volunteers. They found that although the boat's timber was reassuringly in good overall shape, its long immersion had saturated it to the consistency of wet cardboard, meaning that it was too soft to move by normal means. Yet, as they were all too well aware, if it were allowed to dry out its entire cellular structure would collapse. They had but days to come up with a solution, but ingeniously conservator Orna Cohen devised a method of spraying liquid polyurethane over the already exposed inner portions of the vessel, and letting this harden to the boat's exact shape. Protected by an impromptu 'dry dock' of sandbags the volunteers then dug tunnels below the outer part of the boat still embedded in the mud, and threaded fibreglass through these which, with the addition of more polyurethane, provided supportive trusses. After clearing the rest of the mud and spraying on yet more polyurethane, creating a complete protective cocoon, they then removed the sandbags and gently floated the whole ensemble to the nearby Kibbutz Ginnosar, where Yigal Allon Museum staff were waiting to receive it.

Although at the time of writing, the Galilee boat is still at the Yigal

The Galilee boat, the outlines of which became exposed early in 1986 when the Sea of Galilee's water-level was at a record low due to drought. From its mortise-and-tenon joint construction, this boat was quickly identified as being of a very early date, and here on only its second day of excavation its 26-foot length is already revealed. Each bucket of mud removed was carefully numbered so that its contents could be later sifted and the location of any small artefacts identified with precision.

Allon Museum undergoing conservation treatment of a kind similar to that used for England's sixteenth-century *Mary Rose*, it is already clear from the radiocarbon dating of its wood, mostly cedar planking with oak frames, that this dates from between 40 BC and 40 AD, its working life hence having been very close to, if not actually contemporary with, the lifetime of Jesus. Furthermore it has already been sufficiently well studied for an assessment to be made that it is similar, if not identical to the type of vessel repeatedly described in the gospels as used by Jesus and his disciples (Matthew 8: 18, 23-7; 9: 1; 14: 13-14, 22-32; 15: 39; 16: 5; Mark 4: 35-41; 5: 18, 21; 6: 32-4, 45-51; 8: 9-10, 13-14; Luke 6: 1; 8: 22-5, 37, 40; John 6: 16-21). It is twenty-six and a half feet long, seven and a half feet wide and four and a half feet high, with a rounded stern and well-crafted bow, and nautical experts have determined that it could be both sailed and rowed, and would have needed a crew of five, four rowers and a helmsman who steered with a specially shaped steering oar. Additionally it could have carried either a substantial cargo or some ten passengers. The crew complement readily corresponds to the Mark gospel's account of Zebedee's sons James and John leaving their father 'in the boat with the men he employed' when Jesus recruited them (Mark 1: 20), and indicates that those who operated such vessels were by no means at the lowest level of subsistence, but must have needed to be at least moderately well-placed in order to be able to invest in such transport.

Nine days after the commencement of the excavation, and protected by a polyurethane cocoon, the Galilee boat is gently floated to shore before being lifted onto dry land for conservation. From pottery and coins in the mud surrounding the boat, it was tentatively dated to the first century AD, and radiocarbon dating has supported this.

Mosaic of a small boat, as found in a first-century AD house at Migdal, the ancient Magdala, home of Jesus' woman follower Mary Magdalen. Migdal is only a mile from where the Galilee boat was found. The mosaic shows that the boat was powered by four rowers, two on each side, with a fifth man controlling the steering oar, or rudder. This corresponds well with the fishing boat crew indicated in Mark 1: 20.

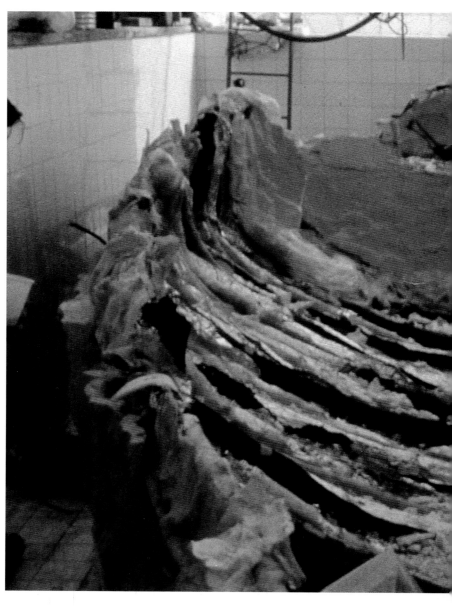

The gospels also convey vivid images of people for whom fish were a central part of their diet and economy, as in the Luke gospel's description of Jesus somehow arranging a record catch of fish after Peter and the others had been out all night in two boats and caught nothing (Luke 5: 1-7). Important for buttressing the gospels' credibility, these elements are not regarded as fanciful even by non-Christians. As has been pointed out by Mendel Nun, a modern-day authority on the Galilee fishing industry, for two boats to have been out overnight, seemingly working in partnership, is totally accurate for the traditional Galilean way of fishing for a large, wily and very edible fish known as musht. Musht (see p.84) are shoal-loving plankton-eaters who will shy from any net deployed during the day, as a result of which the long-established way

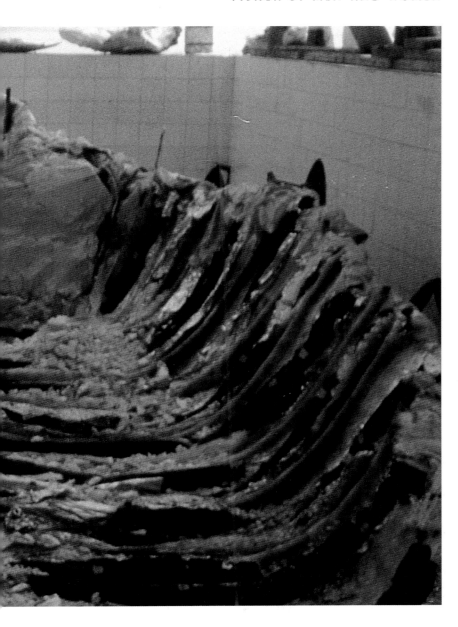

Its protective cocoon removed, the Galilee boat undergoing conservation at the Yigal Allon Museum, where its timbers are being carefully reconsolidated with the aid of the synthetic wax polyethylene glycol. This will eventually enable the boat to be displayed in a dry atmosphere, providing the closest glimpse of the sort of boat in which Jesus travelled with his disciples on the Sea of Galilee.

of catching them is for two boats to go out overnight and fan a trammel net around any shoal they find, trapping the fish in an underwater 'barrel' stretching from the lake bottom to the surface (see p.85). It is an all-or-nothing operation, and as Mendel Nun insists, this is almost certainly what Peter and his companions had been trying unsuccessfully to do until Jesus' apparently miraculous intervention. Elsewhere in the gospels we are told of Jesus eating barbecued fish with his disciples (e.g. John 21: 9). And Migdal, on the Sea of Galilee's eastern shore, where the gospels' Mary Magdalen almost certainly had her origin, has long been where the very plentiful Galilee sardines have been brought for pickling, this variety of fish still representing some half the annual total of those commercially caught in the Sea of Galilee.

Musht, large, edible and shoal-loving fish that have remained very plentiful in the Sea of Galilee from Jesus' time to our own. Often called 'St Peter's fish', this is definitely a misnomer, since musht are not caught singly with hook and line as in the incident with Simon Peter described in Matthew 17: 24-7. However, because of their shoal-loving characteristics, they were almost certainly the particular fish netted in the 'miraculous' catch described in Luke 5: 1-7.

But whatever may have been the status (or lack of it) of Galilean fishermen in Jesus' time, also clear is that these were by no means the only individuals of low esteem whom Jesus gathered to him. According to the Matthew gospel, John the Baptist had attracted 'tax-collectors and prostitutes' (21: 32), and it is very evident that Jesus pointedly drew to him disciples and hangers-on of similar ilk, in line with his openly declared policy that these people were most in need of what he had to offer. Thus it was again from what seems to have been Capernaum, and specifically from the town's customs house, that Jesus reportedly recruited the tax-collector Matthew (Matthew 9: 9), a man who would have been widely disliked because of his necessary collaboration with the forces of occupation. Likewise, immediately after the story of this Matthew's recruitment, we are told of Jesus' entertaining to dinner 'a number of tax-collectors and sinners' at what seems to have been his Capernaum house.

In fact, so frequently do the gospels report Jesus' socializing with obvious undesirables, enjoying meals with them, speaking of himself as 'a glutton and a drunkard' (Luke 7: 34), even declining to join in fasts observed by John the Baptist's disciples, that there can be little doubt that he did behave in precisely this way, the most extreme example of this being his reported acceptance of particularly intimate favours from 'a woman ... who had a bad name in the town' (Luke 7: 37-8). The woman is described as wiping Jesus' feet with her hair, massaging his feet and/or his head with an expensive lotion, and lavishing kisses upon him, all so repugnant for the gospel writers and for the disciples alike that no two accounts are the same. While the Luke author noted the horror felt by Jesus' host at the fact that Jesus had allowed himself to be made impure, or ritually unclean, by such a woman, the Matthew, Mark and John writers all remarked on the disciples' indignation at the waste of money: 'Why this waste of ointment? Ointment like this could have been sold for over three hundred denarii and the money given to the poor' (Mark 14: 4-5). Only Jesus, amidst all the embarrassment and anger, seems to have accepted the woman's clearly sensual favours with a quite shameless equanimity.

For although association with a prostitute was clearly extreme behaviour, feelings would already have been heightened by the fact that in Jesus' day almost any association with a woman outside one's immediate family was frowned upon. For example, the Babylonian Talmud tells of the Galilean Rabbi Yose being scolded for merely asking a woman the way to Lydda: 'You stupid Galilean, have the Sages not commanded "Do not engage in a lengthy conversation with a woman?"' In first-century Jewish society women were second-class citizens, banned from the Inner Courts of the Temple, banned from any part of the Temple during their monthly periods, and, at any time, instantly divorceable by their husbands without any right of redress, merely by the writing of a notice to this effect. This has even given rise to inconsistencies within the New Testament, for because the apostle Paul had never known the human Jesus, and according to some arguments at least wrote before the gospels themselves had been written, he reflected the attitudes of contemporary society towards women rather than what we may now believe to have been Jesus' own ideas. Thus he wrote:

How two Galilean fishing boats would traditionally fish in partnership to catch musht. They would use one net to encircle a shoal in a barrel of mesh, then a second net would be spread on the water's surface and kept afloat with reeds, to trap any fish trying to escape by leaping out of the barrel.
The fish inside the barrel would then be caught with cast nets.

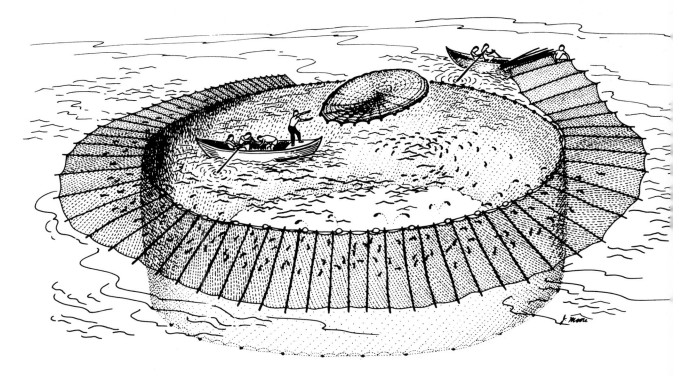

… women are to remain quiet at meetings since they have no permission to speak; they must keep in the background as the Law itself lays it down. If they have any questions to ask, they should ask their husbands at home: it does not seem right for a woman to raise her voice at meetings. (1 Corinthians 14: 35)

By way of contrast, the gospel writers convey Jesus entering into deep conversations with women, as in John 4: 27, 'The disciples returned and were surprised to find him speaking to a woman' and in Luke 10: 38-42, in which he became involved in such a lengthy discourse with Mary, sister of Martha of Bethany, that even the practical Martha thought he had gone too far. And although in general the gospels gloss over the fact, the Luke author, who seems to have had a more liberated outlook than his fellow-evangelists, makes clear that Jesus attracted nearly as many women followers as he did men:

With him went the twelve, as well as certain women who had been cured of evil spirits and ailments: Mary surnamed the Magdalen, from whom seven demons had gone out, Joanna the wife of Herod's steward Chuza, Susanna and several others who provided for them out of their own resources. (Luke 8: 1-3)

It is frustrating that we are told by no means nearly enough concerning these women, how they accompanied this large entourage day and night, and the strength of feelings they must have aroused in those whom they had left behind back home. Particularly interesting is the inclusion in the list of Joanna, the wife of Herod Antipas' steward, Chuza. From Luke's mention of her among 'certain women … cured of evil spirits and ailments' it would seem that Jesus had relieved her of some mental or physical illness. But why are we not told more of Jesus' healing of such a well-to-do woman? It can hardly be doubted that some sort of fluttering in the Herod Antipas camp must have been caused by such a woman leaving her highly placed husband and going off to tramp Galilee's dusty by-ways with her healer.

The inclusion in the list of Mary Magdalen is another case in point. Of Jesus' precise relationship with her we are likewise told very little, but this has not stopped sensationalist writers – from Baigent, Leigh and Lincoln in their best-selling *The Holy Blood and the Holy Grail* to Australian Barbara Thiering in *Jesus The Man* making a whole industry out of speculations on this theme, particularly centring on the idea that Mary Magdalen and Jesus secretly married. A certain fuel to this was provided by the discovery, among the Nag Hammadi hoard, of a 'Gospel of Philip' in which occurs the passage:

… the companion of the [Saviour is] Mary Magdalen. [But Christ loved] her more than [all] the disciples, and asked to kiss her [often] on her [mouth]. The rest of [the disciples were offended] … They said to

Jewish woman's hair, first century AD, from the excavations at Masada. Jesus was noted in the gospels for entering into deep conversations with women, and for treating them with far greater respect and consideration than was normal in his day. He allowed a woman to dry him with her hair (Luke 7: 38).

him, 'Why do you love her more than all of us?' The Saviour answered
and said to them, 'Why do I not love you as [I love] her?'

In fact the 'Gospel of Philip', unlike its companion 'Gospel of Thomas',
has no special claim to an early date, and seems to be merely a Mills &
Boon-style fantasy of a type not at all uncommon among Christian apocryphal literature of the third and fourth centuries. Inevitably the very fact
that Jesus was canonically described as being so intimate with women gives
rise to the entirely legitimate question: if he did not marry – and there is
absolutely no serious evidence that he did – why did he choose not to, particularly since Jewish priests and rabbis of his time were very much expected to do so, and also Peter at least among the disciples certainly had a wife,
as revealed by Jesus' cure of his mother-in-law?

What may well be clues to Jesus' reasons lie in a cryptic remark in the
Matthew gospel: '… there are eunuchs who make themselves that way for
the sake of the kingdom of heaven' (Matthew 19: 12), together with an
equally significant passage in the Luke gospel:

> The children of this world take wives and husbands, but those who are
> judged worthy of a place in the other world and in the resurrection
> from the dead do not marry because they can no longer die, for they are
> the same as angels, and being children of the resurrection they are sons
> of God. (Luke 20: 34-7)

Arguably, Jesus may here have been defining a blueprint for the purest and
most immediate way of reaching the kingdom of God. For although for
most Jews the kingdom of God, long spoken of by the *nabi'im*, was conceived as something between a politically independent state of Israel and a
heavenly dream home for the righteous, for Jesus it seems to have been both
of these – hence his talk of the 'coming' of the kingdom – but also something much more immediate and positive, a releasing of the self from all
earthly ties, the prime among those being property, employment and wife,
not necessarily in that order. As Dr John Robinson beautifully expressed it in
his controversial *Honest to God*, Jesus 'emptied himself utterly of himself thus
abandoning all self-consciousness, all shame, all self-seeking, in order that
God and only God could shine through'. This same ideal, as translated into
the rôle of a Catholic priest, was also superbly expressed in Morris West's
The Shoes of the Fisherman in the response of a priest to a friend who felt that
he, the priest, had thrown away his life the day he was ordained:

> It costs so much to be a full human being that there are very few who
> will have the courage to pay the price. One has to abandon altogether
> the search for security and embrace the world like a lover, and yet
> demand no easy return for love. One has to accept pain as a condition
> of existence. One has to court doubt and darkness as the cost of

knowing. One needs a will stubborn in conflict, but open always to every consequence of living and dying. If a man is centred on himself, the smallest risk is too great for him because both success and failure can destroy. But if he is completely centred on God ... then no risk is too great because success is already guaranteed.

It is important to emphasize, however, that this was an ideal for those who were free so to abandon themselves, as Catholic priests do to this day, rather than any recipe for universal communism and anarchy. For however offbeat and unconventional his behaviour may sometimes have been, Jesus nevertheless firmly upheld the Jewish Law (Matthew 5: 17, 18). Likewise while he may have told the adulterous woman that her sins were forgiven, he also asked her not to repeat them (John 18: 1, 2). Contrary to those who today try to push for more liberal divorce laws, Jesus insisted on stricter ones than those pertaining in his time (Mark 10: 10), pointedly removing the husband's then prerogative of being able to dismiss his wife without an equivalent right on her part. It would seem always to have been the underlying spirit of the Law that he wished to enforce rather than its letter.

Likewise, while Jesus openly and unashamedly consorted with prostitutes and tax-collectors, it was not only such people whom he won over. Those who went on, after his death, to carry out his message, often at great danger to themselves, were people leading ordinary lives who, though they may sometimes have been shocked to observe him saying and doing things not expected of a holy man, followed him nonetheless. And to these he likewise insisted on the nearness of the kingdom of God. The strength of this following by people of all kinds is in fact one of the most striking features of Jesus' recorded life. Repeatedly the gospels refer to the crowds which surrounded him wherever he went, crowds from whom, equally repeatedly, he felt obliged to slip away when the pressure became too great. As the Mark gospel specifically commented on the predicament this presented for him: 'Jesus could no longer go openly into any town, but had to stay outside in places where nobody lived. Even so, people from all around would come to him.' (Mark 1: 45)

So how was it that when Jesus wanted helpers he had merely to say: 'Follow me', and, as the gospels insist, hard-headed fishermen like Andrew and Simon Peter, James and John, mercenary tax-collectors like Matthew, and even suspected near-terrorists like Simon the Zealot (Zealots were a Jewish near-equivalent of the IRA) abandoned all else to do just that? Nor was Jesus' appeal only to Jews. As even Josephus, although a non-Christian, acknowledged in the brief reference to Jesus that we discussed in chapter 3: 'He [Jesus] won over many of the Jews and many of the Greeks'.

Now no teaching alone, however unconventional or innovative, could have made such an impact, particularly upon people who were not of the same nationality. So just what was it about Jesus that could have exerted such a magnetic appeal?

7

MAN OF MAGIC

I f there is one feature of Jesus' activities that repeatedly shines out from the gospels, it is his capacity to work acts of healing and other feats that men have called 'miracles'. The Mark gospel makes quite clear that it was his reputation for these which caused him to be the centre of so much popular attention: '… after sunset they brought to him all who were sick and those who were possessed by devils. The whole town came crowding round the door' (Mark 1: 32).

There was nothing completely new in this, for acts of healing were a common attribute of Jewish holy men both before and after Jesus. Moses and Elisha were accredited with curing a leper or two (Numbers 12: 13; 2 Kings 5: 1-4), and a generation after Jesus a *hasid* or holy man called Hanina ben Dosa, from Araba, ten miles to Nazareth's north, was also accredited with healings.

But the works reported of these were as nothing compared to the cures of paralysis, lameness, fever, catalepsy, haemorrhage, skin disease and mental disorder attributed to Jesus. Miracles were the first aspect of Jesus' ministry that the disciple Simon Peter reportedly recalled after Jesus' death:

Jesus the Nazarene was a man commended to you by God by the miracles and portents and signs that God worked through him when he was among you as you all know. (Acts 2: 22)

Opposite *Jesus depicted healing a woman with a chronic haemorrhaging disorder. From a fresco of the late third century, the cemetery of SS Peter and Marcellinus, Rome.*

This same reputation was clearly what Josephus had in mind when, as we noted earlier, he spoke of Jesus as 'a wise man' who performed 'astonishing feats', or 'paradoxical deeds', the word *paradoxon* that he used commonly denoting 'miracle' in Hellenistic Judaism. In the earliest Christian art, among the most frequent representations of Jesus are ones showing him with a magician's wand, usually being used for raising Lazarus. As reported in Luke's gospel, when asked by the imprisoned John the Baptist whether he was 'the one who is to come (i.e. the super-*nabi* prophesied by Moses, Deuteronomy 18: 15-18), Jesus' reply to John's messengers was, 'Go back and tell John what you have seen and heard: the blind see again, the lame walk, lepers are cleansed, and the deaf hear, the dead are raised to life ...' (Luke 7: 22)

That Jesus performed such deeds is therefore one of the best-attested items of information about him, yet paradoxically, it has been one of the least explored because, as Matthew Arnold succinctly expressed it, 'miracles do not happen'. Under the influence of Kant and Hegel, the German rationalist theologians steadfastly resisted treating the gospel miracle stories with any seriousness, and among many of today's theologians, quite aside from the ordinary general public, this resistance has continued. Nonetheless, some scholars are now favouring the idea that one of the very earliest lost gospels may have been one specifically devoted to accounts of Jesus' miracles. And the leading Anglican scholar Canon Anthony Harvey of Westminster Abbey has laid stress on the convincingness of the very matter-of-fact way in which the canonical gospels' miracle stories are described:

> In general one can say that the miracle stories in the gospels are unlike anything else in ancient literature ... They do not exaggerate the miracle or add sensational details, like the authors of early Christian hagiography [lives of the saints]; but nor do they show the kind of detachment, amounting at times to scepticism, which is found in Herodotus or Lucian ... To a degree that is rare in the writings of antiquity, we can say, to use a modern phrase, that they tell the story straight ...

And indeed if we allow ourselves at least temporarily to suspend incredulity towards miracles per se, we find that some of the gospel stories of this ilk have within them material which we simply cannot dismiss out of hand. For instance, in a manner rare among gospel stories, the writer of the John gospel, in one of his important narrative sections, sets the healing of the so-called paralytic in a historically identifiable building:

> Now at the Sheep Pool in Jerusalem there is a building, called Bethzatha in Hebrew, consisting of five porticoes; and under these were crowds of sick people – blind, lame, paralysed – waiting for the water to move; for at intervals ... the water was disturbed, and the first person to enter the water after this disturbance was cured of any ailment he suffered from ... (John 5: 1-4)

Remains of Herodian building (at the lowest level) thought to have been the five-porticoed edifice called Bethesda (or Beth-zatha) housing the so-called Sheep Pool at which Jesus reportedly healed the paralytic man (John 5: 1-9). Although only part of the original pool has been exposed beneath layers of Christian churches dating back to the fifth century AD, tunnels and soundings show that there were originally two very large pools cut deep into the bedrock, surrounded by porticoes with columns 25 feet high. Probably this same edifice is mentioned in the Dead Sea Scrolls' Copper Scroll as Beth Eshdathayin, or the 'House of the Twin Pools'.

As a result of exhaustive research by Professor Joachim Jeremias, there can be absolutely no doubt that there was a building of this kind in the Jerusalem of Jesus' time, the original natural pool having been used probably as early as the eighth century BC, and developed as two 'Great Pools' around 200 BC. Despite the depredations the city suffered as a result of the Romans' suppression of the Jewish Revolts, the Sheep Pool building of John's gospel seems still to have existed in the fourth century AD, for as reported at that time by Western Europe's earliest-known Christian pilgrim to the Holy Land, the so-called Bordeaux pilgrim:

> Further in the city are twin pools having five porticoes, which are called Bethsaida [from New Testament manuscripts, this seems to have been a corruption of Bethzatha]. There those who have been sick for many years are cured. The pools contain water which is red when it is disturbed.

Sadly, the five porticoes effectively disappeared during subsequent centuries upon the building's conversion into a church, this church in its turn suffering all sorts of vicissitudes as Jerusalem painfully and successively changed hands between Christians and Moslems. But the site has continued to be marked by a church, and just north of what is now the Crusader church of St Anne in Old City Jerusalem's Muslim Quarter, excavations earlier this century revealed two huge, deep rock-cut cisterns, with stairs that originally led to their bottoms, which undoubtedly once comprised the original Sheep Pool described by John, some of the surviving masonry being of the time of Herod the Great, who is known to have embellished the building.

But even if we can actually identify a building where Jesus once reputedly worked a miracle, why should we trust the story of the miracle itself? According to the author of John the paralysed man whom Jesus encountered at the Sheep Pool had had his condition for thirty-eight years, and Jesus cured him with the simple command: 'Get up, pick up your sleeping-mat and walk' (John 5: 8). Although this is obviously scant information on which to base any belief in the story, it is well-known medically that some paralyses are 'hysterical' in origin, that is they have a mental rather than physical cause, usually as a result of some severe emotional stress. Disfiguring skin conditions, blindness, apparent inability to hear or speak, and all manner of seeming mental disorders, can also be induced by hysteria, and while to the patient such ailments seem all too real, and may last for many years, they can sometimes be cured by a reversing or neutralizing of the original, debilitating emotional problem. Although treatment with drugs is of course the most usual way of doing this today, other nonetheless well-recognized approaches are via psychotherapy or hypnosis, the 'cure' as effected by the latter often being dramatically sudden.

It has to be acknowledged that even to this day no-one really knows what hypnosis is, whatever individual hypnotists themselves may claim they know. In essence hypnosis appears to be a belief system shared between two individuals, one, the subject, who abandons himself, in terms of his waking consciousness, to the other, the hypnotist, who by taking charge of the patient's unconscious mind may be able to free elements that the patient's consciousness has previously repressed or held back. So-called 'hysterical' individuals often seem to make particularly good hypnotic subjects and consistently the effects of hypnosis upon these can be in direct proportion to the degree of awe in which they hold the hypnotist. While scientists mostly remain reticent about stating anything too positive about hypnosis because of its continuing mysteries and uncertainties, few would deny that it can and does produce some remarkable phenomena, including spectacular 'cures'.

For instance, the now veteran British hypnotist Peter Casson has on his files the case of a woman who, for fifteen years after a major car accident, had been quite unable to close her hand or to grip with it. Several operations had failed to improve her condition, but on the strength of just one hypnosis session with Peter Casson she found that she could once again close her hand and use it normally. Effectively, Casson achieved her 'cure' by commands little different from those which Jesus is said to have used in curing the paralytic by Jerusalem's Sheep Pool.

An even better attestation of hypnosis's medical potential is a British doctor's highly dramatic use of it as a last resort for a particularly disfiguring skin condition that was well documented, with accompanying photographs, in the *British Medical Journal* of 23 August 1952. The patient was a sixteen-year-old boy who two years earlier had been admitted to East Grinstead's Royal Victoria Hospital suffering from ichthyosis, a most unsightly condition that from ever since he had been born had covered his body with a black, horny, reptilian layer that was as uncomfortable and evil-smelling as it was disfiguring. Although two attempts at plastic surgery had been made, in both the reptilian layer had quickly replaced the skin that had been freshly grafted, so that even Sir Archibald McIndoe, the most eminent plastic surgeon of the day, pronounced further conventional treatment useless.

By chance, however, the boy's plight came to the notice of a young physician with an interest in hypnosis, Dr A.A.Mason, today a psychoanalyst in Beverley Hills, California. Mason asked if he might at least try hypnosis, and on 10 February 1951, having induced a hypnotic state, he suggested to the youth that his left arm's reptilian layer would disappear. There ensued an extraordinary transformation. Within five days the horny covering on this arm simply fell away, and within a further few days the skin was soft, pink and normal for the first time in the boy's life. During the next few weeks hypnotic suggestion was given for the clearance of the reptilian layer on the right arm and then for specific remaining areas of his body, each time with between 50 per cent and 95 per cent success. Although the cure was slower than it might have been in the case of, say, a

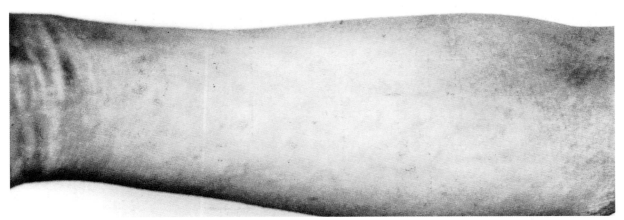

A modern-day 'miracle'? The legs and arms of a sixteen-year-old sufferer from the disfiguring and repulsive skin condition ichthyosis, as seen before and after his hypnotic treatment by the then British physician Dr A.A.Mason. Following Dr Mason's purely verbal suggestions, it took only a few weeks for the horny, reptilian layer to fall away and be replaced by clear, normal skin.

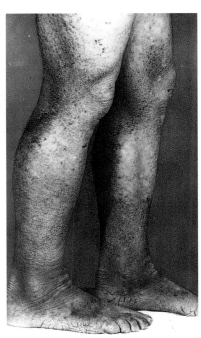

hysterical blindness or paralysis (almost certainly because of the very nature of the disease), it is little short of incredible that it should have happened at all. And a fascinating feature is the fact that, because of ichthyosis's rarity, Dr Mason did not even realize at the time that he was dealing with such a congenital, structural illness. As he has frankly admitted, had he realized he would most likely not have tried hypnosis, because he would have thought it unsuitable for anything so deep-seated. But because he believed he could do it, he succeeded. Accordingly, it is the most striking possible attestation of what mere words, given the hypnotic state, can do.

So could there have been a knowledge of hypnosis in ancient times upon which Jesus drew? Professor Lionel Haward of the University of Surrey psychology department has pointed out that there are Egyptian papyri, such as the Demotic Magical Papyrus preserved in the British Museum, which appear to describe hypnotic inductions and trance states and also classical frescoes that depict individuals in what looks like hypnotic trance. Furthermore, that whatever Jesus was using for his miracles derived not from any quasi-divine power, but could be well within the powers of ordinary men, is quite evident from the gospels themselves, which describe him sending out his disciples to do the same healing work that he undertook himself:

> He summoned his twelve disciples, and gave them authority over unclean spirits with power to cast them out, and to cure all kinds of diseases and sickness. (Matthew 10: 1)

Likewise the book of Acts relates that the disciples were able to carry on his work after his death:

> There were … unclean spirits that came shrieking out of many who were possessed, and several paralytics and cripples were cured. (Acts 8: 7)

Arguably then, hypnosis may help us go at least some way towards recognizing, and believing, in a perfectly rational way, that at least some of Jesus' reputed healing miracles could and did happen along the lines the gospels describe. Furthermore, if we look more closely at one group of these, his exorcisms or cures from 'possession', we find that modern medical and psychological insights can again give us good reason for trusting the gospels' accounts of the disorders that Jesus tackled.

Thus back in the early 1920s, and ironically at the very University of Tübingen which was the setting for so many attacks on the gospels' credibility, psychology professor T.K. Oesterreich made an intensive study of the cases of possession encountered by Jesus. First published in the journal *Deutsche Psychologie*, then developed into a definitive 400-page book, *Possession, Demoniacal and Other*, Professor Oesterreich's findings were that the Mark gospel in particular is very impressive for its concise and

Jesus healing a so-called 'leper' (Mark 1: 40-2). In the ancient world the term 'leprosy' could denote a variety of serious skin disorders. From a fifth-century ivory from Palermo, Sicily, now in the Victoria and Albert Museum, London.

clinical reporting of the cases Jesus tackled. There was the so-called Gerasene demoniac:

> … no sooner had he [Jesus] left the boat than a man with an unclean spirit came out of the tombs towards him. The man lived in the tombs, and no-one could secure him any more, even with a chain; because he had often been secured with fetters and chains but had snapped the chains and broken the fetters and no-one had the strength to control him. All night and all day, among the tombs and in the mountains he would howl and gash himself with stones … (Mark 5: 1-10)

There was the man suffering from convulsions:

> In their synagogue … there was a man possessed by an unclean spirit and it shouted 'What do you want with us, Jesus of Nazareth? Have you come to destroy us?' … But Jesus said sharply 'Be quiet! Come out of him!' And the unclean spirit threw the man into convulsions and with a loud cry went out of him. (Mark 1: 23-7)

There was the youth who foamed at the mouth:

> A man answered him from the crowd, 'Master, I have brought my son to you; there is a spirit of dumbness in him, and when it takes hold of him it throws him to the ground, and he foams at the mouth and grinds his teeth and goes rigid. And I asked your disciples to cast it out and they were unable to' … They brought the boy to him and as soon as the spirit saw Jesus it threw the boy into convulsions, and he fell to the ground and lay writhing there, foaming at the mouth. Jesus asked the father: 'How long has this been happening to him?' 'From childhood', he replied, 'and it has often thrown him into the fire and into the water, in order to destroy him …' (Mark 9: 17-27)

As commented by Professor Oesterreich:

> … the succinct accounts of Jesus' relation to these events, his success and failure together with that of his disciples, as well as the particulars

of his cures, coincide so exactly with what we know of these states from the point of view of present-day psychology that it is impossible to avoid the impression that we are dealing with a tradition which is veracious.

Of course, neither Professor Oesterreich nor any other realistic individual would argue that real demons or unclean spirits were responsible for the disorders being dealt with, as the gospel writers and Jesus seem to suppose. But the point at issue is the power of the belief held by the sufferer, who had come to believe himself so much afflicted, usually as a result of some emotional stress. However extreme and fictional the book and film of William Blatty's *The Exorcist* might seem, it represents a very real phenomenon that has been reported century after century, throughout all sorts of cultures, both before and after the time of Jesus. Church of England vicar the Reverend Christopher Neil-Smith, now living in retirement in Ealing, claims to have been called upon to deal with up to five hundred 'possession' cases a year in just the area in and around London, and although it is a little-known part of its organization, since the 1970s the Church of England has appointed a consultant exorcist for every diocese. For if people try to solve such problems without professional help, sometimes things can go badly wrong, as in 1973, in West Yorkshire, when a 'possessed' young father murdered his wife and the family dog after a failed exorcism by local amateurs.

One form of 'possession' psychiatrically well-recognized is the condition known today as 'multiple personality', of which recent famous cases have been those of Virginia housewife Chris Sizemore (the original 'Eve' of *The Three Faces of Eve*) and Ohio rapist Billy Milligan, who in 1979 committed a series of robberies and rapes while apparently possessed by some nine alternating personalities, ranging from 'Ragan', an aggressive hit-man, to

Site of one of Jesus' healings? The remains of the Roman forum and a colonnaded street at Jerash, Jordan, the very hellenized 'Gerasa' of Jesus' time where, according to Mark 5: 1-10, he healed the deranged 'demoniac' who wandered among the tombs.

Jesus depicted healing a woman with a chronic haemorrhaging disorder. Her cure is described in all three synoptic gospels (Mathew 9: 20-22; Mark 5: 25-34; Luke 8: 43-8). According to later tradition, she came from Caesarea Philippi, and in gratitude erected a statue to Jesus there. From a fresco of the late third century, the cemetery of SS Peter and Marcellinus, Rome.

'Christine', a three-year-old obsessed with painting butterflies. Among many parallels between these cases and those reputedly cured by Jesus is a tendency for one of the personalities to speak for the rest by using the term 'us'. In the very first chapter of the Mark gospel, a possessed man in the Capernaum synagogue reportedly railed at Jesus: 'What do you want with us, Jesus of Nazareth? Have you come to destroy us?' (Mark 1: 24), and the Gerasene demoniac, asked his name by Jesus, responded: 'My name is legion...for there are many of us' (Mark 5: 10), and in the American multiple-personality case 'Sybil', Sybil's 'us' personality told her psychiatrist/ hypnotist '...the rest of us know about Sybil, she knows nothing about any of us...'.

In connection with Jesus' dealings with such phenomena we have no need to believe that he had any formal knowledge of what we now label hypnosis. But that his approach to the physically and mentally sick was powerfully and spontaneously hypnotic is absolutely self-evident from the gospel descriptions of the sharp, authoritative verbal manner in which he conducted his healings: 'Be quiet! Come out of him!' he reportedly told the possessed man in the Capernaum synagogue (Mark 1: 26), *'Ephphatha!'* ('Be opened!') he commanded of the eardrums of the deaf man brought to him in the Decapolis (Mark 7: 34), *'Talitha kum!'* ('Little girl, I tell you to get up!') he ordered the seemingly dead daughter of synagogue official Jairus (Mark 5: 41). The very fact that we have been given, in these last two examples, Jesus' apparent exact original words, untranslated from the Aramaic, is a powerful sign of just how awed had been those present at the time, seemingly prompting them to try to record these 'magical'-seeming formulas for posterity.

But what would it have been that gave Jesus the authority and confidence to be so naturally hypnotic? Two special attributes arguably at least helped. One was his personal conviction that God was speaking and working through him in a manner unparalleled since the days of Moses (the Luke author notably represents him as speaking of 'the finger of God' as being responsible for the success of his exorcisms, Luke 11 : 20). The other was an equally strong belief that at some unpredictable moment the dread 'Last Times' (already spoken of by earlier prophets) would begin, bringing eternal life for those who followed his words, and eternal damnation for those who did not. Fired by such convictions, Jesus would have been a difficult man to ignore, though as we saw earlier some were able to do so, most notably in his own home village of Nazareth.

Yet this very admission that there were circumstances in which he could and did fail is itself interesting for two reasons. First, it is an important indication of the basic honesty of the gospel writers' reporting that they could admit that Jesus had his limitations. And second, he failed precisely where *as a hypnotist* (albeit an unconscious one) we might most expect him to fail, among those who knew him best, those who had seen him grow up as an ordinary child, and knew all his human weaknesses. For largely responsible for any hypnotist's success are the awe and mystery with which he surrounds himself, and these essential factors would have been lacking in Jesus' home town.

Now this idea of Jesus' natural hypnotic talents can be carried further. For instance, his alleged first miracle, the changing of water into wine at Cana of Galilee, exclusively described in the narrative portion of the John gospel (John 2: 1-11), can easily lend itself to an explanation involving hypnosis. As every stage hypnotist knows, one of the most entertaining of demonstrations is to suggest to a group of hypnotized volunteers that they are drinking some highly alcoholic (but in reality totally harmless) liquid, and then watch them roll around the stage in comic states of 'inebriation'. With a set of already inebriated guests at a wedding feast Jesus would have had a very easy group of subjects to persuade that the water they were being given was the finest wine. Likewise, because so many illusions and fantasies are possible via hypnosis, it would be possible to argue that his so-called 'transfiguration' – the incident in which, on a high mountain, he reportedly turned into dazzling light before three disciples (Matthew 17: 1-8; Mark 9: 2-8; Luke 9: 28-36) - was engineered by some clever piece of hypnotic suggestion. Likewise, his apparent feeding of the five thousand, his walking on water, and much more.

Very important, however, is not to stray too far down this road. For, as is human nature, hypnotists, magicians and David Copperfield-type illusionists all perform their tricks and wonders for the normal human motives of commercial gain, entertainment, power, etc. But in Jesus' case, what did he have to gain? When instructing his disciples in healing, he told them, 'You received without charge, give without charge' (Matthew 10: 8). The gospels emphasize his total disinclination to make any personal capital from his miracles. We are told by the writer of John that the paralytic whom Jesus cured at the Sheep Pool did not even know who it was that had cured him: 'The man had no idea who it was, since Jesus had disappeared into the crowd that filled the place' (John 5: 14). Jesus mostly shunned publicity, as in the case of his cure of the deaf man: 'Jesus ordered them to tell no-one about it, but the more he insisted, the more widely they published it' (Mark 7: 36).

Equally importantly, even if all those diverse individuals to whom Jesus brought release from suffering were, in psychological terms, mere hysterics, the sheer scale of what Jesus managed to effect, and the spontaneity with which he is said to have achieved it, go far beyond what even the greatest braggadocio among hypnotists would profess to be able to achieve today.

There is a yet further, sombre, aspect of this issue. For had Jesus been just a clever hypnotist/exorcist he could no doubt have continued happily into old age making a comfortable living from his craft. But whatever Jesus' purpose was it was altogether more serious than this, as is apparent from the most well-attested feature of his life, the way of death that he now began to bring upon himself.

8

THE ROAD TO JERUSALEM

A s theologians have repeatedly emphasized, the gospels are not, and were never intended to be, biographies of Jesus, and it is therefore quite impossible to reconstruct from them any realistic timetable for the events between Jesus' baptism and his last, so fateful days in Jerusalem.

Particularly highlighting our inadequate knowledge of such matters is an incident in the Luke gospel in which Jesus told an un-named but 'very rich' aristocrat that if he wanted to inherit eternal life he had to sell everything he owned and give the money to the poor. During the subsequent lively discussion Simon Peter reportedly remarked, on behalf of both himself and the rest of the disciples: 'What about us? We left all we had to follow you', prompting Jesus to respond 'I tell you solemnly, there is no-one who has left house, wife, brothers, parents or children for the sake of the kingdom of God who will not be given repayment many times over in this present time, and in the world to come…' (Luke 18: 28-30).

Suddenly we are very forcefully reminded that the gospel episodes of Jesus seemingly so casually calling his disciples away from whatever they had previously been doing must in actuality have involved some very strong feelings between them and their families as they left their homes to

Opposite *Aerial view of the Temple Mount as it looks today. In place of the former Jewish Temples built by King Solomon and King Herod, the platform is now dominated by the gold-domed Dome of the Rock, built in the seventh century by the Umayyad Caliph 'Abd-al-Malik, and by the more southerly el Aqsa mosque that occupies part of the site of Herod's Royal Stoa. In 70 AD the Romans flattened all the Herodian buildings throughout the entire 1,300,000-square-foot platform as a reprisal for the Jewish Revolt. On the Mount's western side is the part of the Temple platform, formerly known as the Wailing Wall, where devout Jews perform special devotions as a ritual reminder of the loss of their Temple. The southern part of the Temple platform was revealed by excavations directed by the Israeli archaeologist Benjamin Mazar after the Israelis' successful capture of this area in 1967.*

go with him 'on the road', with 'no purse, no haversack, no sandals' as he would later insist (Luke 10: 4). As the Luke gospel conveys, Jesus even expected them to make their departures without a moment's hesitation or looking back to pay any last-minute respects (Luke 9: 61-2), and on the principle that he must surely have practised what he preached we can only presume that he too must have left his own family much in the same way. This makes it small wonder, as the Mark gospel imparts, that his family initially 'set out to take charge of him, convinced he was out of his mind' (Mark 3: 21).

However, although we are never until the very last hours of his life provided with any remotely sure timetable of what Jesus did when, the gospel writers do at least provide the glimmerings of an itinerary for his earlier travels, albeit subject to some of the geographical gaffes mentioned in an earlier chapter (see p.28). Thus within Galilee's immediate environs he reportedly turned the water into wine at Cana, some ten miles to the north of Nazareth (John 2: 1-12), and on a separate occasion cured a nobleman's son in the same town (John 4: 46-54). At Nain, about six miles to Nazareth's south-east, he brought a widow's son back to life (Luke 7: 11-16). At Bethsaida on the Sea of Galilee's northern shore he 'walked on the water'. And after a boat journey from Bethsaida, he apparently healed many sick at Gennesaret on the north-western shore.

Further afield, he reportedly ventured at least as far north-west as Tyre and Sidon, on the Phoenician coast (Mark 7: 24-30), where he healed the daughter of a Syro-Phoenician woman. To the north-east, the Mark gospel describes him as at least en route to Caesarea Philippi (Mark 8: 27), in which vicinity snow-capped Mount Hermon is favoured by several scholars for the location of his 'transfiguration' on an otherwise un-named 'high mountain' (Matthew 17: 1-13; Mark 9: 2-13; Luke 9: 28-36). The Matthew and Mark gospels also describe him visiting the Decapolis, a confederation of ten mainly Greek-speaking cities east of the Jordan, two of these being Gadara and Gerasa (today Jerash in Jordan), where he reportedly healed the possessed man who lived among the tombs.

Throughout all Jesus' journeys he not only healed, he taught, and one of his most distinctive modes of teaching was by the parable. He did not invent this art form, for earlier Jewish prophets such as Nathan in King David's time had used it, as had Gautama the Buddha back in the fifth century BC. Yet by the keenly observed characters with whom he peopled his parables, and the clever twist he gave to each plot, he exhibited an exceptionally wry and lively mind, and took the teaching aid to new heights.

But as Jesus seems to have been well aware, ultimately the journey that he had to make to fulfil his destiny was southwards, to the Jewish people's holy city of Jerusalem. More than a thousand years before, his reputed ancestor King David had captured Jerusalem from the Jebusites and had made it his capital, David's son, Solomon, thereupon building the first Temple there. The city had undergone a number of vicissitudes, both constructive and destructive, in the subsequent centuries, including savage sack by the Babylonians in 586 BC. But every bit as dramatic was the transformation that had happened to the city shortly before and during Jesus' own lifetime. Ironically it is mostly thanks to the present-day generation of Israelis, from a tradition perennially so disinclined to accept Jesus and his teachings, that our archaeological knowledge of the Jerusalem of Jesus' time has dramatically increased in recent years, particularly regarding places associated with the leading Jewish religious groups with whom Jesus found himself in opposition in the lead-up to his crucifixion.

For most Christians, the Pharisees are the Jewish religious faction most likely to spring to mind as opposing Jesus, not least because in the English language at least, their very name has become a pejorative term, largely owing to what Jesus had to say about them. As represented in the gospels, he lost no opportunity to fulminate against the Pharisees' love of external show (e.g. Matthew 23: 1-7); against their preoccupation for observing the letter rather than the spirit of the Jewish Law (Matthew 23: 13-32); and against their attitudes of self-righteousness towards others, as epitomized by Jesus' parable of the Pharisee and the tax-collector (Luke 18: 9-14). Yet for reasons that are by no means clear, this appears to have been more than a little unfair. Other sources, most notably Josephus and the Talmud, portray the Pharisees altogether more favourably, as experts in scriptural interpretation who remained in close touch with the ordinary people, working alongside them as humble tailors, shoemakers and the like, and engendering much affection for their education of children, for their founding of regional synagogues and for their development of an oral tradition of religious wisdom that despite every attempt (including Christian) to suppress it, flourished into mainstream present-day Judaism.

For in reality the Pharisees seem to have been vigorous and down-to-earth, 'with the multitude on their side', as Josephus expressed it. Although they made no greatly overt opposition to the Roman regime, they did not disguise their lack of love of it, and they even had a paramilitary wing, the Zealots, from whose ranks Jesus appears to have drawn at least one disciple, 'Simon called the Zealot' (Luke 6: 15), also possibly Judas Iscariot, whose surname is thought to mean 'daggerman'. It is a notable aside on the author of the Mark gospel that, ever sensitive to anything too political, he notably side-stepped translating the word for 'Zealot' from its original Aramaic. Particularly in the Luke gospel there are several reported instances in which Pharisees entertained Jesus socially and exhibited genuine concern for his safety (e.g. Luke 7: 36; 13: 31; 14: 1 and elsewhere), and according to Acts (thought also to have been written by the Luke author), it was a Pharisee called Gamaliel who shortly after Jesus' death stepped forward to defend Jerusalem's earliest Christian community before the Jewish Sanhedrin (Acts 5: 34-40). The Pharisees also seem to have shared with the first Christians a belief in both angels and spirits (Acts 23: 8) and a conviction that the body would physically rise from the grave at the end of time, for this reason

Carpet-style mosaic decorating the floor of one of the opulent and tastefully furnished houses in the priestly area of first-century Jerusalem excavated by Nahman Avigad. In keeping with the Second Commandment, the mosaics and frescoes adorning the houses in this area included no human or animal representations, only floral and geometric designs.

insisting that the dead should be buried, not cremated, and that all their bones should be left intact.

Instead, the Jewish religious faction who would seem to have been Jesus' real opponents were the Sadducees, the priestly aristocrats who controlled the Jerusalem Temple. Highly materialistic in their attitudes, they rejected angels and spirits (Acts 23: 8), and the idea of any physical resurrection (Matthew 22: 23), and their love of outward show was sufficient for this to have been written large even in the archaeological record. When in 1967 the Israelis captured Old City Jerusalem's Jewish Quarter, which had lain razed and neglected under Jordanian rule, the then already veteran archaeologist Nahman Avigad seized what seemed an ideal opportunity to excavate this historic area. Trying always to keep one step ahead of planned urban redevelopment, he and his team spent some fourteen years uncovering what can now be determined to be several of the houses owned by the Sadducean priestly aristocracy that lay just to the south-east of the Temple Mount. As today's visitors to Jerusalem can see for themselves from a permanent exhibition of the finds, and from the remains of the houses themselves, cleverly preserved in specially designed basements to modern-day buildings, these chief priests lived in princely style.

By far the most impressive of their houses, though today some twenty feet below the twentieth-century floor level, is the so-called Palatial Mansion, on the eastern edge of the Western Hill overlooking the Temple and the Lower City. With two thousand square feet of floor area, and built on two (possibly even three) storeys around a spacious paved courtyard, the fact that this was fitted out with several *mikveh*, or ritual baths, suggests that it may well have belonged to the Jerusalem Temple's highest functionary, the high priest, perhaps as his official residence, in the manner of the grace-and-favour homes provided for England's Lord Mayors. In every room used for living and for guest accommodation the archaeologists found plastering and traces of fine fresco decoration, which along with a superb glass pitcher and other clues make it quite evident that this house's one-time occupants enjoyed many of Graeco-Roman life's luxuries.

A little to the north-west of this mansion Avigad and his team uncovered another impressive villa, known as the Burnt House, because it had clearly been set ablaze and destroyed during the Roman sack of Jerusalem in 70 AD (see p.165). From the debris again ritual baths emerged, accompanied by the remains of fine furniture and everyday objects. Particularly enabling attribution to a priestly family, and one to which a name could be put, was the finding of a weight inscribed as belonging to the Kathros family. Known to have been one of the 'big four' among Jerusalem's Sadducean mafia of priestly families, the Kathroses feature unfavourably in a satiric folk-song preserved in the Talmud because they used their position for their own gain.

Indicating the rich but undeniably tasteful lifestyle enjoyed by the Palatial Mansion's priestly owners, a reconstruction of what was once a superb glass pitcher.

Plan/reconstruction of the so-called Palatial Mansion in Old City Jerusalem's priestly area. Centred around a large courtyard, possibly the one in which Simon Peter waited at the time of Jesus' arrest, this mansion covered 2,000 square feet and included a 33-by-21-foot reception hall, part of which has survived to a height of more than 11 feet. The mikveh or ritual baths found in the basement strongly indicate priestly ownership.

Last resting place of the Temple high priest of Jesus' time? Ornate limestone ossuary of the first century AD accidentally discovered in 1990 during the construction of a water park in the Peace Forest on the hill of Abu Tor immediately south of Jerusalem. The most elaborately carved of the dozen ossuaries found within the tomb, this particular example is inscribed 'Joseph bar Caiaphas' [Joseph, son of Caiaphas] and is thought to have belonged to the Caiaphas who controlled the Jerusalem Temple in Jesus' time.

This runs:

> Woe unto me because of the House of Kathros, woe unto me because of their reed pens … for they are high priests and their sons are treasurers and their sons-in-law are temple overseers, and their servants smite the people with sticks.

Reinforcing the folk-song's sentiments, the scholar Martin Goodman in his recent book *The Ruling Class of Judaea* has shown that these Temple priests operated a lucrative sideline using the taxes and tithes that they imposed upon the religious faithful in order to buy up small family holdings, resulting – as has happened so often in other countries throughout history – in themselves becoming richer and the poor poorer, with ordinary people who had once owned their own modest patches of land being reduced to tenant farmers or hired labourers.

In fact the gospels make clear that the Sadducean high priest when Jesus came into conflict with this breed was not Kathros but Caiaphas (Matthew 26: 3; also John 11: 49), who held the office c.18-37 AD. And although we cannot be totally sure that this Caiaphas was the occupant of the Palatial Mansion excavated by Avigad, there is now the strongest likelihood that archaeologists have found his bones. When in November 1990 Israeli workmen were building a water park as part of Jerusalem's Peace Forest, just to the south of the Old City, they came across an old cave with several limestone ossuaries or bone boxes in its central chamber. (In Jesus' time it was a common practice for the bones of the dead to be gathered in these often beautifully crafted containers after all the flesh had decomposed.)

As the archaeologists called to the scene quickly deduced, it was likely that these ossuaries dated from around the time of Jesus, since as funerary equipment they ceased in Jerusalem after 70 AD. But the find became really interesting when their study of the inscriptions revealed two to bear the name Qafa, or Caiaphas. The first box, simply inscribed 'Qafa' (ka-FA), contained just the skeletons of four children and an adult woman. But the second, with significantly superior decoration, and twice inscribed 'Yehosef bar Qayafa' (yeh-hoh-SEF bar ka-ya-FA), Joseph, son of Caiaphas, contained the bones of four children, an adult woman, and – most importantly – a man aged about 60. Although the New Testament simply gives the name Caiaphas (Matthew 26: 3, 57; Luke 3: 2; John 11: 49; 18: 13, 14, 24, 28; Acts 4: 6) to the high priest of Jesus' time, Josephus specifically refers to him as 'Joseph who was called Caiaphas of the high priesthood', 'Caiaphas' thereby seeming to have been either a family name or a nick-name. It is therefore a tantalizing possibility that the skeleton of the elderly man in the second ossuary was that of the very high priest of the time of Jesus. Sadly, however, the bones were very quickly re-interred at the behest of ultra-orthodox Jewish extremists, thus depriving both Christians and Jews of any chance of reconstructing Caiaphas' facial features using the methods that have recently been so successful with King Midas, King Philip of Macedon and others.

The control of the Jerusalem Temple's revenues, revenues directly deriving from that institution's monopoly as the only place where sacrifices could be made in atonement for sins, was therefore directly in the hands of men such as Kathros and Caiaphas. And what an emporium their allies, the Herod family, had made of the Temple in order to further this sort of trade! In keeping with his passion for ambitious building projects, back around 20-19 BC Herod the Great had set in motion plans for transforming Jerusalem's Second Temple from its somewhat modest rebuilding of King Solomon's version after the Jews' return from their Babylonian captivity, into the largest and most magnificent religious building in the world. Not satisfied with King Solomon's original foundations, which had partly utilized Jerusalem's highest hill, Herod decided to double this hill in extent, filling in natural valleys to the north and west, extending the original eastern wall and building new western, southern and northern foundation walls to create a vast man-made platform a quarter of a mile long by a fifth of a mile wide. Onto this platform Herod set his engineers to implement his grandest design, an enormous structure that he knew would not be completed in his lifetime, and indeed was continued throughout the time of Herod Antipas, and thereby throughout the lifetime of Jesus. What neither Herod could have believed was that in keeping with Jesus' apparent prophecy (see p.38), this man-made wonder would be all but completely destroyed by the Romans following the Jewish Revolt of 70 AD, so that trying to reconstruct the original by combining archaeological findings with descriptions by contemporary eyewitnesses such as Josephus demands a great deal of detective work.

However, thanks to exhaustive efforts by American archaeological architect Leen Ritmeyer and his Irish-born archaeologist wife Kathleen, and also by English model-maker Alec Garrard, enormous advances in recapturing the Herod Temple's magnificence have been made in recent years. As noted by the Ritmeyers, Josephus wrote of the Temple: 'To approaching strangers it appeared from a distance like a snow-clad mountain, for all that was not overlaid with gold was of purest white'. Making up much of the structure of this man-made mountain were precision-cut blocks of limestone, some up to thirty-five feet long and weighing up to eighty tons which had to be hauled by oxen from the nearest quarries over a mile distant. Even in the Temple's present near totally razed state some of these blocks remain over a hundred feet

Side-view of the same ossuary, showing the 'Joseph bar Caiaphas' inscription. The Matthew, Luke and John gospels all identify the high priest who presided over Jesus' interrogation simply as 'Caiaphas' (Matthew 26: 57; Luke 3: 2; John 18: 13-14). But according to Josephus' Antiquities *'Joseph Caiaphas' was the high priest from 18 to 36 AD, i.e. the period within which Jesus was crucified. And elsewhere in his* Antiquities *Josephus refers to this same individual as 'Joseph who was called Caiaphas of the high priesthood'. There is therefore a strong likelihood that the man of about sixty years old whose skeleton was among the six interred in this ossuary was indeed the Caiaphas who encountered Jesus.*

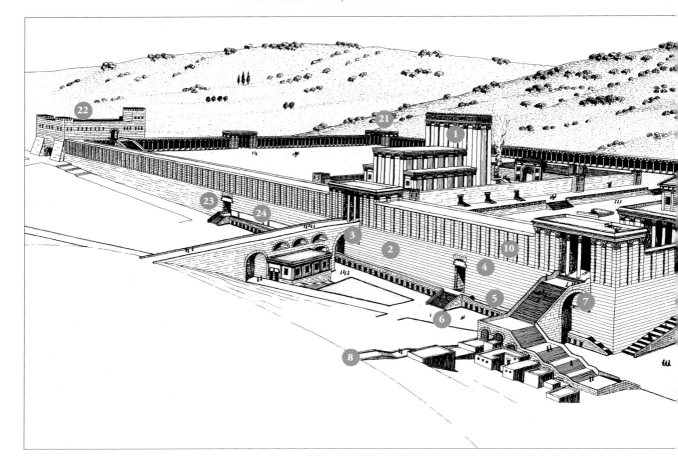

KEY TO THE TEMPLE MOUNT

1. THE SECOND TEMPLE
2. WESTERN WALL
3. WILSON'S ARCH
4. BARCLAY'S GATE
5. SMALL SHOPS
6. MAIN N-S STREET
7. ROBINSON'S ARCH
8. UPPER CITY
9. ROYAL STOA
10. PILASTERS
11. DOUBLE GATE
12. TRIPLE GATE
13. STAIRWAY
14. PLAZA
15. RITUAL BATHOUSE
16. COUNCIL HOUSE
17. ROW OF WINDOWS
18. BURNT ARCHES ·
19. BURNT ARCHES
20. STAIRWAY
21. HERODIAN TOWER
22. ANTONIA FORTRESS
23. WARREN'S GATE
24. LARGEST ASHLARS

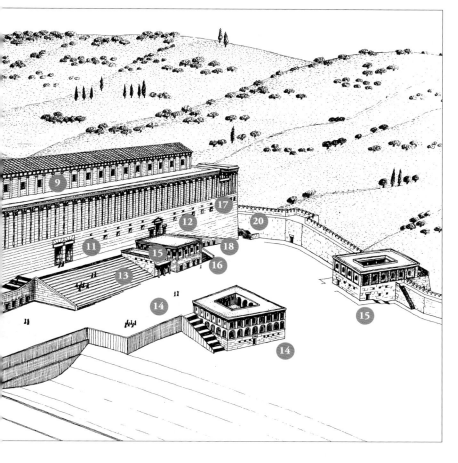

*The Temple Mount in Jesus' time.
Reconstruction by architect-artist Leen
Ritmeyer and his wife, Kathleen, of
how the Jerusalem Temple would have
looked as a result of the ambitious and
elaborate building programme
initiated by Herod the Great. After
using huge stone blocks to double the
size of the natural platform on which
King Solomon had built his Temple,
Herod rebuilt the then 500-year-old
Second Temple (1) and embellished it
with a series of magnificent buildings
that made the whole structure one of
the wonders of the world in Jesus' time.
For the southern approach from
Jerusalem's Lower City, Herod's
architects designed the Royal Stoa (9),
a grand multi-columned hall stretching
the entire east-west width of the Temple
platform, which pilgrims approached
via an imposing Double Gate (11),
while priests used a Triple Gate (12) to
reach the store-rooms containing the
items they needed for their rituals. For
the aristocracy living in Jerusalem's
Upper City (8) a special bridge (3)
enabled them to avoid having to mix
with the ordinary pilgrims
approaching from the south. Natural
valleys protected the Temple from
every side except the north, where the
Romans, presumably with the Temple
priesthood's consent, stationed their
Antonia fortress. According to Josephus,
Herod began the Temple project in the
eighteenth year of his reign (19 BC),
and work on the Temple itself took only
eighteen months. However, in John
2: 20 'the Jews' tell Jesus: 'It has taken
forty-six years to build this sanctuary',
indicating that construction had
continued well into Jesus' lifetime.*

above the foundations, and the awe they created among Jesus' disciples is a matter of gospel record (e.g. Matthew 24: 1).

Also clear is that on the Temple Mount's western side Herod provided the chief priests and aristocracy with their own special bridge from the Upper City across the Tyropoeon valley and onto the Mount, while for those coming from the Lower City to the south, wide steps led up to a Double Gate and Triple Gate opening into what is called the Royal Stoa. This, a basilica-like structure, was lined with Corinthian columns which according to Josephus were so wide that it took three men with out-stretched arms to encircle them. Money-changers for changing image-bearing Roman coins for image-less ones approved by the Jewish Law, together with hawkers of animals and birds to be used for sacrifices, are thought to have plied their business in the aisles provided by these columns, one of several places around the Temple where they did so, while at the Stoa's eastern end was an assembly room for the Sanhedrin, the Jewish central religious and legislative council.

North of the Stoa lay a series of increasingly exclusive courts, the pro-hibition of Gentiles on pain of death being marked by special stone notices, two of which survive, one near complete in the Archaeological Museum,

Jesus almost certainly walked up and down these steps. These led to and from the southern entrance-way to the Temple, commanded by the Royal Stoa (see 13 on previous reconstruction), and are one of the very few usable areas to have survived. Although they are not high, Herod the Great's engineers carefully made them of alternating depths, one 12 inches deep, the next 35 inches deep, then back to 12 inches, preventing those ascending and descending from doing so in anything but a slow, methodical manner.

How Herod's stonemasons achieved very accurate rectangular shapes for the huge limestone blocks used in the Temple's construction. First a channel would be cut into the natural 'grain' line of a limestone block, then water poured over logs inserted the length of this channel. Swelling of the wood would cause the limestone to split along the relatively straight natural fault line, creating neat, rectangular blocks with relative ease. The quarries were only a mile from the Temple, and once stonecutters had properly dressed the blocks teams of oxen would then haul them to the site with the aid of wooden rollers.

Huge Herodian blocks still in situ as part of the platform of the Temple Mount. Some of these measure 39 feet in length, and weigh over 100 tons.

Istanbul, the other, more fragmentary, in the Rockefeller Museum, Jerusalem. At the approach to the Temple itself a so-called Court of the Women marked the point beyond which all women were excluded. From this court a portico led into the Court of the Priests (see reconstruction, p.122) where animals, from pigeons to heifers, many purchased from the traders in the preceding areas, were brought to be sacrificed on an altar on which two fires were kept constantly alight, and a third acted as an auxiliary. Reputedly the very spot where Abraham had once stayed his hand in sacrificing his son Isaac, this was the one place where every good Jew of Jesus' time was expected at least once a year to bring an animal sacrifice accompanied by suitable money offerings. Beyond this lay the Temple itself, with its mysterious Holy of Holies reserved only for the high priest. Some twenty thousand functionaries were said to be employed in the day-to-day running of this vast enterprise, and another sixteen thousand craftsmen and labourers kept busy on the construction work.

It is against this overall setting that we must now try to see Jesus and his disciples as they completed their fateful journey to Jerusalem, and to the Temple, that would culminate in Jesus' death. As with so many circumstances of Jesus' life, such as his enjoyment of food, and his acceptance of the endearments of prostitutes, we find him acting in a particularly offbeat

way on his arrival. Normally expected of any pilgrim on visiting the holy city of Jerusalem was that he or she would make the final stages of the journey on foot as a sign of respect and devotion. Thus even as recently as 1917 Britain's General Allenby,

ΜΗΘΕΝΑΑΛΛΟΓΕΝΗΕΙϹΠΟΡΕΥΕϹΘΑΙ
ΕΝΤΟϹΤΟΥΠΕΡΙΤΟΙΕΡΟΝΤΡΥ
ΦΑΚΤΟΥΚΑΙΠΕΡΙΒΟΛΟΥΟϹΔΑΝ
ΛΗΦΘΗΑΥΤΩΙΑΙΤΙΟϹΕϹΤΑΙ
ΔΙΑΤΟΕΞΑΚΟΛΟΥΘΕΙΝ
ΘΑΝΑΤΟΝ

Notice warning Gentiles on pain of death to keep out of the Temple's inner precincts. According to Josephus, several such notices were displayed on a screen surrounding the Temple courts, 'some in Greek and some in Roman characters', warning that 'no foreigner was to enter the holy area'. This example was found in 1935, near Jerusalem's St Stephen's Gate (the Lion's Gate) and is today in Jerusalem's Rockefeller Museum. Its reconstruction (below) is possible from a near-complete version found in the late nineteenth century and now in the Archaeological Museum, Istanbul.

Jesus rides into Jerusalem on a donkey (Matthew 21: 1-10). His riding into the Holy City in this way can only be interpreted as intentionally provocative, particularly towards the priestly aristocracy who controlled the Temple. From the sarcophagus of Junius Bassus, city prefect of Rome 359 AD, now preserved in the Vatican Grottoes, Rome.

upon capturing Jerusalem from the Turks, pointedly dismounted from his horse at the Jaffa Gate before making his entry.

Fascinatingly however, the gospels portray Jesus doing the very reverse. While throughout the rest of the gospels there is not the slightest reference to him ever using animal transport, for his entry into Jerusalem he is specifically described as going to elaborate lengths to procure a donkey to ride on (e.g. Luke 19: 28 ff.). And his choice of animal is particularly interesting. A horse would have seemed ostentatious, grandiose and militaristic. Indeed had Jesus chosen this we might have been obliged to treat more seriously the claims of Professor S.G.F. Brandon, Hyam Maccoby and others that Jesus was a guerrilla leader whose actual use of violence was written out by the gospel writers in order to make his message more acceptable to Gentiles.

But a donkey, as much in Jesus' time as now, could only be viewed as a humble beast. Furthermore, as Jesus would have been well aware, more than five hundred years earlier the *nabi* Zechariah had 'prophesied' that the promised Messiah's coming would be in precisely this manner:

> Shout with gladness, daughter of Jerusalem!
> See now, your king comes to you.
> He is victorious, he is triumphant,
> humble and riding on a donkey...
> He will proclaim peace for the nations.
> His empire will stretch from sea to sea...
>
> (Zechariah 9: 9-10)

Acclaiming Jesus on his entry, the gospels tell us, was a crowd waving palm branches and singing, 'Hosannah, blessed is he who comes in the name of the Lord', words from Psalm 118. As has been pointed out by Westminster Abbey's Canon Anthony Harvey, this scene strongly recalls the triumphant purification and rededication of the Jerusalem Temple by the Hasmonean Simon Maccabeus after it had been defiled by Antiochus Epiphanes in the second century BC, readily confirmed from even the most casual glance at the relevant passage in the first book of Maccabees: 'The Jews made their entry ... with acclamations and carrying palms ... chanting hymns and canticles.' (1 Maccabees 13: 51)

So if this was how Jesus entered Jerusalem, who was this gesture aimed at? Was it the occupying Romans, as might be expected if Jesus had genuinely been a guerrilla leader? Or was it the Sadducean aristocracy, with all their materialism, their lucrative concessions to money-changers and animal traders, and their concern only with the outward forms of religion? There can be no greater confirmation that it was the latter than the account (in all four gospels, though the John writer puts it almost at the very beginning of his) of Jesus' famous 'cleansing' of the Temple, the most violent physical act recorded of him throughout all four gospels. Reportedly he knocked over the money-changers' tables, laid about the traders themselves with whips, and released the animals and pigeons intended for sacrifice, loudly declaiming 'Take all this out of here and stop turning my Father's house into a market' (John 2: 16).

Now this was the man who, with John the Baptist, had already told the populace (following the theme, 'What I want is mercy not sacrifice', Matthew 9: 13 and elsewhere, after Hosea 6: 6) that repentance was what was truly necessary for the forgiveness of sins, not the paying of a Sadducean priest to sacrifice some innocent animal. So if this had not been challenge enough to the Sadducees' monopoly, now, by turning out the traders and money-changers, he had made his feelings crystal clear: to him the Sadducees' money-dominated running of the Temple was every bit as much a defilement and abomination of God's Holy Place as the pagan Antiochus Epiphanes' erection of a statue of Zeus had been two centuries before.

We have every reason to believe that the news of his high-handedness was quickly relayed to the chief priests and other members of the Sadducean aristocracy, for sure enough they were seemingly instantly upon the scene the very next time that Jesus showed his face in the Temple. According to the Mark gospel, 'the chief priests, and the scribes and the elders came to him' demanding 'What authority have you for acting like this?', prompting Jesus' characteristically cryptic response: 'John's baptism, did it come from heaven, or from man?' (Mark 11: 30). Modern-day psychologists are notoriously fond of answering a question with a question, and the gospels convey Jesus' mastery of this device long before them, making particularly adroit use of it when someone tried to trap him.

But of course the real import of Jesus' response was its challenge to his questioners' authority. If they had been prepared to acknowledge that John had been a mouthpiece of God, then Jesus, as John's successor, could have claimed the same, and thereby authority over matters concerning the Temple. We are told that those who had put their question to Jesus extricated themselves as best they could by mumbling that they did not know, but with little doubt they had sensed the trap and astutely recognized that they were dealing with a man who threatened their whole grip on the affairs of the Temple, and the comfortable living that went with this.

Accordingly, there can be absolutely no doubt that from this point on Jesus was a marked man. Because of the popular support he had attracted he represented such a serious danger to the ruling Sadducean and Herodian aristocracy that, as the John gospel chillingly conveys, they 'determined to kill him' (John 11: 52). So, this decision taken, their course now was to find the best means to effect this with the least opposition (Luke 19: 47, 48) and with the least blame falling upon themselves.

'Take all this out of here and stop turning my Father's house into a market!'
Jesus expelling the traders from the Temple, from the famous painting by El Greco in the National Gallery, London. The most violent act recorded of Jesus, it seems to have been this which prompted the Temple's controlling Sadducean priesthood to decide that he could no longer be allowed to live.

9

THE ROAD TO THE CROSS

J ust as earlier in this book we found it impossible to determine the year in which Jesus was born, so similar uncertainty shrouds the exact year of his death, chiefly because of gospel contradictions. According to the authors of the four canonical gospels, also the Roman historian Tacitus and also the de-Christianized version of Josephus' text, Jesus was executed sometime during Pontius Pilate's governorship of Judaea. This Pontius Pilate's existence is readily confirmed by extensive mention of him in other contexts in the writings of Josephus. Also, in 1961, excavation of the ruins of a Roman temple at Caesarea revealed a Roman dedicatory inscription bearing Pilate's name as *praefectus* or governor of Judaea, the first known reference to him in a non-literary context. And his term as *praefectus* has been reliably determined as between 27 and 36 AD.

This term of office therefore usefully provides us with a narrower set of years for Jesus' death than the equivalent for Caiaphas as high priest, which was between c.18 and 37 AD. But it is still not narrow enough, for the gospels badly let us down on what might otherwise be a useful chrono-logical pointer provided by the Last Supper. According to all three synoptic gospels this Supper was very definitely the Passover Meal of Jesus and his disciples (Matthew 26: 17-20; Mark 14: 12-17; Luke 22: 7-14), a meal all

Above *Attestation of Pilate's governorship of Judaea, independent of the gospels, is provided by this fragmentary inscription discovered in 1961 in the first-century theatre at Caesarea Maritima during excavations by Italian archaeologists. The text appears to read '[CAESARIEN]S [IBUS] ... TIBERIEVM ... [PON]TIVS PILATVS [PRAEF]ECTVS IVDA[EA]E' ('To the people of Caesarea ...Tiberieum ... Pontius Pilate, Prefect of Judaea').*

Opposite *Among the very few contemporary visual representations of crucifixion, a crude graffito showing the victim with knees apart, and appearing to have been hung facing the cross. From Pozzuoli, near Naples.*

Jesus' Last Supper, in which he asked his followers to share bread and wine together, in memory of the sacrifice he was about to make of his body and blood. He closely modelled the rite on the Jewish Kiddush. From a fresco of the first half of the third century in the Capella Graeca, cemetery of Priscilla.

practising Jews know as the Seder and which they celebrate on a very specific night of the year to give thanks for their apparently divine deliverance from bondage in ancient Egypt. Since the Passover always falls on the Jewish 15 Nisan (Nisan roughly corresponds to our April), and all gospels are agreed that the day after Jesus' crucifixion was a Sabbath (making the crucifixion day a Friday and the day of the Last Supper a Thursday), it ought to be possible to fix the date of Jesus' death by finding on which year or years between 27 and 36 AD the 15 Nisan fell on a Thursday. However the author of the John gospel ruins any such calculations by stating that the day of the crucifixion, which he agrees to have been a Friday, was 'Passover Preparation Day' (John 19: 14), meaning, if he was right, that the Last Supper could not have been a Passover meal, and that we should be looking for a year in which 15 Nisan fell on a Friday.

Ingenious attempts have been made to reconcile the differences by suggesting that Jesus and his disciples, along with the Essenes of the Dead Sea Scrolls, may have celebrated the Passover according to an ancient solar calendar different from that observed by the Jews of Jerusalem. Another possibility is that Mark, as the first of the synoptics, simply got his facts wrong, and that the authors of Matthew and Luke, because they copied from Mark, made the same error, John thereby providing the only true date. Yet another possibility is that it was the author of John, in his desire to represent Jesus as the new 'paschal lamb', who distorted historical truth by altering the true moment of crucifixion to coincide with the time when lambs would have been slaughtered in the Jerusalem Temple in preparation for the Passover.

Equally fraught is any attempt to fix the year of Jesus' death from the Luke gospel's dating of Jesus' baptism to the fifteenth year of the reign of the Emperor Tiberius (Luke 3: 1). Since this is readily calculable as 29 AD, and the synoptic gospels suggest Jesus' public ministry lasted no longer than a year, this would mean that Jesus died in 30 AD. But again the John gospel complicates matters by suggesting that Jesus' ministry spanned some three years after his baptism. This has led to a widespread, but still thinly founded idea that the true year was 33 AD, hence the holding of a Holy Year in 1933. Among theologians the likeliest dates have been calculated to be 30, 33 and 27 AD, in that order of probability, though the late Hugh Schonfield, author of the famous *Passover Plot*, preferred 36 AD. But the only honest verdict can be that we simply do not know the exact year when Jesus died.

Whatever the exact year we are dealing with, however, it would seem to have been on a Thursday very close to Passover time that Jesus shared with his disciples the meal now known as the Last Supper. Supporting the synoptic view that this was the Passover meal we are told that there was wine on the table, indicating a celebration, and also that, by way of introducing the meal, Jesus reportedly used words very close to those of the Jewish Kiddush or Blessing, traditionally said by the head of a Jewish family before a Sabbath or on the eve of a major festival. This rooting of what we now know as the Christian Eucharist in the Jewish Kiddush is very obvious:

Jewish wooden eating bowls of the early second century AD, found among objects left in caves near the Dead Sea by Jewish guerrillas holding out against the Romans during the Second Jewish Revolt. Bowls such as these would very likely have been used at the Last Supper.

JEWISH KIDDUSH

Blessed are you, O Lord our God, King of the universe, who creates the fruit of the vine ...

Blessed are you, O Lord our God, King of the Universe, who brings forth bread from the earth.

CHRISTIAN EUCHARIST

Blessed are you, Lord, God of all creation, through your goodness we have this wine to offer, fruit of the vine and work of human hands ...

Blessed are you, Lord, God of all creation, through your goodness we have this bread to offer, which earth has given and human hands have made.

However, as in so much else that he said and did, Jesus introduced a quite new element into this rite, and an extremely chilling one, which was to liken the bread and wine that all were sharing with his own flesh and blood that was about to be sacrificed: 'This is my body which will be given for you' (Luke 22: 21); 'this is my blood, the blood of the covenant, which is to be poured out for many for the forgiveness of sins' (Matthew 26: 28).

There can be no mistaking the novelty of this way of thinking. While the Jewish Kiddush simply acknowledged God as Creator of bread and wine, ignoring the additional 'human hands' factor that contributed to both these products, Jesus pointedly recognized the additional human contribution, emphasizing that the same also applied to his own body and blood which was now, like the bread and wine, about to be sacrificed. Whereas perhaps two thousand years before – purportedly on the very spot occupied by the Jerusalem Temple – God had chosen to stay the Jews' ancestor Abraham from killing his son in sacrifice, now, with a little help from Joseph and Mary, God was providing the victim, for man to make his choice whether to stay his hand, or otherwise. So would Abraham's descendants, in the form of the Jewish priesthood, continue with their declared aim to shed Jesus' blood – slaughtering him just as they daily slaughtered the animals and birds brought to them? Or would they stay their hand, just as God had done with Abraham's son, Isaac?

The Jewish priests, of course, had no conception that their killing of Jesus might have any role cleansing people's sins, in the manner of their more normal sacrificing of animals. But Jesus' insistence that his new version of the Kiddush and its accompanying celebratory meal was specifically for the forgiveness of sins, and that it should be repeated in perpetuity in his memory, underlines the importance that he attached to his words. His seriousness of purpose is also all too evident from the bloodiness of the events that so swiftly followed. According to the gospels it was one of his own disciples, Judas Iscariot, who turned traitor and sold the vital information that would enable the Temple priesthood to make their seizure when the ordinary people had the least opportunity to come to Jesus' aid. Although it is impossible to be sure exactly what went on in Judas' mind, the author of the John gospel, without stating as

The Jerusalem Temple's place of sacrifice, the inner court, or Court of the Priests, where animals brought in offering for the forgiveness of sins were slaughtered by the Temple priests. Detail from a meticulously researched reconstruction of the Temple made by East Anglian model-builder Alec Garrard.

much, gave him a real motive apart from the famous 'thirty pieces of silver'. According to John, Judas' responsibility was looking after 'the common fund' (that is, the money that Jesus and all his followers shared between them for their needs), and a few days before the Passover he had been deeply angered by the wastefulness with which Jesus had allowed Mary of Bethany to lavish on him some highly expensive perfume, feeling that this went against all Jesus' avowed principles of giving all to the poor.

Whatever Judas' thinking, however, the gospels agree that Jesus and his disciples did not stay that night in the house where they had shared his Last Supper. Instead they went on to the Mount of Olives, to what the Matthew and Mark authors both describe as 'a small estate called Gethsemane' (Matthew 26: 36; Mark 14: 32). In the original Greek Gethsemane is described as a *chorion*, a very general term that simply denotes an estate or property. But because the John gospel (John 18: 1) mentions Jesus and his disciples going (in what seems to be the same context) 'into' a 'garden' (Greek *kepos*), it has long been assumed that Gethsemane was a garden, the oddity being that Jesus and his disciples should apparently quite regularly (John 18: 2) sleep rough in such a place at a time of year when Jerusalem could be very chilly, which we know from Peter being described as warming himself by a fire later that same night (Luke 22: 55-6).

As recently pointed out by New Zealand lecturer Joan Taylor, the explanation may be that Gethsemane, which (as *gat-shemanim* in Aramaic and Hebrew) means 'olive oil press', may not have been a garden at all but instead a large cave used for the pressing of olives into oil. Precisely such a cave, undoubtedly used in early centuries for pressing olives and equipped with a cistern for catching winter rainwater, is located just seventy yards north of the present-day 'garden'. Although in the autumn this would have been filled with olives awaiting processing, in Passover's springtime it would have been empty and ideal for overnight shelter, and historical sources strongly suggest that it was this, rather than the 'garden', that the earliest Christian pilgrims venerated as the true 'Gethsemane'. Certainly it is the sort of shelter that Jesus and his disciples might well have used overnight at a time when accommodation in Jerusalem would have been very scarce because of the crush of Passover pilgrims.

The Luke author informs us that on this occasion Jesus' group had two swords with them (Luke 22: 38), information that it is important to interpret carefully since some have used it to fuel arguments that Jesus was a guerrilla leader. In fact, Josephus says that even the monastic Essenes were allowed 'weapons to keep off bandits', as a result of which it seems perfectly reasonable to regard the swords as a sensible, minimal deterrence to protect the 'common fund' from being seized by undeserving hands. Even the philosophy of going the second mile and giving away cloak as well as tunic needed to be treated sensibly, rather than to the absolute letter.

Whatever number of swords Jesus' group had with them, there is no suggestion that Gethsemane, whether it was a cave or a garden, had any

The true location of Jesus' arrest? Gethsemane, where Jesus spent his last night with his disciples before his arrest, has long been supposed to have been a garden. But nowhere in the gospels is it directly described as a garden. Instead, the name actually means 'olive oil press', and new researches by Joan Taylor, of the University of Waikato, New Zealand, suggest that the true 'Gethsemane' of the gospels was this still extant natural cave 70 yards north of the present-day tourists' 'Garden of Gethsemane'. It was undoubtedly used in ancient times for pressing olives to produce oil, and in the spring months, as at Passover time, it would have lain idle and would have been ideal for overnight shelter for Jesus and his disciples. Today the cave is used as a chapel.

defence capabilities, seemingly prompting Judas, who we are told knew it well (John 18:2), to choose it as the best location for Jesus to be seized with the least amount of fuss. Ironically, there virtually had to be a Judas for Jesus to suffer the fate he clearly believed the Messiah had to suffer, and thirty years ago in his best-selling *The Passover Plot* Jewish writer the late Hugh J. Schonfield made a very plausible case for Jesus having almost psychologically pressured Judas into carrying out his unsavoury role. Certainly this remains rather more convincing than the argument by Schonfield's fellow-Jew Hyam Maccoby that Judas never did betray Jesus, as advanced in his recent *Judas Iscariot and the Myth of Jewish Evil*.

For certainly the Luke gospel in particular conveys Jesus as going through some very convincing human emotions during that last night of his life, as he waited for the results of that betrayal and the consequent harrowing fate which he had effectively brought upon himself. It is exclusively reported by the Luke writer, who in this instance certainly seems to have had access to someone who directly witnessed Jesus' plight, that: 'in his [Jesus'] anguish … his sweat fell to the ground like great drops of blood' (Luke 22: 44). Considerable interest in this information has been expressed by forensic pathologist Dr Frederick Zugibe, Chief Medical Examiner of Rockland County, New York, who has pointed out that the 'bloody sweat' strongly suggests a rare medical condition called haematidrosis, in which anything from one to thousands of subcutaneous blood vessels rupture into the exocrine sweat glands, causing the sufferer literally to 'sweat blood'. Since the condition is comparatively little known, and is invariably triggered by extreme emotional stress, for someone to have observed Jesus suffering this at the crisis time at Gethsemane (and when he was supposed to be alone) gives us another of those tantalizing glimpses of him as a flesh-and-blood human being.

However inadequately, we are able to feel something of what a terrible moment of aloneness it must have been for Jesus. Knowing the physical torment that he had committed himself to, and knowing the disbelief and ignorance among his companions regarding what he had told them of his fate, he might easily at this moment have run away from it all, while there was still time. Yet he seems quite deliberately to have chosen this particular time and place for his ultimate act of self-sacrifice. As represented in the gospels, while many of his followers, even though they had been sleeping, took the opportunity to slip away as they heard the approach of the arrest squad, Jesus, who had reportedly so often made himself scarce on previous occasions with surprising ease (e.g. Luke 4: 30; John 10: 39), this time resolutely stood his ground, even forbidding any resistance on the part of those companions who temporarily stayed.

As the gospels also make clear, the arrest squad was composed of 'a number of men armed with swords and clubs, sent by the chief priests and the scribes and the elders' (Mark 14: 43; also with slight variants Matthew 26: 47 and Luke 22: 52). These therefore seem to have been the chief priests' servants behaving 'with sticks' in much the same manner portrayed in the Talmud's poem about the Kathros family (see p.108). And while we may question the John writer's isolated mention (John 18: 3) of the part that the Pharisees played in the arrest, also his equally isolated mention of the seemingly Roman 'cohort', the hand of the 'chief priests' in the operation is agreed by all.

Thus it was, therefore, that on that very same night Jesus found himself on trial for his life before the very men whose conduct of religious affairs he had so outspokenly questioned. Although according to Mark and the other synoptic writers, the trial was conducted by 'the chief priests and the elders and the scribes ... the whole Sanhedrin' (Mark 14: 53-5), several Jewish scholars have convincingly argued that for the full Sanhedrin, the supreme Jewish council, to have held an overnight or even dawn meeting is historically extremely doubtful, since no normal Sanhedrin meeting ever took place at night, and the difficulties of summoning appropriate representatives from their beds at festival time would have been far greater than simply holding Jesus overnight, or indeed over several nights had there been any legitimate trial.

We may therefore find the John gospel's account rather more convincing, suggesting that there was no formal trial, but that Jesus was simply shuttled between two high priestly houses, that of Caiaphas and that of Caiaphas' father-in-law, Annas, both these individuals having much to lose if Jesus' popularity went unchecked. If this were the case then we may perhaps picture Jesus' 'trial' as little more than a hasty overnight interrogation by two Sadducees whose motives were rather more those of self-interest than a desire for justice. We may even quite reasonably conjecture

Jesus being brought before his accusers in one of the Palatial Mansion's upper rooms as revealed by Israeli archaeologist Nahman Avigad's excavations, while the chief disciple Peter waited 'below in the courtyard', just as described in Mark 14: 46.

But what of the charges on which Jesus is said to have been condemned? The Mark gospel represents the high priest as asking him: 'Are you the Messiah, the Son of the Blessed One?' (Mark 14: 61), thereupon tearing his robes at the apparent blasphemy when Jesus answers in the affirmative. As modern Jewish scholars have pointed out, it was surely not the Messiah claim as such that could have caused Caiaphas such offence, for someone, sometime, had to be he. For instance, according to the Jewish Midrash, at the time of the Second Jewish Revolt of 132 AD the great Rabbi Akiba specifically acclaimed rebel leader Simon Bar-Kokhba with the words: 'This is the king Messiah!', and although Akiba's companion reportedly scoffed: 'Akiba, grass will grow in your jawbones and he will still not have come!', Akiba's claim as such was no offence.

The John gospel, for its part, says the charge on which the priests brought Jesus before Pilate for execution was 'because he has claimed to be the Son of God' (John 19: 7), and here it seems to be the use of the definite article, i.e. the Son of God, as also in the Mark version, that brings us nearer to the issue on which Jesus' life hung. Any Messiah's claim to being a son of God was already recognized, the link being made in Psalm 2, for instance, and in some Dead Sea Scroll references. But as the high priest seems to have been already aware, perhaps via Judas, Jesus' claim for himself, overt or otherwise, went far deeper - to the extent, if accepted as such, of carrying authority in God's name over the whole enterprise that he, Caiaphas, currently controlled to such advantage.

Clearly this upstart Galilean could not be allowed to live, and with this decided Jesus' inquisitors are described as handing him over to Pilate because: 'We are not allowed to put a man to death' (John 18: 31). No doubt there was something to this effect in the small print of the alliance between the Temple authorities and the Romans, but that in practice the Temple authorities could put a man to death if they so chose is evident from the fact that the book of Acts describes the martyr Stephen being stoned by the Jerusalem Sanhedrin (Acts: 7: 59-60) for an apparently similar blasphemy shortly after Jesus' death. Although some have argued that this was a mere mob lynching, the likelihood that the Sadducean chief priests possessed at least some power of execution, albeit most likely reserved for special offences against the Temple, is further indicated by the Temple's still extant stone notices threatening death to any Gentile trespasser, as featured in the previous chapter (see p.113).

So whilst there is little doubt the 'chief priests' could have publicly killed Jesus there and then had they felt they were acting with the full approval of the Jewish people, there is every reason to suppose that they would have been extremely unpopular had they openly done so, and it must have seemed much more expedient for them to have Pontius Pilate take care of their dirty work. From the gospels' mention of the governor's custom of releasing a prisoner, Pilate seems to have made a regular practice to come to Jerusalem to keep an eye on events during Passover (he was normally based at Caesarea). And despite the chief priests' own Temple security force, it would have been Pilate who had the far superior military capability to deal with any disturbance.

But what of the gospels' portrayal of Pilate as finding no fault with Jesus, and pointedly washing his hands of any responsibility for Jesus' death? Fortunately the Jewish historian Josephus includes in his writings mention of two attempts by Pilate to put down demonstrations of Jewish passive resistance which provide important clues to the Roman's mentality. The first of these demonstrations had arisen because Pilate had provocatively ordered the display of his legion's image-bearing standards in Jerusalem. This had prompted an 'angry city mob ... joined by a huge influx of people from the country' to surround Pilate's residence in Caesarea, calling for him to remove the offending objects, whereupon on his refusal they all 'fell prone all round his house and remained motionless for five days and nights'. Concerned to rid himself of this nuisance, Pilate ordered the gathering to be surrounded by a ring of soldiers three deep, who advanced with drawn swords. But at this, according to Josephus,

> ... the Jews as though by agreement fell to the ground in a body and bent their necks, shouting that they were ready to be killed rather than transgress the Law. Amazed at the intensity of their fervour Pilate ordered the standards to be removed from Jerusalem forthwith.

The second demonstration described by Josephus was provoked by Pilate's use of some of the Temple tax for the building of an aqueduct. In his response to this Pilate seems to have tried hard to be more cunning, for he had his soldiers '... mix with the mob, wearing civilian clothing over their armour. Furthermore they were ordered not to draw their swords but to use clubs on the obstreperous'. Even so the result was hardly a triumph for public order. According to Josephus, '... many died from the blows, and many were trampled on by their friends as they fled.'

The interest value of these episodes is that first, and quite independently of anything in the gospels, the incident of the standards in particular shows Jews of Jesus' time using passive resistance methods of which even Mahatma Gandhi could scarce not have been proud. Although we are told nothing about who led those who bared their necks to Pilate's soldiers, their actions accord unerringly with the message of the man who taught: 'offer the wicked man no resistance ... if anyone hits you on the right cheek, offer him the other as well' (Matthew 5: 38).

Secondly, the incidents are mentioned by Josephus in his book *Antiquities* specifically just before his controversial reference to Jesus that was discussed

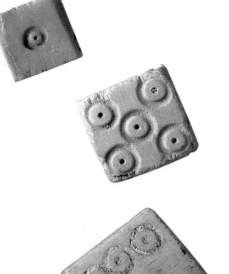

Roman dice found at Sepphoris, of a kind typical of the first century AD. Made of bone, such dice are often found at sites associated with Roman troops, and are arranged almost identically to modern dice (i.e. opposite faces always add up to seven). According to the John gospel the Roman soldiers responsible for Jesus' crucifixion used dice at the foot of his cross to decide who should have his 'seamless undergarment' (John 19: 24).

in chapter 3. As was noted there, this reference was tampered with, and most commentators, such as Paul Winter and others, recognize that part of the text is now missing. So in his original did Josephus directly link Jesus with some third popular demonstration that mediaeval Christian copyists felt obliged to suppress? Could this have been the incident Luke's gospel hints at: 'It was just about this time that some people arrived and told him [Jesus] about the Galileans whose blood Pilate had mingled with that of their sacrifices' (Luke 13: 1).

Likewise, is there some significance in Mark's cryptic reference to Barabbas as one who had been thrown into prison 'with the rioters who had committed murder during the uprising' (Mark 15: 7)? We may take comfort from the probability that whatever was suppressed is unlikely to have been earth-shattering, for we would otherwise have heard about it from those commentators on Josephus, such as Origen, who were writing before the text was mutilated. But even so there are grounds for suspicion that Jesus, albeit passively, had stirred up greater popular Jewish fervour than the Gentile gospels convey.

A third point of interest is Pilate's reaction to the passive resistance methods. He acts neither as the insensitive butcher that some modern authors have tried to label him, nor as the pusillanimous capitulator to mob demands portrayed by the gospel writers. A man clearly used to the ways of violence – he was, after all, regionally responsible for the world's most efficient fighting machine, the Roman army – he nonetheless exhibits a superstitious awe of individuals ready to lay down their lives for what to him would have seemed trifling religious niceties. It is possible therefore that he may genuinely have raised some objection to putting Jesus to death just to satisfy the demands of the Sadducean high priesthood. In this regard, and given the gospels' portrayal of a Jewish crowd positively baying for Jesus' blood when Pilate suggested he might be spared, many writers have remarked on the strange and seemingly unexplained change that seems to have happened from the effusive welcome that Jesus had reportedly been given on his arrival in Jerusalem just a few days before. One possible explanation is that Jesus was disowned by those who had welcomed him to Jerusalem because he had failed to sanction the abortive uprising against the Romans that arguably they had launched in his name. If the latter were the case, it would inevitably have been accompanied by disillusionment and bitterness against Jesus as a betrayer of those who had given their lives in his cause. But arguably the likelier explanation is that the second, blood-thirsty crowd was one carefully orchestrated by the Sadducees using their own paid employees. With an estimated twenty thousand Temple servants and eighteen thousand workmen on their payroll, they would scarcely have had difficulty in finding a mob to perform to their tune. This is further suggested by Josephus' bald statement, 'Upon an indictment *by leading members of our society,* Pilate sentenced him [Jesus] to the cross'.

Of the details of this crucifixion, all the gospels relate that Jesus was beaten as a preliminary and also that he was scourged, that is, lashed repeatedly with a pellet-studded whip (Matthew 27: 26; Mark 15: 15; John 19: 2). Apparently seriously weakened by this maltreatment, he reportedly had difficulty carrying his 'cross' to the crucifixion site (although this is generally thought to have been just the beam from which he would be suspended, it would have been quite heavy enough). This necessitated the aid of the bystander Simon of Cyrene. Once at the execution site Jesus was stripped of all his clothes, and although we are not directly told that nails were driven through his hands and feet, this may be assumed from John 20: 25.

Otherwise the gospel writers seem to have been concerned to spare their readers the more harrowing details of the procedure, no doubt because these were all too familiar at the time. Earlier employed by Scythians, Assyrians and Carthaginians – none of them the most squeamish of people – crucifixion was universally execrated as a form of punishment, even the Romans reserving it only for slaves and for foreign rebels. Again, because crucifixion was so abhorred, only the scantest of contemporary information about it has survived. Mostly this has been in the form of artistic representations, two of these crude graffiti, one from Pozzuoli, just outside Naples, the other from the Palatine Hill, near Rome, and two others tiny depictions on gems, one of these in the Pereire Collection in Paris.

Also, despite many thousands having been crucified during the Roman era – in 71 BC alone the Roman consul Crassus had six thousand rebels of the Spartacus uprising strung up along Italy's Via Appia – there has been a

Among the very few contemporary visual representations of crucifixion, a crude graffito showing the victim with knees apart, and appearing to have been hung facing the cross. From Pozzuoli, near Naples.

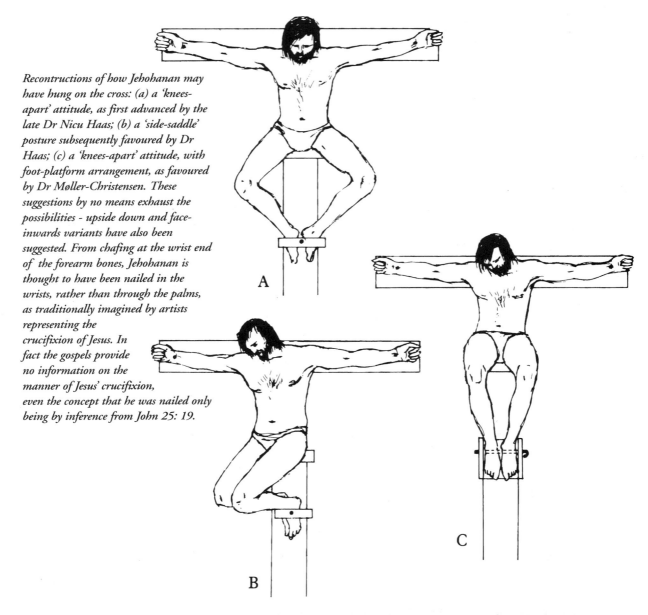

Reconstructions of how Jehohanan may have hung on the cross: (a) a 'knees-apart' attitude, as first advanced by the late Dr Nicu Haas; (b) a 'side-saddle' posture subsequently favoured by Dr Haas; (c) a 'knees-apart' attitude, with foot-platform arrangement, as favoured by Dr Møller-Christensen. These suggestions by no means exhaust the possibilities - upside down and face-inwards variants have also been suggested. From chafing at the wrist end of the forearm bones, Jehohanan is thought to have been nailed in the wrists, rather than through the palms, as traditionally imagined by artists representing the crucifixion of Jesus. In fact the gospels provide no information on the manner of Jesus' crucifixion, even the concept that he was nailed only being by inference from John 25: 19.

The breaking of the legs of the crucified. The bones of Jehohanan's legs can be seen to have been broken by 'a single, strong blow' shortly before death, in precisely the manner recorded of the robbers crucified alongside Jesus (John 19: 31-2). A measure that would have prevented the crucified from raising himself in order to breathe (thus hastening death), this is a notable instance of archaeology confirming the gospel record.

Ankle-bones of a first-century Jew called Jehohanan, joined by a six-and-a-half-inch crucifixion nail. The only known victim of crucifixion so far scientifically excavated, Jehohanan's skeleton was found in an ossuary in an extensive Jewish cemetery of Jesus' time discovered in 1968 in the northern Jerusalem suburb of Giv'at ha-Mivtar. Forensic examination revealed that in life Jehohanan had been slightly disfigured by a cleft palate, and that he was crucified while in his mid-twenties. Traces of wood found either side of the ankle-bones have been variously explained as from the titulus or notice recording Jehohanan's crime, or from a foot-platform to which his feet were nailed.

marked dearth of identifiable skeletal remains for them. One of the reasons for this seems to have been a medical black market for crucifixion nails in antiquity, for they were thought to be effective against bee-stings, fevers and epilepsy, and if withdrawn from the body no easily identifiable trace was left on the skeleton. In 1968, however, following the discovery of an ancient Jewish cemetery at Giv'at ha-Mivtar in northern Jerusalem, several ossuaries or bone boxes came to light, one of which was found to contain an adult male skeleton whose two heel bones were securely joined together by a nail nearly six and a half inches long. The ossuary's inscription identified this individual as one 'Jehohanan', and it is evident from the skeletal remains that he was a gracefully built, cleft-palated male in his mid-twenties, who undoubtedly died of crucifixion.

The discovery has raised lively interest among both Christians and Jews, with no little controversy regarding the exact form the crucifixion took. The Israeli anatomist Dr Nicu Haas, who conducted the main forensic examination, favoured the legs having been forced into an awkward side-saddle position, but renowned Israeli archaeologist the late Dr Yigael Yadin thought otherwise, opting instead for the knees having been kept apart. According to Yadin, although the ossuary's inscription is difficult to decipher, it may well read: 'Jehohanan ... the one hanged with his knees apart', and such a position certainly corresponds with the Pozzuoli graffito and the Pereire Collection gem. Another possible reconstruction has come from the Copenhagen Medical Museum specialist Dr Møller-Christensen who has deduced from traces of wood on both sides of Jehohanan's ankles that his feet had been forced into a crude wooden frame and were then locked in with a transverse nail.

Of course, whatever the exact method used, Jesus was not necessarily

Magical gem of the Roman period depicting a crucifixion, this time with the victim clearly suspended face outwards, but again with the legs wide apart. From a magical gem formerly in the Pereire Collection, Paris.

crucified the same way as Jehohanan, for crucifixion procedures are known to have varied, the disciple Peter, for instance, reputedly having been crucified upside down. But there is one feature of Dr Nicu Haas' observations on Jehohanan's skeleton which has a particular importance in suggesting that the gospels are, at least to some extent, eyewitness accounts. Dr Haas noted:

> The right tibia and the left calf bones (tibia and fibula) were all broken in their last third at the same level, but in a different manner: the right tibia had brutally been fractured, by comminution, into sharp slivers; the left tibia and fibula were broken by a simple, oblique, dentate-serrate line. Both types of fractures are characteristic in fresh bone. The fracture of the right tibial bone (the fibula being unavailable for study) was produced by a single, strong blow. This direct, deliberate blow may be attributed to the final 'coup de grâce'.

Essentially, Jehohanan had his legs savagely smashed, immediately recalling the breaking of the legs of Jesus' two crucifixion companions exclusively reported in the John gospel:

> ... to prevent the bodies remaining on the cross during the Sabbath ... the Jews asked Pilate to have the legs broken and the bodies taken away. Consequently the soldiers came and broke the legs of the first man who had been crucified with him and then of the other. When they came to Jesus they found he was already dead, and so instead of breaking his legs one of the soldiers pierced his side with a lance ... (John 19: 31-4)

The 'breaking of the legs' would seem to have been a procedure carried out only on Jewish crucifixion victims, for in other countries they would be left on the cross during the night, and it might take up to three days for them to expire. But in deference to the Mosaic prohibition on the leaving of a body on a cross after sundown, the Romans broke the legs of crucified Jews to hasten death, John's report thereby providing an authentic detail of which a Gentile writer, working from a distance, could not be expected to have been aware. Accordingly, whereas the old German theologians supposed the 'breaking of the legs' to have been an invention of the gospel writer in order to fulfil the Messianic prophecy of Psalm 34: 20, 'God rescues him ... Taking care of every bone ... God will not let one be broken', modern archaeology has proved them wrong, finding instead that it argues for the gospel's veracity. There is also medical support for the view that the John gospel's narrative content at least embodies other authentic, eyewitness detail, as in its writer's claim in respect of another crucifixion detail, the physiological effects of the lance reportedly thrust into Jesus' side:

… immediately there came out blood and water. This is the evidence of one who saw it – trustworthy evidence, and he knows he speaks the truth … (John 19: 34, 35)

According to some medical specialists, the 'water' would have been from fluid that had accumulated in lungs badly damaged from the beatings that Jesus suffered.

All the canonical gospels report as the final act of the crucifixion saga the arrival on the scene, after Jesus' death, of a hitherto unmentioned secret disciple, a 'rich man' called Joseph of Arimathea, who took charge of Jesus' body. Mystery surrounds the reasons why such a man, apparently influential enough to gain ready access to Pilate, should have emerged only at this moment, and also why not a single one of the associates of Jesus who might have been expected to have tried to organize some form of burial for him appears to have done so. Joseph, we are told, provided the grave linen and spices for the burial, and the tomb itself. Although a Jew would normally have been buried in his Sabbath-best clothes, Jesus had had all his clothes removed and shared out as part of the pickings by the execution squad, and Joseph is described as purchasing a length of linen in which to wrap the otherwise naked corpse.

Inevitably thoughts turn to the now notorious Turin Shroud, a length of linen in Turin Cathedral which bears seeming imprints of a naked, crucified body. Although the Shroud's history could be traced with certainty only back to the 1350s, the discovery in 1898 of its life-like photographic image when seen in negative revolutionized serious interest, so much so that evidence steadily mounted that it could be the very cloth purchased by Joseph of Arimathea – until 1988. In that year radiocarbon dating carried out by three separate laboratories showed the Shroud's fabric

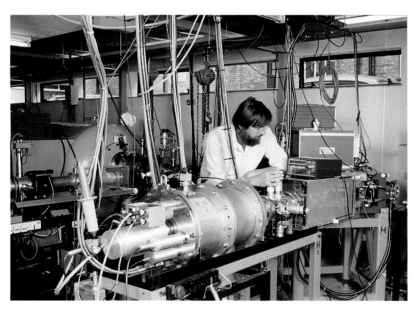

The radiocarbon dating laboratory at Oxford University, one of three which tested small samples of the Shroud's linen in 1988. According to the laboratories' instrumentation, the flax from which the Shroud was woven 'died' sometime between 1260 and 1390, thereby strongly suggesting it to be a mediaeval fake. However, no truly satisfactory explanation has yet been forthcoming for how such a convincingly photographic image could have been created so long before the age of photography. Despite widespread popular belief that the Shroud has been 'proved' a fake, carbon dating readings are not necessarily infallible, and some as yet undetermined anomaly to these remains an open possibility.

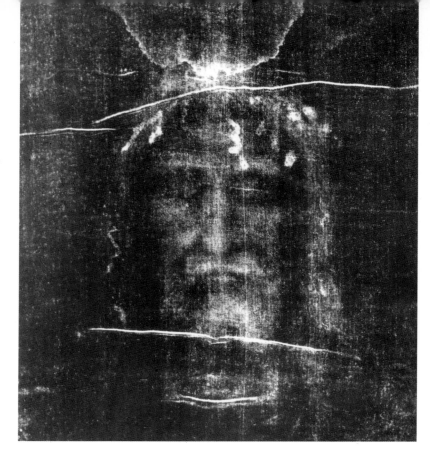

The famous negative of the facial image on the Turin Shroud, once widely reputed to be the cloth which wrapped Jesus in the tomb. Whenever the Shroud is photographed using black and white film, the ghostly imprint faintly visible on the cloth itself becomes transformed into this convincingly photographic likeness.

to have been made sometime between 1260 and 1390 AD, its mysterious image thereby being most likely the work of a mediaeval forger. Subsequently the Turin cloth has been the subject of a variety of absurd claims ranging from deliberate 'rigging' of the carbon dating to the proposition that it was a 'photograph' invented by none other than Leonardo da Vinci. Even so, its mystery remains very far from being resolved. Medically the Shroud's body image and apparent bloodstains are so convincing that dozens of well-respected specialists continue to contend that the cloth genuinely wrapped someone crucified in a manner identical to that recorded of Jesus. Historians can show that some form of cloth mysteriously imprinted with Jesus' likeness was recorded at least as far back as the sixth century – well over six centuries before the earliest date claimed by the carbon dating. And some highly talented professional artists have confessed themselves baffled how anyone, of any century, could have so convincingly 'forged' facial and body images of the Shroud's astonishing subtlety. Because of certain anomalies now emerging concerning radiocarbon dating's claimed margins of accuracy, the much-publicized scientific 'proof' of the Shroud's fraudulence may yet be in need of some serious revision.

But although the Shroud, if genuine, can provide the most powerful data on Jesus' 'way of the cross' – effectively taking on the rôle of a Fifth Gospel – it is by no means central to our understanding of Jesus. The same cannot be said, however, of the mystery surrounding what happened to his body within just a few hours of the time when he was first laid, to all appearances dead, in Joseph of Arimathea's brand new tomb.

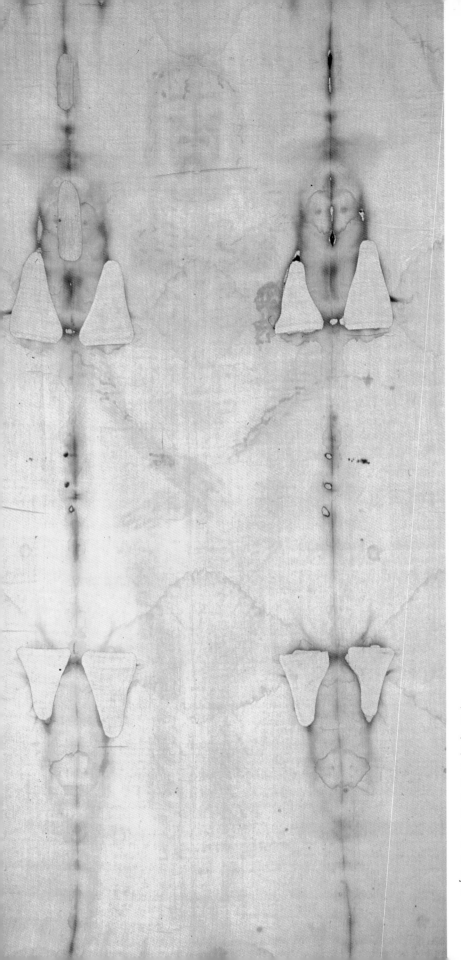

Image of the frontal half of the whole body image imprinted on the Shroud, seen as it appears to the naked eye. Nailing is notably indicated through the wrists, reminiscent of the crucifixion of Jehohanan. A flow of what seems to be blood from a wound in the chest readily corresponds with the action of the lance thrust into Jesus' side described in John 19: 34. The triangular shapes are patches from a fire which nearly destroyed the cloth in 1532.

10

DID JESUS REALLY RISE FROM THE DEAD?

According to the gospels, Joseph of Arimathea laid Jesus in his own new, rock-cut tomb 'in which no-one had yet been buried' (John 19: 41). This is described as having been in a garden, close to Golgotha (John 19: 41-2), and with a 'very big' stone rolled across the entrance-way (Matthew 27: 60; Mark 15: 46; 16: 3-4). More than sixty examples of such rolling-stone tombs can still be seen in and around Jerusalem. Their entrance boulders can weigh up to two tons, though if on level ground they can with a little effort be rolled aside by just one person. Although the John gospel's information that 'no-one had yet been buried' in the tomb might appear puzzling, in fact this is consistent with the evidence of Jewish rock-cut tombs from Jesus' time that have been excavated in recent years.

Thus, as was found, for instance, during the earlier-mentioned excavations at Giv'at ha-Mivtar, a single Jewish tomb might contain one or more benches or 'laying-out' places, together with as many as eight or more chambers cut into the rock (see overleaf) to accommodate ossuaries, the stone boxes in which the bones were gathered once the corpse had decomposed. Since each tomb-chamber might contain two or three ossuaries, and each ossuary several sets of bones, a single tomb could be used for thirty or

Opposite *Rolling-stone tomb in the environs of Jerusalem. This example is one of several tombs that feature a large 'rolling-stone' boulder which could be rolled across to seal their entrance-way. Such a boulder readily corresponds to the gospel account of the women visiting Jesus' tomb asking: 'Who will roll away the stone for us from the entrance to the tomb?' (Mark 16: 3). According to the Mark gospel, the stone used for Jesus' tomb was 'very big'. Surviving examples can sometimes weigh up to two tons, but if on level ground it is possible for them to be moved by just one person, albeit with effort.*

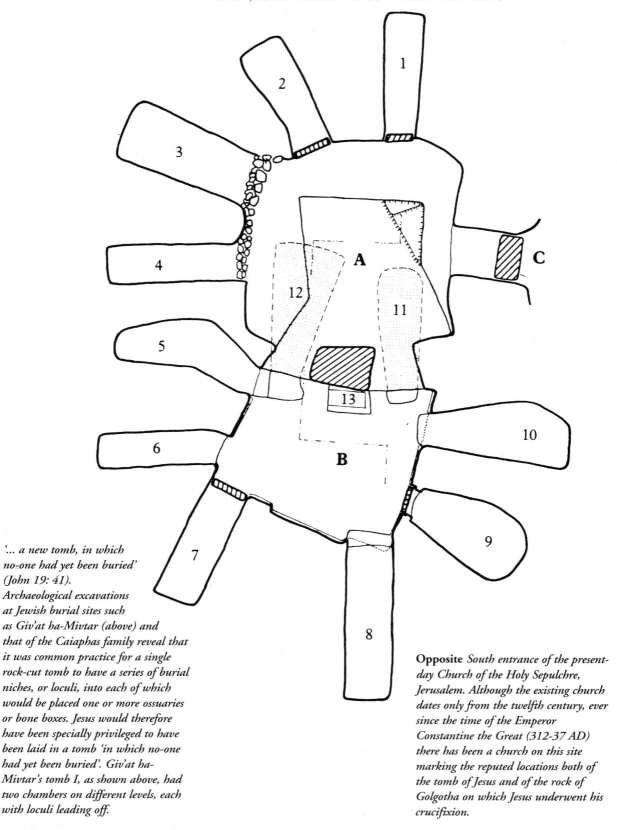

'... a new tomb, in which no-one had yet been buried' (John 19: 41). Archaeological excavations at Jewish burial sites such as Giv'at ha-Mivtar (above) and that of the Caiaphas family reveal that it was common practice for a single rock-cut tomb to have a series of burial niches, or loculi, into each of which would be placed one or more ossuaries or bone boxes. Jesus would therefore have been specially privileged to have been laid in a tomb 'in which no-one had yet been buried'. Giv'at ha-Mivtar's tomb I, as shown above, had two chambers on different levels, each with loculi leading off.

Opposite South entrance of the present-day Church of the Holy Sepulchre, Jerusalem. Although the existing church dates only from the twelfth century, ever since the time of the Emperor Constantine the Great (312-37 AD) there has been a church on this site marking the reputed locations both of the tomb of Jesus and of the rock of Golgotha on which Jesus underwent his crucifixion.

Plan of Jerusalem showing the relation of the present-day Church of the Holy Sepulchre to the nearby city walls. The so-called Third Wall was built by Herod Agrippa between 41 and 44 AD, shortly after Jesus' crucifixion. At the time of the crucifixion, however, the site was outside the city - or 'not far from the city' as Golgotha is described in John 19: 20. This therefore supports the authenticity of the Church of the Holy Sepulchre's location.

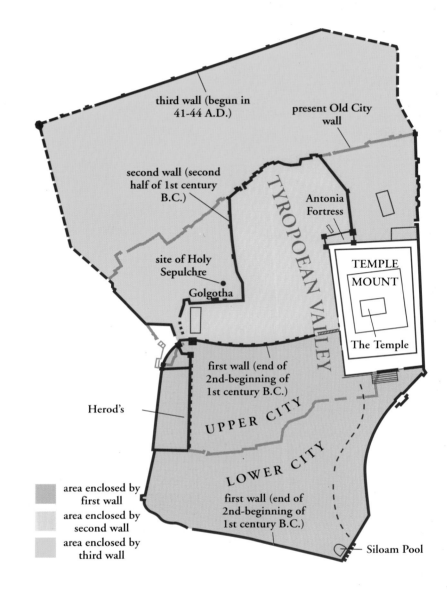

third wall (begun in 41-44 A.D.)

present Old City wall

second wall (second half of 1st century B.C.)

TYROPOEAN VALLEY

Antonia Fortress

site of Holy Sepulchre

Golgotha

TEMPLE MOUNT

The Temple

first wall (end of 2nd-beginning of 1st century B.C.)

Herod's

UPPER CITY

LOWER CITY

area enclosed by first wall

area enclosed by second wall

area enclosed by third wall

first wall (end of 2nd-beginning of 1st century B.C.)

Siloam Pool

Opposite *The nineteenth-century edicule within the Church of the Holy Sepulchre, enshrining what remains of the reputed tomb of Jesus. Constantine the Great's architects rather too enthusiastically cut away much of the hillside around the tomb in order to expose the interior chamber, thus even at that early time ruining the tomb's original appearance.*

more people over a period of decades. For a tomb to be one in which 'no-one had yet been buried' would therefore be at least worthy of comment. It also provides an element of authentic Jewish detail bearing in mind that, for the Romans and other Gentiles of Jesus's time, cremation was the norm.

But where was Jesus' tomb located in relation to present-day Jerusalem? Today the traditional site is marked by the mainly Crusader-built Church of the Holy Sepulchre, a bewildering rabbit-warren of an edifice, always under repair and teeming with tourists, with in its midst a rather ugly, many times rebuilt edicule, or 'little building', housing a carefully protected marble slab covering all that remains of the purported bench on which Jesus was laid out in death. This location has been identified as Jesus' burial place at least since the time when Helena, mother of the first Christian

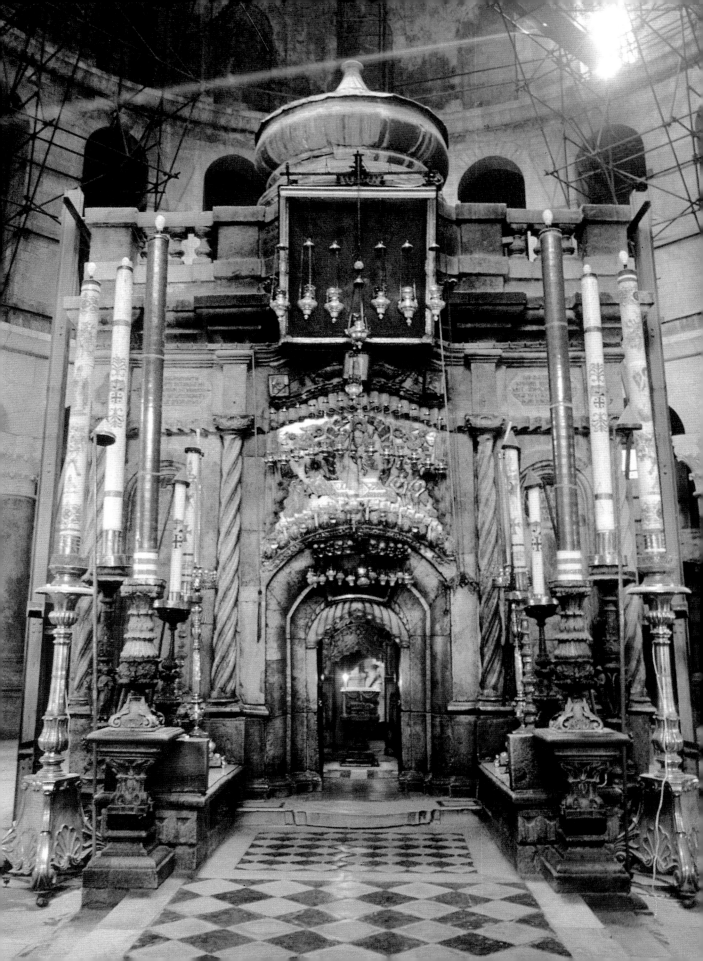

Roman Emperor Constantine the Great, reputedly 'discovered' it back in the fourth century AD. As recounted by the near-contemporary church historian Socrates Scholasticus:

> Helena went to Jerusalem, to find what had been that city as desolate as 'a lodge in a garden of cucumbers' ... after the Passion Christians paid great devotion to Christ's tomb, but those who hated Christianity covered the spot with a mound of earth, built a temple of Aphrodite on it, and set up her statue there, so that the place would not be forgotten. The device was successful for a long time – until, in fact, it became known to the Emperor's [i.e. Constantine the Great's] mother. She had the statue thrown down, the earth removed and the site cleared, and found three crosses in the tomb ... With them was also found the *titulum* on which Pilate had written in various languages that the Christ crucified was the king of the Jews ...

From one of those three crosses found by Helena came most of the pieces of the 'True Cross' venerated in numerous churches and cathedrals throughout the world. What purports to be the *titulus* can also still be seen in Rome's Basilica of Santa Croce in Gerusalemme, a puzzling piece of work with an inscription just decipherable as 'Jesus the Nazarene, King of the Jews', written in Aramaic, Greek and Latin (see John 19: 19). The authenticity of this has to be considered doubtful, likewise probably the pieces of the cross, though no-one can be sure.

But in view of the early attested marking of the spot with the Temple of Aphrodite (known to have been built by the Emperor Hadrian), there is a more than reasonable case for accepting the Church of the Holy Sepulchre as genuinely enshrining the one-time tomb in which Jesus' body was laid. Although according to the gospels Jesus' tomb was located outside Jerusalem's walls, by Helena's time these walls had been rebuilt, the reputed tomb being found inside them. There must, therefore, have been something very compelling about the location for Helena to have ignored the gospels' clear descriptions. As archaeologist Dr Kathleen Kenyon discovered in the 1960s, the Church of the Holy Sepulchre site *was* outside the city walls of Jesus' time, and would seem to have been within a quarry then being used for burials.

Frustratingly, however, Constantine the Great's engineers cut away the rock into which the tomb had been set, leaving it first free standing, and then before the end of the fourth century surrounded by a rotunda within a grandiose church. This church and the tomb alike subsequently became subjected to sometimes exhaustive Moslem attacks so that today almost every vestige of how it looked if and when Jesus was laid in it has been lost. This has prompted many Christian pilgrims to turn instead to the altogether more authentic-looking 'Garden Tomb', which General Gordon of Khartoum, on visiting Jerusalem in 1883, suggested might have been the true one used for Jesus. Located just a short walk north of Old City Jerusalem's Damascus Gate, this is today beautifully maintained as an inter-denominational place of prayer, though as even its guides admit there is very little evidence in favour of it having been the original.

But the real question is: what happened to Jesus' body as laid in the true tomb, wherever this was, and whatever it looked like? According to every available early source, Jesus died on the cross at the hands of the world's most efficient executioners, the Romans. Before his body was taken down from the cross the Roman governor Pontius Pilate reportedly sent a senior officer to ensure that he was genuinely dead (Mark 15: 45). The author of the John gospel observed that in order to leave nothing to chance a lance was plunged into his chest, whereupon blood and a watery fluid oozed out (John 19: 34). According to the Matthew gospel's author, a guard was even mounted and official seals affixed to the entrance stone in order to prevent any possibility of trickery (Matthew 27: 66).

Because the Matthew gospel alone tells the story of the guard, also of a 'violent earthquake' and of the 'angel of the Lord' rolling away the entrance stone, it is probably safest to regard these as pious embroideries by an author demonstrably over-fond of the miraculous. It is equally impossible to know quite what to make of the differing accounts of the young man or men encountered at the tomb (Mark 16: 5; Luke 24: 4; see the parallel passages featured earlier on p.27), except that the bench on which Jesus' body would have been laid, as still to be seen in surviving rolling-stone tombs, certainly would have provided sufficient space for individuals to be seated at both head and foot. But altogether more important is the agree-ment of all sources that just two days after Jesus had been laid in the tomb not only had his body mysteriously disappeared but people who had known him well began to have strange experiences of seeing him among them. Sometimes, distrusting their own senses, they reported seeing him pass through locked doors, yet he was able to talk and eat with them (Luke 24: 43). Reportedly he even felt like a living person to the touch (John 20: 27, 28). The convincingness of these encounters to those on the receiving end is powerfully conveyed by the speech attributed to Peter in the tenth chapter of Acts:

Now I and those with me can witness to everything he did throughout the countryside of Judaea and in Jerusalem itself: and also to the fact that they killed him by hanging him on a tree, yet three days afterwards God raised him to life and allowed him to be seen, not by the whole people, but only by certain witnesses God had chosen beforehand. Now we are those witnesses – we have eaten and drunk with him after his resurrection from the dead … (Acts 10: 39-42)

As even 'Jesus-did-not-exist' exponent Professor G. A. Wells has acknow-ledged, this powerful belief caught on very soon after the events described,

Exterior (left) and interior views of the so-called 'Garden Tomb', which General Gordon of Khartoum suggested could have been the true tomb of Christ. Spared much of the historical destructions and accretions that have ruined what remains of the tomb within the Church of the Holy Sepulchre, the 'Garden Tomb' often appeals to Christian visitors to Jerusalem because it conforms to how they imagine Jesus' true tomb once looked. However, as even the 'Garden Tomb's custodians acknowledge, there is no serious evidence that it was the true location.

at least one attestor to the resurrection, the apostle Paul, being readily date-able. In Acts 18: 12 Paul is said to have appeared before the Achaean pro-consul Gallio while on his second mission, and since an inscription found at Delphi enables Gallio's administration to be accurately dated to 51-2 AD, simple back calculation establishes that Paul must have believed in Jesus' resurrection c. 40 AD, and according to some authorities, perhaps even as early as 36 AD. So what had happened to account for the fact that Paul and others held this belief? In this ostensibly simple question lies the central mystery of the Christian religion, and one for which there remains no uncontested rational answer.

The various accounts of the scene at the empty tomb on the first Easter morning are so full of inconsistencies that it is easy for sceptics to deride them. The writer of the John gospel describes Mary Magdalen arriving at the tomb alone, discovering the tomb to be empty and imparting the news to Peter and an unnamed 'other disciple, the one Jesus loved' (John 20: 2), generally identified as John. The Matthew author relates that Mary Magdalen was accompanied by 'Mary the mother of James and Joseph'. Mark adds a further companion, a woman called Salome, referred to in the Thomas gospel. Luke, who knows nothing of any Salome, speaks only of one 'Joanna' (presumably royal treasurer Chuza's wife – see p.87), together with other women who go off to tell the disciples what they have seen, though according to Mark, the women, 'frightened out of their wits ... said nothing to a soul, for they were afraid' (Mark 16: 8).

Similar discrepancies occur in the reports of what was seen at the empty tomb. John's Mary Magdalen saw first two angels sitting in the tomb and then Jesus, whom she was not allowed to touch. Matthew's two Marys saw one seated angel, and then Jesus. Mark's three women saw a young man in a white robe, and Mary Magdalen alone saw Jesus. Luke's group of women saw two men in brilliant clothes who suddenly appeared at their side, but not Jesus himself, who was seen only by two disciples on the road to Emmaus. All four gospels describe Jesus subsequently appearing to the full group of disciples, but while Matthew and Mark set these appearances in Galilee, the Luke and John gospels suggest that the setting was Jerusalem. Luke also indirectly mentions an earlier appearance of Jesus to Simon Peter, one which seems to have gone unnoticed elsewhere in the gospels. But it is one of Paul's letters which gives the fullest information of all:

> ... he [Jesus] appeared first to Cephas [Peter] and secondly to the Twelve. Next he appeared to more than five hundred of the brothers at the same time, most of whom are still alive, though some have died; then he appeared to James and then to all the apostles; and last of all he appeared to me too ... (1 Corinthians 15: 5-8)

The documentation is an almost hopeless jumble of confusion, scarcely helped by the fact that the ever enigmatic Mary Magdalen, the only witness mentioned in every account except Paul's – for whom women didn't count – was obviously so unbalanced that she had needed to be cured by Jesus of 'seven devils'. The lack of a proper ending to the Mark gospel, as revealed by the *Sinaiticus* and *Vaticanus* manuscripts, merely adds to the problem. Yet had someone wholly invented the resurrection story one might have expected them to do so more convincingly than, for instance, representing women as the prime witnesses, when women's testimony carried a particularly low weight in Jewish Law. And in their own way the garblings and inconsistencies have the same quality as the memories of witnesses after a road accident, which are, after all, personal and often highly confused versions of the same true story.

Any number of theories have been advanced in an attempt to explain what really happened, but all may be reduced to permutations of six basic hypotheses:

1. The women went to the wrong tomb.
2. Unknown to the disciples, some independent person removed the body.
3. The disciples themselves removed the body and invented the whole story.
4. The disciples saw not the real Jesus, but hallucinations.
5. Jesus did not actually die on the cross, but was resuscitated, or in some other way survived.
6. Jesus really did rise from the grave.

Although it is impossible within a single chapter to do justice to these different hypotheses, quite clear is that the disciples and gospel writers anticipated that the first four theories would be proposed to explain the mystery. All the synoptic writers emphasize, for instance, how the women had carefully taken note of where Jesus was laid (Matthew 27: 61; Mark 15: 47; Luke 23: 55). The John gospel puts into the mind of Mary Magdalen the idea that the man she mistook for a gardener (in reality Jesus, as yet unrecognized) had for some reason taken the body away (John 20: 15). The writer of Matthew acknowledged that in his time there was a story in circulation that the disciples had stolen the body. He accused 'the Jews' of having bribed the guards posted at Jesus' tomb to say this. With regard to the possibility of hallucination, both the Luke and the John gospels emphasize the disciples' own incredulity at the solidity of what they were seeing, the Luke author, for instance, wonderingly reporting '…they offered him a piece of fish which he took and ate before their eyes' (Luke 24: 43). The John author noted the disciple Thomas' insistence that he was not prepared to believe unless he was able to put his fingers into the wound in Jesus' side, and recorded that Thomas was specifically allowed to do this.

In fact, quite aside from the gospel writers' evident anticipation of them, the first four hypotheses bear little serious scrutiny. Had there simply been a mistake over the location of the tomb, it would have been an easy

Jesus' resurrection appearance to Mary Magdalen, from a panel painting in the London National Gallery by the Italian Gothic artist Orcagna. Although according to the gospels Mary was one of the prime witnesses of Jesus rising from the dead, for Jews her testimony as a woman would have carried very low weight. However Mary was but one of more than five hundred who claimed to have experienced the resurrected Jesus, many of whom were prepared to die attesting the validity of this.

matter for any sceptic to go to the right location, show the body still there and set the whole matter at rest. Had Jesus' body been taken away either by a person unknown or by the disciples, we might surely have expected someone, sometime, to produce it. Such a hypothesis also fails to account for the repeated attestations of Jesus being seen alive and well. With regard to the possibility of hallucinations, it might of course be possible to envisage some bizarre mass post-hypnotic suggestion that made Jesus seem to appear to those so hypnotized, to seem to eat with them, and even to feel solid to their touch. But this still totally fails to account for the reportedly very real emptiness of Jesus' tomb.

Perhaps because the gospel writers do not take account of it, the fifth hypothesis, that Jesus did not die on the cross, has been particularly favoured by sceptics and sensationalists in recent years. In his *The Passover Plot* the late Hugh J. Schonfield advanced the ingenious theory that the sponge offered to Jesus on the cross (John 19: 29, 30) was soaked not in vinegar but in a drug to induce the appearance of death. This was so that he could be taken to the tomb by Joseph of Arimathea and there resuscitated, the lance thrust into Jesus' side being the unexpected eventuality that caused the plot to misfire. According to Schonfield, the man seen by Mary Magdalen was simply someone who had been deputed to help revive Jesus, and the 'resurrection' was therefore nothing more than a case of mistaken identity, Jesus' body having been quietly buried elsewhere.

Both before and after Schonfield all sorts of variants to this theory have been offered. In D.H. Lawrence's short story 'The Man who Died', Jesus was taken down too early from the cross, revived in the tomb, petrified his followers, who assumed he was dead, 'resurrected', and then slipped away to Egypt to enjoy conjugal relations with a priestess of Isis. The supposedly factual *The Holy Blood and the Holy Grail* by Baigent, Leigh and Lincoln represents Jesus' paramour as Mary Magdalen and their place of refuge as the south of France, but it follows essentially the same plot, with Jesus even going on to father a family. Within the last few years Dr Barbara Thiering of the University of Sydney has resurrected the same idea in her *Jesus: The Man*, as have the German writers Holger Kersten and Elmar Gruber with their *The Jesus Conspiracy*. Thiering has based her arguments on the idea that the gospels were all written in a code, so that virtually everything in them has to be re-interpreted in the light of that code. Kersten and Gruber have contended that the Vatican conspired with radiocarbon dating scientists to ensure that the Turin Shroud was dated to the Middle Ages so that its purported 'big secret', that it 'proves' that Jesus was still alive when laid inside it, should not be allowed to destroy the Christian faith. Despite the ingeniousness of such arguments, they merit scant serious scrutiny.

The problem for all hypotheses of this kind, certainly those postulating some form of resuscitation, was outlined more than a hundred years ago by the controversial Tübingen lecturer David Strauss, one of those nineteenth-century German theologians who in so many ways cast doubts on the gospel story. As Strauss wrote in his *New Life of Jesus,* published in 1865:

> It is impossible that a being who had stolen half dead out of the sepulchre, who crept about weak and ill, wanting medical treatment, who required bandaging, strengthening and indulgence ... could have given the disciples the impression that he was a Conqueror over death and the grave, the Prince of Life, an impression which lay at the bottom of their future ministry. Such a resuscitation ... could by no possibility have changed their sorrow into enthusiasm, have elevated their reverence into worship!

In support of this, and in full favour of the hypothesis that Jesus genuinely rose from the grave, is the sheer confidence about this that became exhibited by the previously denying and demoralized disciple Simon Peter. This is evident from his first post-crucifixion public speech to the inhabitants of Jerusalem and their fellow-Judaeans reported in the book of Acts:

> Men of Israel ... Jesus the Nazarene was a man commended to you by God ... This man ... you took and had crucified by men outside the Law. You killed him, but God raised him to life ... and all of us are witnesses to that. (Acts 2: 22-4, 32)

Peter went on to speak with similar passion on subsequently addressing non-Jews in Caesarea:

> Now I, and those with me, can witness to everything he [Jesus] did throughout the countryside of Judaea and in Jerusalem itself; and also to the fact that they killed him by hanging him on a tree, yet three days afterwards God raised him to life and allowed him to be seen, not by the whole people, but by certain witnesses God had chosen beforehand. Now we are those witnesses – we have eaten and drunk with him after his resurrection from the dead ... (Acts 10: 39-42)

Likewise meriting considerable weight as evidence is St Paul's clear and unequivocal statement in his letter to the Corinthians that the resurrected Jesus had been seen not only by himself, by Simon Peter, by the other disciples and by James but also by more than five hundred people at one time, most of whom he claimed to be still alive when he was setting his pen to papyrus. As pointed out by Dr Edwin M. Yamauchi, Associate Professor of History at Oxford, Ohio:

> What gives a special authority to ... [Paul's] list as historical evidence is the reference to most of the five hundred brethren being still alive. St Paul says in effect, 'If you do not believe me, you can ask them.'

Such a statement in an admitted genuine letter written within thirty years of the event is almost as strong evidence as one could hope to get for something that happened nearly two thousand years ago.

Overall then, while there are undeniable reporting flaws regarding Jesus' claimed resurrection, and at a time distance of nearly two thousand years knowledge of exactly what happened is beyond us, the evidence that something like it actually happened is rather better than sceptics care to admit. And quite incontrovertibly, belief in it spread like wildfire very soon after the crucifixion.

Thus the book of Acts mentions as one of the first new believers a Hellenistic Jew called Stephen. Although their ancestry and religion was Jewish, Hellenistic Jews lived in the fashionable Graeco-Roman style, and spoke the Greek language. From Josephus' information that Jesus' teaching 'attracted many Jews and many of the Greeks', Stephen's adherence need not be considered out of the ordinary. But whatever his background, he chose, just like Jesus had, to attack the material vanity of the Jerusalem Temple, harking back to the Isaiah text:

> With heaven my throne
> and earth my footstool,
> what house could you build me,
> what place could you make for my rest?
> Was not all this made by my hand?

(Isaiah 66: 1, 2)

Stephen then went on fearlessly to accuse the Jerusalem Temple authorities of having, in executing Jesus, murdered the great prophet foretold by Moses. That same Jesus, he impassionedly declared, he could see there and then 'standing at God's right hand'. Without in this instance even pausing to refer their prisoner to the Roman governor, those whom Stephen had attacked peremptorily stoned him to death.

Stephen was but the first of many who would take up this same cause – including, as we shall see, previously reticent members of Jesus' own family. They would firmly profess Jesus as the Messiah or Christ predicted in the Jewish scriptures, and emphatically attest that he had come back to life again after having suffered the most public of deaths. What cannot be emphasized enough is that those who made such claims had absolutely no expectation of any material gain for their outspokenness. Their reward instead, as the following decades and centuries would demonstrate, was all too frequently to be faced with some form of violent death, from being stoned, to being torn to pieces by wild animals in a Roman arena, to being crucified in some yet more grotesque and painful manner.

The really unnerving feature is that time after time they accepted such terrors with an astonishing cheerfulness, totally confident that what they professed was truth, that death had been conquered, and that their eventual reward far outweighed whatever tortures ordinary mortals might try to inflict upon them in the meantime. And few of the men and women who took up this challenge would have counted themselves natural martyrs, or anything out of the ordinary. Although some were high-born, most were from every stratum of society, whether Jewish or Graeco-Roman.

We can only conclude, therefore, that whether these were among the first five hundred-plus direct witnesses, or whether they had merely come to know one or more of those witnesses at first or second hand, something very powerful had fired into them such resoluteness of belief. So, given such attestation, can the resurrection of Jesus be accepted as a real historical event? And was the one-time flesh-and-blood Jesus genuinely rather more than just an ordinary man? Whatever the answer, already born was a faith in such matters powerful enough to survive not only the early years of persecution, but even through to our own time.

11
A FAITH
IS BORN

A kindly Jewish rabbi from Cardiff once explained to me why most Jews have never accepted Jesus as their promised Messiah. He told me that according to the Hebrew prophets the true Messiah would bring in a kingdom of peace (e.g. Isaiah 11: 6-8). My response was to counter that the resurrected Jesus' first words to his disciples were 'Peace be with you' (Luke 24: 37; John 20: 19), also that Christians throughout nearly twenty centuries have believed Jesus' kingdom of peace to be in their hearts. But on a historical level, at least, the rabbi has to be accounted right.

For it is quite clear from the New Testament that from the very outset Jesus' followers were not even at peace with each other, let alone with the rest of the world, one serious cause of their dissension emanating from the self-styled apostle Paul, originally named Saul. As related in the book of Acts, Saul, a Hellenistic, or Greek-speaking, Jewish tentmaker from the Greek city of Tarsus in Asia Minor, had been approvingly present when the first martyr Stephen was stoned to death, and had subsequently made it his mission to hunt down other followers of Jesus on behalf of the Sadducean authorities.

Then, as described in one of the New Testament's best-known episodes,

Opposite *Head of an apostle often identified as Jesus' disciple Simon Peter, from a fresco of the mid-third century in the hypogeum of the Aurelii, Rome.*

at the height of Saul's persecuting he was dramatically stopped in his tracks on the Damascus road, and blinded for three days. As he subsequently related, he experienced the resurrected Jesus, he had his sight restored by a follower of Jesus called Ananias and was thereupon baptized as a Christian, taking the new 'Christian' name Paul.

Now while any other recruit to this new religion of Jesus might have been expected to take time to go and meet some of the original disciples, and to learn some background details of Jesus' life and teachings, Paul seems by nature to have been far too impatient for this. Even the strongly pro-Pauline Acts remarks that it was 'only a few days' before he began actively evangelizing for Jesus, and he himself described the process as even more swift:

> I did not stop to discuss this with any human being, nor did I go up to Jerusalem to see those who were already apostles before me, but I went off to Arabia at once, and later went straight back from there to Damascus. Even when after three years I went to Jerusalem to visit Cephas [Peter] and stayed with him for fifteen days, I did not see any of the other apostles. (Galatians 1: 16-19)

Paul therefore seems to have had little interest in Jesus' crucifixion as an actual and recent event, associated with flesh-and-blood individuals such as Pontius Pilate and the self-centred Jewish high priests – hence his failure even to mention these in his writings, as noted in an earlier chapter. Instead the experience of the resurrected Jesus was all that he felt he needed: '… the Good News I preached is not a human message that I was given by men, it is something I learned only through a revelation of Jesus Christ.'

Thus Paul saw Jesus' death on an other-worldly level of faith, a divine plan thought out 'before the aeons', whereby the 'powers that rule the world' crucified in ignorance a supernatural 'Lord of glory' (1 Corinthians 2: 8). And instead of referring to Jesus as 'the Christ', which would have been the correct translation of 'the Messiah' into Greek, he adopted the fashion of calling Jesus 'Christ' as if this were his proper name, ignoring its political connotations, likewise referring to him as the Son of God (Acts 9: 20). Furthermore, on the strength of his profound conversion experience, and being himself merely a Hellenistic Jew, he apparently decided that it should be perfectly permissible for Gentile converts to Jesus' teaching to discard the traditional requirements of the Jewish Law such as circumcision and prohibition of the eating of 'unclean' meats, requirements that Jews had laid down their lives to defend during the Maccabean revolt.

At this point we begin to find that Paul was by no means necessarily as universally revered a figure among members of the earliest Church as is often popularly supposed. When this idea was first put forward by the great Tübingen theologian Ferdinand Christian Baur back in the nineteenth cen-tury, it seemed daring at the time, yet it becomes obvious enough to anyone who reads Paul's letters not as religious documents but for their historical content that it must be true. Thus in Paul's letter to those whom he had converted in Galatia not long before, he mentioned certain others who had been there after him with 'a different version of the Good News' (Galatians 1: 6). In his first letter to the Corinthians, generally regarded as written about 57 AD, he noted regretfully:

> … there are serious differences among you. What I mean are all these slogans that you have, like 'I am for Paul', 'I am for Cephas [Peter]', 'I am for Christ'. (1 Corinthians 1: 11-12)

Although Paul studiously omitted to mention who his mysterious opponents are, he happened to let slip, in a typically exasperated remark in his second letter to the Corinthians,

> As far as I can tell, these arch-apostles have nothing more than I have. (2 Corinthians 2: 5)

Arch-apostles? From the well organized nature of these opponents, their close marking of Paul's activities and his obvious embarrassed reluctance to name them, modern scholars are in general agreement that these were Jesus' original fully Jewish followers who during Paul's lifetime remained based in Jerusalem. It is all too rarely appreciated just how little the surviving documentation tells us of the activities of these pioneering followers of Jesus – historically, a really serious loss – but Acts does give us the occasional important though tantalizing glimpse:

> The many miracles and signs worked through the apostles made a deep impression on everyone. The faithful all lived together and owned everything in common; they sold their goods and possessions and shared out the proceeds among themselves according to what each one needed. They went as a body to the Temple every day but met in their houses for the breaking of bread; they shared their food gladly and generously; they praised God and were looked up to by everyone. (Acts 2: 43-7)

In this brief description we get a picture of a group carrying out Jesus' teachings to the letter, and continuing to worship in the tradition of the old Jewish religion, just as Jesus himself had done. But, strangely, what we are not told is anything about this group's leadership. Acts makes it clear that there was a major controversy over whether uncircumcised Gentiles should receive baptism, with Jesus' disciple Simon Peter being sympathetic to a Roman centurion's eagerness to follow Jesus, and having a dream in which he apparently received divine sanction for the eating of 'unclean' foods. From Acts we also learn that Peter expounded this revelation at a council meeting in Jerusalem, that Paul became apostle to the uncircumcised, and that an individual called James (quoted as using the words 'I rule...') apparently agreed to less strictly orthodox rules being applied to pagan converts.

But there is an uncomfortable suggestion here that all is not being told quite straight, an impression which gains greater cogency from Paul's letter to the Galatians, in which Peter is described as initially eating with, and therefore expressing sympathy towards, uncircumcised Gentiles, but then receiving a visit from 'certain friends of James' who urged him to abandon his pro-Gentile stance. This Peter dutifully agreed to apparently for 'fear of the group that insisted on circumcision' (Galatians 2: 12), whereupon a clearly angry Paul tells us: 'When Cephas [Peter] came to Antioch... I opposed him to his face, since he was manifestly in the wrong' (Galatians 2: 11).

Here considerable interest surrounds the identity of this mysterious James, who apparently had the authority to rule on matters of doctrine and adherence to traditional Jewish ways, even to the extent of overruling Peter. Why should the book of Acts be so reticent about him? Despite the popular supposition that Peter was first head of the Church, from a variety of sources it is apparent that this James was its first true leader. This is explicit in the Nag Hammadi 'Gospel of Thomas', which in Logion 12 represents Jesus naming 'James the Righteous' [an appellation to distinguish him from the disciple of the same name] as the disciples' leader after his own departure. It is equally explicit in the writings of the second-century Jewish author Hegesippus and the fourth-century Eusebius of Caesarea. The latter, who quoted from Hegesippus, unequivocally described James the Righteous as 'first to be elected to the episcopal throne of the Jerusalem Church'.

What is quite astonishing to discover, however, is that this James was none other than Jesus' brother. This is attested by Josephus who, describing with genuine sadness James' unjust execution at the hands of a Sadducean high priest in 62 AD, explicitly referred to him as 'the brother of Jesus called the Christ'. That this was no slip of Josephus' pen is firmly corroborated by Paul who remarked of a trip he had made to Jerusalem, 'I only saw James, the brother of the Lord' (Galatians 1: 20). It is also corroborated in the writings of Hegesippus and Eusebius. And in fact the same information checks out with the Mark gospel (which of course has no account of Jesus' 'virgin' birth) in a passage in which the people of Nazareth say of Jesus:

> This is the carpenter, surely, the son of Mary, the brother of James and Joset and Jude and Simon? His sisters too, are they not with us? (Mark 6: 3)

Although there are often attempts to explain away this passage on the grounds that 'brothers' can mean 'cousins' among Near Eastern peoples, the Josephus and other references provide every justification for believing that the use of the words 'brothers' and 'sisters' was intended to mean just that in this particular context.

So why was there such reluctance to acknowledge someone as important and interesting as Jesus' brother? Another sign of this reluctance is that although Paul, as earlier quoted from his letter to the Corinthians (1,15: 8), reported that Jesus had made a resurrection appearance to James, not one of the gospels has any report of this, the only other indication of it occurring in a tantalizingly cryptic extract from the lost 'Gospel of the Hebrews' that happened to be quoted in a later century by St Jerome:

> But the Lord, when he had given the shroud to the high priest's servant, went to James and appeared to him. For James had sworn that he would not eat bread from that hour when he had drunk the Lord's cup until he saw him rising from those who sleep... 'Bring', says the Lord, 'a table and bread'. He took bread and blessed it and broke it and gave it to James the Righteous, and said to him, 'My brother, eat your bread, for the Son of Man has risen from those who sleep'.

Family tree of Jesus, based on the assumption that the 'brothers and sisters' listed in Mark 6: 3, and mentioned elsewhere (John 7: 2; Acts 1: 14; 1 Corinthians 9: 5), were Jesus' immediate family. This is certainly how they were regarded by early authorities such as Tertullian and Hegesippus. Note how headship of the Jerusalem followers of Jesus passed to members of Jesus' family, his brother, James, then his cousin Simeon. A similar family tradition is to be noted among leadership of the Zealots.

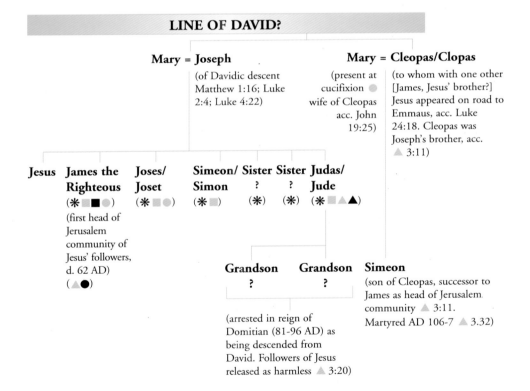

LINE OF DAVID?

Mary = Joseph
(of Davidic descent
Matthew 1:16; Luke
2:4; Luke 4:22)

Mary = Cleopas/Clopas
(present at
cucifixion ●
wife of Cleopas
acc. John
19:25)

(to whom with one other
[James, Jesus' brother?]
Jesus appeared on road to
Emmaus, acc. Luke
24:18. Cleopas was
Joseph's brother, acc.
▲ 3:11)

Jesus

James the Righteous
(✳■■●)
(first head of
Jerusalem
community of
Jesus' followers,
d. 62 AD)
(▲●)

Joses/ Joset
(✳■●)

Simeon/ Simon
(✳■)

Sister
?
(✳)

Sister
?
(✳)

Judas/ Jude
(✳■▲▲)

Grandson
?

Grandson
?

(arrested in reign of
Domitian (81-96 AD) as
being descended from
David. Followers of Jesus
released as harmless ▲ 3:20)

Simeon
(son of Cleopas, successor to
James as head of Jerusalem
community ▲ 3:11.
Martyred AD 106-7 ▲ 3.32)

KEY

✳ Mark 6:3   ■ Matthew 13.55   ■ Galatians 1:19   ● Mark 15:40
● Josephus *Antiquities* 20:9.1 (200-3)   ▲ Hegesippus, as preserved in Eusebius'
History of the Church (references are to the Eusebius text)
▲ Jude 1

Whatever we may make of the 'Gospel of the Hebrews' passage, we seem to be faced with a straight, first-century clash of theologies, Paul's on the one hand, based on his other-wordly experience, and James' on the other, based on his fraternal knowledge of the human Jesus. And, despite the authority which should be due to the latter, it would seem to be Paul's that is all that has been allowed to come down to us. Or, in fairness, almost all.

For one of the most neglected of all New Testament documents is a letter traditionally attributed to this very James, brother of Jesus, and which would indeed appear to have been by him. Although this was dismissed by Martin Luther as 'a right strawy epistle', and tossed aside by the nineteenth-century German theologians as a work of the late second century, Dr John Robinson in his *Redating the New Testament* argued very cogently for James' authorship, and the most serious objection, that the Greek is too good for a Galilean Jew, has recently been almost totally undermined by the latest findings on the quality and quantity of Greek spoken in Jesus' Galilee (see p.63). As noted by the editors of today's Jerusalem Bible, the James letter, despite its good Greek, is full of hebraisms, it exhibits a close similarity to Jesus' Sermon on the Mount teachings and reveals its early composition by portraying Jesus' followers still worshipping within the Jewish religion. But particularly significant is its gentle but firm stance on the importance of Jesus' teaching on communal living, as distinct from Paul's stress on a Christ of faith. In James' words:

> Take the case, my brothers, of someone who has never done a single good act, but claims he has faith. Will that faith save him? If one of the brothers or one of the sisters is in need of clothes and has not enough food to live on, and one of you says to them: 'I wish you well; keep yourself warm and eat plenty' without giving them these bare necessities of life, then what good is that? Faith is like that: if good works do not go with it, it is quite dead. (James 2: 14-17)

That James was intensely devout (as indeed suggested by the 'Gospel of the Hebrews' reference), and actually led a very much more outwardly pious lifestyle than that of his self-confessedly gluttonous and wine-bibbing brother, is quite evident from the lost writings of the second-century historian Hegesippus, as preserved by the fourth-century church historian Eusebius.

> He [James] drank no wine or intoxicating liquor and ate no animal food; no razor came near to his head; he did not smear himself with oil, and took no baths. He alone was permitted to enter the Holy Place [of the Jerusalem Temple] for his garments were not of wool, but of linen. He used to enter the Sanctuary alone, and was often found on his knees beseeching forgiveness for the people, so that his knees grew hard like a camel's from his continually bending them in worship of God.

Yet equally clear is that whatever reservations he may earlier have had about his brother (he was presumably one of the family members who had set out to take charge of Jesus, 'convinced he was out of his mind'; Mark 3: 21), James now firmly recognized Jesus as the great Messiah recorded by the prophets, who had died to save men's sins, and who had risen from the dead. Hegesippus continued:

> Representatives of the seven popular [Jewish religious] sects ... asked him [James] what was meant by 'the door of Jesus' and he replied that Jesus was the Saviour. Some of them came to believe that Jesus was the Christ ... those who did come to believe did so because of James. Since therefore many even of the ruling class believed, there was an uproar among the Jews and Scribes and Pharisees, who said there was a danger that the entire people would expect Jesus as the Christ.

Hegesippus went on to describe James making himself yet more explicit by proclaiming from the Temple parapet, possibly from the same spot on which trumpeters signalled the start and end of the Sabbath, that Jesus as the Son of Man was now 'sitting at the right hand of the Great Power' and would come again 'on the clouds of heaven'. That bold affirmation, which had already proved so fatal in the case of Stephen, again proved far too much for the Temple's controlling Sadducean priesthood who, like Caiaphas and his cronies before them, decided that James now had to be forever silenced. As described by Josephus, when Festus, a successor to Pontius Pilate, died in 62 AD, this left a short vacuum while Festus' appointed replacement, Albinus, journeyed from Rome, providing the then high priest, Ananus, with the opportunity he needed to arrange for James' death with the least likelihood of opposition. In Josephus' words:

> The younger Ananus ... was headstrong in character and audacious in the extreme. He belonged to the sect of the Sadducees, who in judging offenders are cruel beyond any of the Jews, as I have already made clear. Being a man of this kind Ananus thought he had a convenient opportunity as Festus was dead and Albinus still on the way. So he assembled a council of judges and brought before it James, the brother of Jesus, known as Christ, and several others, on a charge of breaking the Law, and handed them over to be stoned.

Before 'the most fair-minded people in the City' had time to intervene, Ananus' lackeys hurled James from the Temple parapet, stoned him on seeing that he was still alive, then finally beat him over the head with a fuller's club. James, for his part, apparently asked for divine forgiveness for them to his dying breath, just as his brother had done before him.

It is clear then that even as early as the three decades immediately following Jesus' crucifixion there were serious divisions between different

Head of an apostle often identified as Jesus' disciple Simon Peter. Peter is believed to have been crucified in Rome during Nero's reign of terror, and a skeleton that some have argued to be Peter's was found during excavations beneath the high altar of St Peter's, Rome. These same excavations revealed a very early shrine seemingly built to Peter's memory.

Most famous of Roman arenas, the Colosseum, Rome, inaugurated by Titus in 80 AD. Many early Christians are believed to have met their deaths here as entertainment for the Roman populace, though direct evidence of this is scanty.

groups of Jesus' followers, both Jews and Gentiles, as well as serious trouble from traditional Jewish groups who opposed them. Inspired by appealing side-aspects of Jesus' teaching, there was also in embryo stages a bewildering variety of fringe groups, loosely collectively termed Gnostics. Some of these would not properly emerge for a century or so, but among them were Docetists (pronounced Do-see-tists), who conceived of Jesus as being such a heavenly being that he must have merely appeared to be human; Montanists, who practised glossolalia or 'speaking with tongues'; Marcionites, who appointed women as priests and bishops; and Carpocratians who, according to their enemies at least, contended that every mortal sin needed to be experienced in order for the soul to reach heaven.

But alike for all varieties of the earliest Christians and for their conforming Jewish counterparts, it was the decade that we now know as 60-70 AD that was to prove the most terrible. When, whether by deliberate arson or otherwise, a huge part of Rome was destroyed by fire in 64 AD, it suited the Emperor Nero to blame the Christians, and it was in recording this that the Roman historian Tacitus made his famous reference to Jesus. In Tacitus' words:

Nero fabricated scapegoats – and punished with every refinement the notoriously depraved Christians (as they were popularly called). Their originator, Christ, had been executed in Tiberius' reign by the governor of Judaea, Pontius Pilate. But in spite of this temporary setback the deadly superstition had broken out afresh, not only in Judaea (where the mischief had started), but even in Rome... First Nero had self-acknowledged Christians arrested. Then, on their information, large numbers of others were condemned – not so much for incendiarism as for their anti-social tendencies. Their deaths were made farcical. Dressed in wild animals' skins, they were torn to pieces by dogs, or crucified, or made into torches to be ignited after dark as substitutes for daylight. Nero provided his Gardens for the spectacle, and exhibited displays in the Circus, at which he mingled with the crowd ...

The Galilean Simon Peter had reportedly made his way to Rome sometime before these atrocities, and it is more than a little testimony to the earliness of the New Testament books, particularly a historical one such as Acts, clearly a follow-up to the Luke gospel, that while reporting earlier episodes of his life they nowhere record his death. Only via later tradition do we learn he was probably among those whom Nero put to death during this terrible time, reputedly at his own request being crucified upside down through his feeling unworthy at being crucified exactly as Jesus had been. Paul for his part seems to have gone to Rome around 60 AD, finding, as Acts records, an already established community of 'brothers' to greet him (Acts 28: 15), but having the fortune to depart before the Neronian terror,

only to find himself, as we learn from 2 Timothy, back there awaiting trial around 67 AD. Again, despite the New Testament incorporating so much of his life and letters, it has no record of the outcome of this, or the manner of his death – as if, as it were, the relevant books 'went to press' before this.

But whatever torments James, Peter, Paul and the Rome community of Christians went through, these were but curtain-raisers for what the rest of the 60-70 AD decade had in store. The gospels convey Jesus as warning his disciples explicitly enough of the sufferings they and their followers would have to undergo in his name: 'They will hand you over to be tortured and put to death, and you will be hated by all the nations on account of my name' (Matthew 24: 9). 'Men will seize you and persecute you; they will hand you over to the synagogues and to imprisonment, and bring you before kings and governors because of my name... You will be betrayed even by parents and brothers, relations and friends, and some of you will be put to death' (Luke 21: 12, 16). Nothing, however, could have been more specific or (at the time) more unbelievable than his dread prophecy of the Jerusalem Temple's destruction. In the words of the Matthew gospel,

> Jesus drew his [disciples'] attention to the Temple buildings. He said to them... 'You see all these? I tell you solemnly, not a single stone will be left on another: everything will be destroyed'. (Matthew 24: 1-2; also Mark 13: 1-4 and Luke 21: 5-7)

Those words, of course, related to the most terrible event ever to befall trouble-torn Jewry, the fall of Jerusalem and wholesale destruction of the Temple in 70 AD, following the revolt against the Romans that had broken out four years earlier. But, as touched on in an earlier chapter, did the gospel writers simply put the prophecy into the mouth of Jesus after the event? Or, if writing before the event, did they record an absolutely genuine prophecy on his part? In favour of the latter, it would surely have been almost irresistible for anyone writing afterwards not to make considerable capital out of this incredible prophecy having been so dramatically fulfilled. Yet not one of the gospel-writers alludes to it.

Whatever the answer, the actuality and sheer terror of Jerusalem's fall is a matter of absolutely firm record. This may be gauged historically, from chroniclers such as Josephus, and archaeologically from the almost complete erasure of the Herodian period edifices on the Temple Mount. Most vivid and indeed poignant of all, however, is a hitherto unmentioned discovery by Israeli archaeologist Nahman Avigad and his fellow-excavators in the house of the priestly Kathros family (see pp.107-8). Lifting up a fire-blackened piece of masonry they found beneath this a thick layer of charred wood, ashes and soot which accompanying pottery showed to date to around the first century AD, and which was dated even more exactly by a coin inscribed 'Year four of the Redemption of Zion' (that is, the fourth year of the Jewish Revolt), corresponding to our 69 AD. But the real chiller

Graphic evidence of the fall of Jerusalem: the arm and finger-bones of a young woman who died during the Romans' savage sack of the city in 70 AD. Found in the so-called 'Burnt House' associated with the Kathros family, her fingers can be seen frozen in the act of clutching at a step, and she seems to have been overcome by smoke when the Romans set fire to the house as part of their general destruction of the city.

was the unearthing, amidst all the debris, of the arm-bones of a young woman, her fingers still fixed in the last movement she made in life, clutching at a step. As the archaeologists deduced, this poor girl most likely suffocated as the fire burned around her. And that fire needed little identification, for Josephus had described it all too vividly in his account of Jerusalem's fall:

> They [the Romans] ... blocked the narrow streets with corpses, deluging the whole city with gore ... At dusk the slaughter ceased, but in the night the fire gained mastery, and on the 8th of Gorpaios [roughly our September] the sun rose over Jerusalem in flames ...

The Matthew gospel records Jesus having forewarned his disciples of this time of troubles, advising them:

> 'When you see Jerusalem surrounded by armies, you must realize that she will soon be laid desolate. Then those in Judaea must escape to the mountains, those inside the city must leave it, and those in country districts must not take refuge in it'. (Luke: 21 20,21)

That some of his Jewish-born followers heeded this at around the time of Jerusalem's fall is attested by a Church tradition that a contingent of them headed for Pella on the east bank of the Jordan. These, later variously

Remains of the Jewish Christians' first-century church on Jerusalem's Mount Zion? Well-dressed Herodian stone blocks, thought to have been re-used from the rubble of the destroyed Jerusalem Temple, are seen here forming part of a so-called 'Tomb of David' on Mount Zion. According to Benedictine monk Bargil Pixner, this 'tomb' was actually a synagogue (see below), and was built by the Judaeo-Christian community of disciples when they returned to Jerusalem around 74 AD, four years after the Romans had destroyed the Temple and much of the surrounding city.

to be labelled 'Nazarenes' and 'Judaeo-Christians', appear to have had as their gospels both an early Aramaic version of the Matthew gospel and the 'Gospel of the Hebrews', both long lost. As some evidence of their settlement in Pella, excavations in 1967 of Pella's ancient West Church revealed a sarcophagus beneath the apse, which judging from its Jewish style of decoration and Christian context may once have belonged to an early leader of this same community.

But according to the tenth-century patriarch Eutychius, who seems to have had access to early documents no longer extant, at least some of these Judaeo-Christians 'returned to Jerusalem in the fourth year of the Emperor Vespasian [i.e. 73 AD] and built there their church'. What may well be remains from this church have recently been identified by Benedictine monk Bargil Pixner in a dressed stone edifice erroneously labelled 'the Tomb of David' tucked amidst a complex of buildings next to the Dormition Church on Jerusalem's south-western hill today called Mount Zion. Comprising part of a later Church of the Apostles (thought to mark the house with the upper room where the apostles assembled after Jesus' ascension), this edifice has in the lower parts of its walls massive and beautifully dressed stones of exactly the type used for Herod's Temple. From the stones' chipped corners and different heights, they seem to have been rescued from the rubble of the Temple site (a salvage operation we might expect of the Temple-going Jerusalem Christians described in Acts 2: 43-7), and used for a synagogue-style building, in which regard a particularly tell-tale feature is

Drawing of eastern wall of the 'Tomb of David' showing in its lower portions the unevenly laid Herodian blocks that are thought to have formed part of the Judaeo-Christians' synagogue on Mount Zion. From a drawing by the French priest and archaeologist Louis Hugues Vincent (1872-1960).

that this is oriented not to the Temple, as any true synagogue would have
been, but to the tomb of Jesus as marked by the site of the Church of the
Holy Sepulchre.

If this thinking is correct, this very early church would have been constructed on the orders of Simeon, son of Cleopas, who is recorded to have
succeeded James, brother of Jesus, as head of Jerusalem's Judaeo-Christian
community. Since Simeon's father, Cleopas (almost certainly the same
Cleopas to whom Jesus appeared on the road to Emmaus, Luke 24: 13-35),
was the brother of Jesus and James' father, Joseph, Simeon would have
continued Jesus and James' own Davidic blood-line, there apparently
having followed thirteen other 'Bishops' of Jerusalem, some also with this
same blood-line.

In 132 AD, however, following another Jewish revolt, the Romans
expelled all Jews, including Judaeo-Christians, from Jerusalem, and made it
into a totally new Roman metropolis under the name Aelia Capitolina.
Jesus and James' enemies, the Sadducees, had already been finished by their
Temple's destruction after the First Revolt, but those mainly Pharisaic
members of the Sanhedrin who survived now made Sepphoris in Galilee
their new seat, largely because Sepphoris had escaped destruction since its
strongly pro-Roman citizens refused to join the Revolt. Accordingly, it was
from thoroughly Roman Sepphoris, ironically filled with pictorial works of
art that flouted the old Jewish Law (see below), that the *Mishnah* began to
be compiled around 200 AD.

*Near perfection in human portraiture:
a breathtakingly beautiful mosaic head
of a girl, dating from the third century
AD, uncovered by archaeologists
excavating at Sepphoris in 1987. The
Graeco-Roman artist who created this
must virtually have rubbed shoulders
with the Jews who compiled the
Mishnah at Sepphoris at around this
time. For these latter such pictorial
representation of a human likeness
would have been strictly forbidden.*

Well before the Second Revolt, however, Jews and Christians had started what became their irretrievable drift apart, with Judaeo-Christians, who had previously continued to worship in traditional Jewish synagogues, being deterred from doing so, and eventually dwindling away, and Gentile Christians, despite occasional periods of persecution, steadily winning further converts throughout the Graeco-Roman world. It was of course somewhat easier for the latter in view of the intense wave of anti-Jewish feeling across the Roman Empire in the wake of the Revolt. And, as explained earlier, this was almost certainly why the gospels of Jesus that have survived were edited and adapted to a Gentile standpoint, with Jesus' association with the Jewish people deliberately down-played, and attention deflected from the activities of those Jewish Christians led by James and his successors.

From these tangled beginnings there therefore emerged what can now, for the first time, legitimately be labelled 'Christianity' as a distinct religion in its own right, rather than a mere branch of the old Jewish religion. Even Tacitus, who described the Rome Christians as 'notoriously depraved', acknowledged that the city's ordinary citizens had taken pity on their sufferings, and although under the emperors Domitian (81-96 AD), Decius (249-51 AD) and Diocletian (284-305 AD) there were fresh persecutions of a savagery rivalling those of Nero, more enlightened emperors such as Hadrian (117-38 AD) and Antoninus Pius (138-61 AD) allowed long periods of unofficial toleration. In Hadrian's reign, for instance, Rome's Christians enjoyed sufficient toleration to organize their religion under presbyters, bishops and deacons and even to build a proper shrine over the earth grave in which Jesus' disciple Peter was believed to have been laid. From this shrine's archaeological discovery within the last few decades, it is apparent that it originally formed part of a walled structure, complete with a courtyard for public assembly and in one corner a low doorway leading into what seems to have been a baptistry. There can be little doubt that it was a very early church building, and in this respect it, the Mount Zion synagogue and the 'St Peter's house' discovered at Capernaum jostle each other for priority as the earliest examples.

Christianity received a further boost when in October 312 AD a vigorous young Roman blue-blood called Constantine fought and won under the Christian 'Chi-Rho' monogram the battle of the Milvian Bridge, gaining for himself the Roman Empire and for Christianity not only toleration but what would soon become the status of an official religion. For many Christians who had all too recently suffered blinding and mutilations under Diocletian's persecutions this must have seemed like an answer to their prayers, and church building could now begin to flourish as never before.

But whatever Jesus may or may not have intended for the promulgation of his Good News, this new official status was not necessarily all blessing. With it came councils, such as Nicaea (325 AD), at which arbitrary decisions on doctrinal issues would be made which would split one

Christian faction from another even more than they had been in the first century. It is true that some of these issues, such as the fixing of an arbitrary date for celebrating Jesus' birthday, were ultimately matters of very little real importance (future department store profits notwithstanding).

But others were altogether profound, in particular the deepest and most difficult issue of all: just who was Jesus? And just to what extent was he, and is he, God's Son? Was he some all-time divine entity, 'eternally begotten of the Father', who had always existed since the beginning of time, and had merely appeared human when he took on flesh sometime around 4 BC? Or was he an ordinary man of human parentage somehow specially chosen by God to convey his all-time message about how humans should behave to one another, a message so heartlessly returned by humankind signed in very real blood? These questions were potent enough causes of squabbling among the Nicaea delegates back in the year 325 AD. But they remain every bit as difficult and controversial to this very day.

Typifying Christianity's establishment as an official religion of the Roman Empire is this depiction of Jesus in a manner very reminiscent of the Roman god Apollo, but with the 'Chi-Rho' monogram clearly identifying him as Christ. Mosaic from a Roman villa at Hinton St Mary, Dorset, now in the British Museum, London.

12
THE REAL
JESUS

Today we live on the very eve of the third millennium of Jesus' birth. Indeed, if our historical assessments of the true date of his birth have any validity, we are already into that millennium, making whatever celebrations are planned for the early hours of 1 January 2000 AD somewhat mis-timed. But likewise making those celebrations more than a little hollow is the fact that the society we live in is arguably more pagan and less Christian than throughout most of those last two thousand years. Millions upon millions go about their daily lives without a moment's thought for Jesus, except perhaps to use his name as an expletive. They may happily exchange gifts on the day arbitrarily chosen as his birthday. They may send out dozens of so-called 'Christmas' cards to their friends. But it will not occur to them to enter a church unless for a wedding, a funeral, or out of historical curiosity. For them Jesus has long since been bypassed by the age of science and moral freedoms. Even if they accept that he lived, they will probably dismiss him as just some obscure preacher who died a long time ago and about whom tall stories of his rising from the dead got out of hand. For those who think thus, Jesus has long lost any interest or relevance, and two thousand years of Christianity, with all its accompanying paraphernalia of churches and art works, have been an expensive waste of time.

Opposite *'I gazed into the visions of the night. And I saw, coming on the clouds of heaven, one like the son of man…' (Daniel 7: 13). Jesus seen coming 'on the clouds of heaven', as in Daniel's prophecy, from a mosaic in the apse of the basilica of SS Cosmas and Damian, Rome.*

The easy option would be for us to conclude likewise. After all, we have seen that the gospels are not exactly infallible in the information they contain, and their reporting is by no means entirely of the direct eyewitness variety. We have established that the Matthew and Luke birth stories are more than a little inconsistent with each other. We have learned how at least some of the miracles might be explained by some form of hypnosis. Admittedly we found Jesus' teachings appealing, and were impressed by the intensity of belief in his resurrection on the part of those who witnessed this. But we might still question whether these can persuade us that he was, as defined in the Nicene creed : 'the only son of God, eternally begotten of the Father, God from God, Light from Light, true God from true God, begotten not made, of one being with the Father' through whom 'all things were made'. We know that the council of bishops at Nicaea who devised this formula entirely lacked our present-day scientific knowledge that 'all things made' took many millions of years to manifest into the form known as humankind, which makes their idea that Jesus was already around at the time of some cosmic 'Big Bang' seem all the more insubstantial and far-fetched.

But would the flesh-and-blood Jesus who tramped the byways of Galilee himself have necessarily expected or held to any belief that he was 'God from God' and 'eternally begotten, not made'? To get some perspective on this it may be helpful to take ourselves back to the times in which Christianity came into being, during which it was surprisingly easy for an ordinary man to be believed to be a god. At least as early as the reign of Tiberius, who was Jesus' contemporary, Roman emperors worked hard to cultivate a divine image, just as kings and pharaohs had done for centuries before them. It was commonplace for artists and sculptors to be commissioned to portray the emperor as Zeus/Jupiter or Heracles, and for the emperor's image on legionary standards to be worshipped by Roman armies. When Tiberius' nephew Germanicus died a beautiful cameo was made of him being received into the heavenly pantheon, with the former Emperor Augustus among the gods.

That such deification could be believed of more ordinary men, even practising Christians, is quite evident from the account in Acts of Paul and Barnabas healing a cripple in the Asia Minor town of Lystra, in Lycaonia:

A man sat there (in Lystra) who had never walked in his life, because his feet were crippled from birth; and as he listened to Paul preaching, he managed to catch his eye. Seeing that the man had the faith to be cured, Paul said in a loud voice, 'Get to your feet – stand up' and the cripple jumped up and began to walk. When the crowd saw what Paul had done they shouted in the language of Lycaonia, 'These people are gods who have come down to us disguised as men'. They addressed Barnabas as Zeus, and since Paul was the principal speaker, they called him Hermes. The priests of Zeus-outside-the-Gate, proposing that all the

One of the earliest depictions of Jesus as bearded and long-haired. As a Jew this would have been his likeliest mode of hairdressing, although the gospels do not mention a single detail of his human appearance, whether he was bearded or clean-shaven, tall or short, fat or thin, handsome or ugly. From a fourth-century ceiling fresco in the cemetery of Commodilla, Rome.

people should offer sacrifice with them, brought garlanded oxen to the gates. When the apostles Barnabas and Paul heard what was happening, they tore their clothes and rushed into the crowd shouting 'Friends, what do you think you are doing? We are only human beings like you ...' Even this speech, however, was scarcely enough to stop the crowd offering them sacrifice. (Acts 14: 8-18)

Even the Jewish world, surrounded and permeated as it was with Hellenism, was susceptible to such ideas. The story was told of Herod the Great's grandson, Herod Agrippa, who in the decade that Jesus was crucified was thrown into prison for suspected treachery against Tiberius. When on his first day of captivity an owl alighted on a branch above Agrippa's head, an old German prisoner told him it was a good omen: he would shortly be released and regain his royal status. But he also warned Agrippa that when he saw the bird again, he would die within five days. Just as predicted, Agrippa was released, and in 37 AD became King of the Jews, ruling over Herod the Great's former territories. At the height of his power, in 44 AD he attended in great style the quadrennial Roman games at Caesarea, appearing in dazzling robes of silver, which sparkled in the sunshine. Sycophants around him cried out that he was a god, not a man, and Agrippa, flattered, failed to reprove them. It was his fatal mistake. He looked up ... and there was the owl, flying towards him. Seized by sudden stomach pains he died in agony five days later, 'eaten away with worms', as noted with relish in Acts 12: 23. Whether or not this is just a good story, it is the clearest possible example of how easily pagans could and would acclaim a man as a god, and what a fatal blasphemy it was for a Jew even to think in these terms.

So, given all that we have learned, could Jesus have regarded himself as God? Ostensibly, no. In the Mark gospel, the most consistent in conveying Jesus' humanity, a man reportedly ran up to him and addressed him with the words 'Good master'. Jesus' response was a firm rebuke: 'Why do you call me good? No one is good but God alone' (Mark 10: 18). In the John gospel, the one with the most accent on Jesus' divinity, he is quoted as stating quite categorically, 'the Father is greater than I' (John 14: 28). If Jesus had really wanted people to believe he was on any sort of equal footing with God the Father, a convenient opportunity came when, as described in the Mark gospel, a scribe reportedly asked him: 'Which is the first of all the commandments?' But instead of introducing some new formula to link himself to God, or to a Trinity, Jesus unhesitatingly looked to his traditional Jewish roots, quoting the great *Shema Israel* ('Listen Israel'), the confession of faith which every practising Jew recites morning and evening every day of his life:

This is the first: Listen Israel, the Lord our God is the *one* Lord [italics mine], and you must love the Lord your God with all your heart, with all your soul, with all your mind, and with all your strength. (Mark 12: 29, 30)

What, then, about the idea that Jesus was God's son? Might he have believed this? For twenty centuries for unbelievers the centrality of such a title to Christianity has represented by far the biggest stumbling block about Jesus, from the Sadducean priests who interrogated him after his arrest (e.g. Mark 14: 61-4), to the Hindu Mahatma Gandhi (who declined to accept the 'God's son' appellation but otherwise revered him as 'one of the greatest teachers humanity has ever had'), to that large majority of present-day Westerners who never think of attending any Christian church.

In genuine deference to these unbelievers' difficulties, we have ourselves already seen that the gospel stories of Jesus' purportedly 'divine' birth feature only in the Matthew and Luke gospels, and then contradictorily. They also lack the convincing quality of much else of the gospel material, and are never alluded to again. Also noticeable is the fact that when described teaching his disciples Jesus is never represented as directly using the title 'Son of God' of himself, consistently preferring instead the enigmatic, and far more humble-sounding, 'Son of Man'. Features such as these have encouraged theologians of the old German stable to downgrade Jesus' perception of himself so that, for example, the distinguished New Testament scholar Helmut Koester, Professor of New Testament Studies at Harvard Divinity School, has concluded:

> It is a simple historical fact that Jesus was an Israelite from Galilee and that he understood himself to be nothing else but a prophet in Israel and for Israel.

But despite Professor Koester, it is important that we ask ourselves what exactly Jesus meant when he used the term 'Son of Man'? In the New Testament this is to be found, with just one exception (Acts 7: 56), solely in the gospels and solely from the reported words of Jesus himself when he was speaking of himself. And when we look into the Old Testament for his source of it, we find this unmistakably in Daniel's great prophecy:

> I gazed into the visions of the night,
> And I saw, coming on the clouds of heaven,
> one *like a son of man* [italics mine].
> He came to the one of great age
> And was led into his presence.
> On him was conferred sovereignty,
> glory and kingship,
> and men of all peoples, nations and languages became
> his servants.
> His sovereignty is an eternal sovereignty
> which shall never pass away ...
>
> (Daniel 7: 13-14)

'Son of God' in the Dead Sea Scrolls. Among the most interesting of the 15,000 scroll fragments found in the Dead Sea Scrolls' Cave Four is this one, designated 4Q246. As translated by the Roman Catholic scholar Joseph Fitzmyer, part of this reads: '... all shall serve [him and he] shall be called [son of] the [gr]eat God, and by his name shall he be named. He shall be hailed the Son of God, and they shall call him Son of the Most High. As comets [flash] to the sight, so shall their kingdom...'. Although this cannot be regarded as a reference specifically to Jesus, it clearly shows that some Jews of Jesus' time expected their great Messiah to come to carry the title 'Son of God'.

Now as the gospels make clear, Jesus was very careful to stress the very earthly sufferings he would have to undergo when he spoke of himself as the Son of Man (e.g. Matthew 17: 22, 23). But there can also be absolutely no doubt that he quite deliberately and pointedly identified himself with this exalted heavenly being 'seen' by Daniel, a being specially appointed by God (the one 'of great age'), to rule as Messiah/King an eternal and universal kingdom.

Also clear is that he accepted that with this same being went the title 'Son of God'. It is particularly notable from the Mark gospel that early in Jesus' ministry madmen reportedly acclaimed him as this, only for him sternly to warn them 'not to make him known' (Mark 3: 12), which we may interpret as a tacit acknowledgement that this is nevertheless what he knew himself to be. But then came the dread moment when he was seized and put on trial for his life before the Sadducean priesthood, with Caiaphas coldly and calculatingly putting to him: 'Are you the Christ, the Son of the Blessed One?'

Fascinatingly, Jesus this time neither equivocated, nor tried any psychologists' tricks, like answering a question with a question. Instead, he forthrightly responded:

I am, and you will see the Son of Man seated at the right hand of the Power and coming with the clouds of heaven. (Mark 14: 62)

That he was there and then, perhaps in one of the rooms of the Palatial Mansion excavated by Nahman Avigad, identifying himself with the God-appointed universal king of Daniel's prophecy is as unmistakable to us today as it was then to the high priest Caiaphas whose more temporal power had brought him there. As will be recalled, both the first Christian martyr, Stephen, and Jesus' brother, James, would later make affirmations about Jesus in almost identical circumstances, with almost identical words, and with similarly fatal results. Further underlining that Jesus really did see himself as God's son (any human paternity by Joseph notwithstanding) and as the rightful heir to God's universal kingdom, is a revealing parable quoted of him that is far too characteristic to have been invented by anyone else. The parable of the wicked husbandmen, or tenant farmers, this appears not only in all three synoptic gospels (Mark 12: 1-12; Matthew 21: 33-46; Luke 20: 9-19) but also in a particularly explicit and primitive form in the Nag Hammadi 'Gospel of Thomas':

Jesus seen coming 'on the clouds of heaven', as in Daniel's prophecy: 'I gazed into the visions of the night. And I saw, coming on the clouds of heaven, one like the son of man...' (Daniel 7:13)

> He [Jesus] said, 'There was a good man who owned a vineyard. He leased it to tenant farmers so that they might work it and he might collect the produce from them. He sent his servant so that the tenants might give him the produce of the vineyard. They seized his servant and beat him, all but killing him. The servant went back and told his master. The master said, 'Perhaps [they] did not recognize [him]'. He sent another servant. The tenants beat this one as well. Then the owner sent his son and said, 'Perhaps they will show respect to my son.' Because the tenants knew that it was he who was the heir to the vineyard, they seized him and killed him. Let him who has ears hear ...

The meaning of this parable is of course quite unmistakable. The 'good' vineyard owner is God, the vineyard his kingdom and his tenant farmers mankind/the house of Israel. The servants are the Old Testament prophets, some of whom were indeed badly treated in their time. But quite distinct from these, and suffering a far worse fate, is the vineyard owner's son. Jesus could hardly have spelled out more plainly his role in a future drama that he would play out with his own life, or that, as 'the son', his relationship with God and his right to inherit his Father's kingdom was unique and different from that of anyone who had gone before. Most eerily and disturbingly, here we also see him, to all appearances a flesh-and-blood Galilean of the first century AD, calmly explaining in advance the excruciating death that with our hindsight we know he would undergo, as matter-of-factly as if he were watching it all through a window.

Now it is at this point that all our previous, modern-minded complacency that Jesus was probably just some God-inspired teacher necessarily receives its severest jolt. If this man could so clearly and dispassionately look into the future – and not only his own future, for we have earlier suggested the genuineness of his 'destruction of the Temple' prophecies – did the past, the time before his own human birth, likewise have no barriers for him? Was this how, during his so-called 'Transfiguration', a dumbfounded trio of his disciples saw him in the company of Moses, who died at least as early as 1200 BC, and Elijah, who died back in the ninth century BC (Matthew 17: 1-13; Mark 9: 2-13; Luke 9: 28-36)? Did space likewise hold no normal bounds for him, hence his reported walking on water, and his sudden appearances in a variety of places, including passing through closed doors, after his resurrection?

For the sceptical-minded reader it might seem unacceptable, in an otherwise objective book, now to be apparently accepting at face value such matters supernatural. But it is only the truth of this sheer bounds-of-time-and-space-defying power, verberating and reverberating among the far from simple peoples of first-century Galilee and Judaea, that can explain the sudden confident abandonment of any fear of death that was taken on by men such as Simon Peter, and Stephen and James, and that gave birth to Christianity. Likewise, and no less importantly, only the equally clear and fearful recognition of this same power on the part of the hard-hearted men who controlled the Temple can explain their so malevolent and repeated concern to snuff it out whenever it showed itself to them. As will be recalled from the earlier-quoted parable, the tenant farmers (with whom we may particularly identify the Temple priesthood) 'knew he [the vineyard owner's son, and therefore Jesus] was the heir to the vineyard' and determined to kill him. Likewise evident, particularly from Mark's gospel, is that those who were reputedly possessed by devils were quickest to recognize Jesus as 'Son of God'.

This clear recognition of the power of good by the power of evil, and the perennial and seemingly insatiable anxiety of the latter to stamp out the former, is supremely important because, as many a committed Christian of today can corroborate, it is very real and remains every bit as active as it was in Jesus' time. As Father Thomas Keating has expressed it in his book *The Mystery of Christ*:

> ... union with Christ is not some kind of spiritual happy hour. It is a war with the powers of evil that killed Jesus and that might kill us, too, if we get in their way. Because we live in the human condition, the divine light is constantly being challenged by the repressive and regressive forces within us as individuals and within society, neither of which wants to hear about love, certainly not about self-giving love.

Speaking personally, one of my most painful and yet illuminating experiences, having as a writer expressed my beliefs in Jesus in the 1984 version of this book and also in the otherwise so discredited Turin Shroud, has been to be most deviously targeted in efforts to undermine these beliefs by certain plausible-sounding and publicity-seeking people with absolutely no concern for truth. The illuminating aspect is that for modern-day people to be so motivated can only mean that they actually do recognize truth, but like Caiaphas, see it as too threatening to their own quite different priorities for it to be allowed to live.

This is but one reason why, although I regard my brand of Christianity as one still fettered by my historical training and by what was once a very strong agnosticism, I can conclude with now much greater conviction than in 1984 not only that there was a very real flesh-and-blood Jesus of Nazareth who walked the byways of Galilee two thousand years ago and was very publicly crucified by the conniving of Caiaphas and his cronies, but also that in a very real sense he lives on as Lord of all humankind, and will do so throughout eternity.

As we noted in the last chapter, Jesus' brother James spoke of Jesus as 'the door', the important supplement to that particular imagery being that in each of our lives that door is always open, and we have but to walk through to find our past failings forgiven and our daily earthly cares as nothing.

Of course, Christians and non-Christians alike will always squabble over issues such as whether Jesus was born by some form of divine insemination of his mother Mary, whether he forms part of a Trinity, whether he was around from the beginning of Creation, whether he really died when he was crucified, and much else. As has been beautifully expressed by Birmingham lecturer Frances Young:

> ... there are as many different responses to Jesus Christ as there are different fingerprints ... Attempts to produce creeds are inevitably divisive or compromising ... What we need is not new creeds but a new openness.

Which is why ultimately all that is really important is that, unlike any human being, however saintly, throughout history, Jesus still *is*. In a way still beyond our human understanding, two thousand years ago something of God was made flesh in him, and shone through him and spoke through him, so that the sick were healed and miracles happened. And because he was such a perfect vessel of God, on death he did not die as other humankind but passed through that so illusory barrier to become the open door to the divine, and to the eternal values of truth and love.

This is the real Jesus, and the free choice (and it is one that does have the bounds of our individual spans of mortality) is whether we continue to live as if Caiaphas really succeeded in silencing Jesus two thousand years ago – or we boldly go through that door to find him still very much alive...

13
REFERENCES, BIBLIOGRAPHY AND INDEX

The following notes and bibliography are intended for readers wishing to explore further the issues raised in *Jesus: The Evidence*. In the interests of simplicity, sources appear in the notes only in an abbreviated form, except in the case of very specialized publications. Full publishing details will be found in the bibliography.

REFERENCES
1
GETTING BACK TO THE BASICS

p.12 **Dr John Covel:** See the extracts from Dr Covel's diaries in *Early Voyages* by J.T. Brent.

p.12 **Hon. Robert Curzon:** The quotation derives from his *Visit to the Monasteries*, p.366.

p.12 **Constantin Tischendorf:** For an excellent account of the discovery of *Sinaiticus*, and that of other early biblical manuscripts, see Deuel's *Testaments of Time*, also Tischendorf's own account, *Codex Sinaiticus: Tischendorf's Story and Argument Related by Himself*.

p.14 **Tischendorf's alleged theft of Sinaiticus:** The monks of Sinai still regard Tischendorf as having stolen their manuscript, and display a letter in which Tischendorf acknowledges that he has the manuscript merely on loan (see G.H. Forsyth, 'Island of Faith', p.91). But this letter was written before the monastery had accepted a substantial payment from Tsar Nicholas, a payment negotiated by Tischendorf, apparently for the purchase of *Sinaiticus*. For the announcement of the British acquisition of *Sinaiticus*, see *The Times*, 21 December 1933, p.15.

pp.18-19   **Oxyrhynchus excavations:** The quotation from Grenfell derives from his article 'The Oldest Record...', p.1030. For details of the other manuscript fragments discovered by Grenfell and Hunt, see their multi-volume *The Oxyrhynchus Papyri* published by the Egypt Exploration Fund. Their work was carried on by others after their deaths.

p.19   **Nag Hammadi discovery:** The manuscripts were almost certainly originally hidden by someone from the nearby monastery of St Pachomius. For background on the whole story, and an appraisal of the manuscripts themselves, see Elaine Pagels, *The Gnostic Gospels*. Full translations of the manuscripts are to be found in James M. Robinson, *The Nag Hammadi Library*, from which the 'Gospel of Thomas' and other extracts quoted in this book are derived.

p.20   **Egerton Papyrus 2:** A full translation and definitive appraisal is to be found in Bell and Skeat, *Fragments of an Unknown Gospel*.

p.21   **Chester Beatty Collection:** News of the Chester Beatty acquisition was announced in an article by Sir Frederic George Kenyon, *The Times*, 19 November 1931, p.13. See also Kenyon's *The Chester Beatty Biblical Papyri* for a definitive appraisal. The exact location where the papyri were found remains unknown.

p.21   **Rylands Papyrus:** See C.H. Roberts, *An Unpublished Fragment of the Fourth Gospel*.

p.21   **Quotation from Bruce Metzger:** This derives from his 'Recently published Greek Papyri of the New Testament', *Biblical Archaeologist*, 10, 2 May 1947, p.38.

pp.22-3   **Magdalen Papyrus MS.Gr.17:** See Matthew D'Ancona, 'Eyewitness to Christ', *The Times*, 24 December 1994.

p.22   **Colin Roberts on the Magdalen Papyrus:** See Colin Roberts, 'An Early Papyrus of the First Gospel', *Harvard Theological Review*, 46, 1953, pp.233-7.

pp.22-3   **Dr Thiede on the Magdalen Papyrus:** See Carsten Peter Thiede, 'Papyrus Magdalen Greek 17 (Gregory-Aland $\mathfrak{p}^{64}$): A Reappraisal', *Zeitschrift für Papyrologie und Epigraphik*, 105 (1995), pp.13-20.

2

HOW MUCH CAN THE GOSPELS BE TRUSTED?

p.26   **Manuscript punctuation, dating, etc.:** For a lucid, modern summary of the technical details, see Metzger, *Manuscripts of the Greek Bible.*

p.27   **Parallel passage technique:** For examples of this technique as applied to the synoptic gospels, see Throckmorton, *Gospel Parallels.*

p.27   **Reimarus' 'On the Aims of Jesus ...':** The original German title of Reimarus' work was *Von dem Zwecke Jesu und seiner Jünger.* This was the last of the so-called Wolfenbüttel Fragments, published by G.E. Lessing after Reimarus' death (see Lessing in bibliography).

pp.27-8   **Strauss' 'The Life of Jesus ...':** The original German title of Strauss's work was *Das Leben Jesu ...* The first English-language version, translated by George Eliot, was published in 1846.

p.28   **F.C. Baur:** Although Baur's output was prodigious, only two of his works have been translated into English, *Paul the Apostle of Jesus Christ* (1873-5) and *The Church History of the First Three Centuries* (1878-9). For an excellent appraisal of his signifcance, see Stephen Neill, *The Interpretation of the New Testament,* pp.19-28.

p.28   **Mark as secretary or interpreter for Peter:** According to the second-century bishop Papias, as quoted in Eusebius, *History of the Church,* book 3: 'This too the presbyter used to say: "Mark, who had been Peter's interpreter, wrote down carefully, but not in order, all that he remembered of the Lord's sayings and doings. For he had not heard the Lord, or been one of his followers, but later, as I said, one of Peter's ..."' Eusebius, *History,* translated by Williamson, p.152.

p.29   **John gospel written at Ephesus:** This is attested by, among others, the early church father Irenaeus (c.130-c.200 AD).

p.29   **Wrede:** The original German title of Wrede's work was *Das Messiasgeheimnis in den Evangelien,* published at Göttingen in 1901. It has never been translated into English, but for a summary of its content, see Albert Schweitzer, *The Quest of the Historical Jesus,* pp.328 ff.

pp.29-30   **Schweitzer:** The original German title of Schweitzer's book was *Von Reimarus zu Wrede,* published in 1905. The quotation derives from the English-language edition, p.396.

p.30   **Bultmann:** For Bultmann's own elucidation of the principles of 'form criticism', see his *Die Geschichte der synoptischen Tradition,* 1921, published in English as *The History of the Synoptic Tradition,* 1963.

p.31   **Quotation from Bultmann:** This derives from his *Jesus and the Word,* p.14.

p.31 **Dr Vermes on the Bultmann school:** The comment derives from Vermes, "Quest for the Historical Jesus"', *Jewish Chronicle Literary Supplement,* 12 December 1969.

p.32 **Don Cupitt:** Don Cupitt's remarks on the *zakkau/dakkau* misreading, to which I am indebted, derive from Cupitt & Armstrong, *Who was Jesus?,* pp.52, 53.

p.34 **Manual of Discipline:** The quotation derives from Vermes' *The Dead Sea Scrolls in English,* p.93.

pp.34-5 **Early Aramaic element in the John gospel:** According to C.F. Burney, speaking of himself: '...the writer turned seriously to tackle the question of the original language of the Fourth Gospel; and quickly convincing himself that the theory of an original Aramaic document was no chimera, but a fact which was capable of the fullest verification, set himself to collect and classify the evidence in a form which he trusts may justify the reasonableness of his opinion not merely to other Aramaic scholars, but to all New Testament scholars who will take the pains to follow out his arguments' (Burney, *The Aramaic Origin of the Fourth Gospel,* p.30). Olmstead somewhat arbitrarily separated the narrative and discourse elements of the gospel, arguing that the former represented the earliest and most authentic source of biographical information on Jesus. Variants of the same argument have subsequently been adopted by Professor Charles H. Dodd in his *Historical Tradition in the Fourth Gospel* (see especially p.120), and by Dr John A.T. Robinson in his *Redating the New Testament.*

pp.34-5 **The Gabbatha or Pavement:** For the arguments identifying the Sion Convent pavement with that referred to by the writer of the John gospel, see Fr L.H. Vincent, 'Le lithostrotos évangelique', also P. Benoit, 'Prétoire, Lothostroton et Gabbatha'.

p.35 **Quotation from Papias:** See Eusebius, op.cit., p.153.

p.37 **Professor Brandon and pro-Roman slant of the Mark gospel:** See Professor Brandon, *The Fall of Jerusalem and the Christian Church.*

pp.37-8 **Kümmel dating of the gospels:** See his *Introduction to the New Testament.*

p.39 **Quotation from Nicholas Sherwin-White:** This derives from p.191 of his *Roman Society and Roman Law in the New Testament.*

3

CAN WE BE SURE OF ANYTHING ABOUT JESUS' BIRTH?

pp.41-2   **John Allegro and Professor G.A. Wells:** For details of the works of these writers, see bibliography. John Allegro was forcefully refuted in *The Times,* 26 May 1970, and an acerbic review of Wells, *Did Jesus Exist?,* written by Dr John Robinson, appeared in the October 1976 *Journal of Theological Studies,* pp.447-9.

p.42   **Tacitus:** The reference to 'Christ' occurs in his *Annals of Imperial Rome,* book 15, 44. See Penguin translation by Michael Grant, p.354.

p.42   **Suetonius:** The full reference reads: 'Because the Jews at Rome caused continuous disturbances at the instigation of Chrestus, he [Claudius] expelled them from the city.' *The Twelve Caesars,* Penguin, translated by Robert Graves, p.197.

p.42   **Pliny:** The reference to Christians derives from his Letters, X, 96-7. For the best English translation, see B. Radice, *The Letters of the Younger Pliny* (Penguin, Harmondsworth, 1963), pp. 293-5.

pp.43-4   **Josephus on Jesus:** The passage describing Jesus as a 'wise man' occurs in *Antiquities* XX 3, 3 (63-4). The reference to James as brother of Jesus derives from *Antiquities* XX, 9, I (200-3). For a definitive appraisal of these passages, and the extent to which they have suffered alteration, see Excursus II 'Josephus on Jesus and James' in Schürer's *History of the Jewish People,* pp.428-41.

p.44   **Origen on Josephus and Jesus:** See his *Comm. in Matthaeum,* 10, 17 (referring to Matthew 13: 55); also *Contra Celsum,* 1, 47. Origen provides crucial corroboration that Josephus did refer to Jesus, but did not believe that he was the Messiah, or Christ.

p.44   **Agapius on Josephus:** See Shlomo Pines' *An Arabic Version of the Testimonium Flavianum and its Implications.*

p.45   **Quotations from 'Baraitha' and 'Tosefta':** These derive as follows:

1. Baraitha, *Babylonian Talmud,* Sanhedrin 43a.

2. *Ibid.*

3. Tosefta, *Hullin (Profane Things),* II, 22, 23.

4. Tosefta, *Hullin* II, 24.

For the fullest discussion of these extracts, see Rabbi Goldstein, *Jesus in the Jewish Tradition,* especially pp.22-51.

p.47   **Census of Quirinius:** For a definitive appraisal of the Luke gospel's deficiencies concerning this census, see Excursus I, 'The Census of

Quirinius', in Schürer's *History of the Jewish People* (1973 edition), pp.400-27.

p.48   **Kepler:** Kepler's original book describing his astronomical findings was *De Jesus Christi Salvatoris Nostri Vero Anno Natalitio,* published in 1606.

p.48   **Clark, Parkinson and Stephenson:** See bibliography.

4
WHAT OF JESUS' UPBRINGING?

p.52   **Jesus' education:** The Luke gospel story of Jesus astonishing the doctors in the Temple (Luke 2: 41-50) should be regarded with some caution, for Josephus tells a very similar story of himself at the age of fourteen. But there is no reason to believe Jesus was not well educated. As theologian C.F.D. Moule remarked: 'It seems fair to assume that, broadly speaking, the average Jew was better educated than the average Gentile, if only because Jewish family life was the soundest in the empire, and also the education which Jewish children received in the synagogue school was, within its limits, more conscientious and thorough than the teaching given by Gentile schoolmasters who had not necessarily the intensity of vocation belonging to a devout teacher of the Torah' (C.F.D. Moule, *The Birth of the New Testament,* p.157).

p.52   **Pantera, Panthera:** For a full discussion, with sources, see Goldstein, *Jesus in the Jewish Tradition,* pp.35-9.

p.52   **Origen's reference to Panthera:** As quoted by Origen, this reads: 'Mary was turned out by her husband, a carpenter by profession, after she had been convicted of unfaithfulness. Cast off by her spouse, and wandering about in disgrace, she then in obscurity gave birth to Jesus by a certain soldier Panthera' (Origen, *Contra Celsum,* refutation 1, 28).

p.52   **Panthera tombstone:** For a full appraisal, see A. Deissmann, *Light from the Ancient East,* pp.74, 75.

p.53   **Relatives of Jesus arrested for their descent from King David:** See Eusebius, *History,* III, 20, translated by Williamson, pp.126, 127.

p.53   **Gospel references to Nazareth:** In the Mark gospel, already noted as most likely the earliest, specific reference to Nazareth occurs only in chapter 1, verse 9. In four later passages (Mark 1: 24; 10: 47; 14: 67 and 16: 6) the original Greek refers to Jesus as 'the Nazarene'.

p.53   **Quotation from Rabbi Goldstein:** See his *Jesus in the Jewish Tradition,* p.24.

pp.54-5 **Jesus the countryman:** For Dr Geza Vermes' remarks on Jesus as a countryman, see his *Jesus the Jew,* pp.48, 49.

p.55 **References to 'Eleazar', 'Lazar' and 'Laze':** For a description of a Jewish ossuary bearing the name 'Eliazar', see *Gli scavi del 'Dominus Flevit',* I, *Tipographia dei P. Franciscani,* (Jerusalem, 1958), p.92. For examples of 'Lazar' and 'Laze' at Beth She'arim, see M. Schwabe and B. Lifshitz, *Beth She'arim* II, no.177, p.73; no.93, p.34.

p.56-7 **Sepphoris:** For excellent background to James F. Strange's excavations, see Richard A.Batey, *Jesus and the Forgotten City.*

p.59 **Herod the Great's Caesarea:** For a useful introduction, see Kenneth G. Holum, Robert Hohlfelder, Robert J.Bull and Avner Raban, *King Herod's Dream: Caesarea by the Sea;* also Barbara Burrell, Kathryn Gleason and Ehud Netzer, 'Uncovering Herod's Seaside Palace', *Biblical Archaeology Review,* 19, 3, May/June 1993, p.50 ff.

p.61 **Quotation from Shirley Jackson Chase:** See Chase, *Jesus: A New Biography,* pp.205 ff.; also 'Jesus and Sepphoris', *Journal of Biblical Literature,* 45 (1926) p.18.

pp.62-3 **Hypocrite:** For useful discussion of this, and sources, see Richard A. Batey, 'Sepphoris: An Urban Portrait of Jesus', *Biblical Archaeology Review,* 18, 3, May/June 1992, pp.59 ff.

p.63 **Professor Fitzmyer on Jesus' knowledge of Greek:** See Joseph A. Fitzmyer, 'Did Jesus Speak Greek?', *Biblical Archaeology Review,* 18, 5, Sept/Oct 1992, p.58 ff.

5

HOW DID HE ACQUIRE HIS SENSE OF MISSION?

p.66 **Quotation from Josephus on John the Baptist:** This derives from *Antiquities* 18, pp.116-19.

p.66 **W.F. Albright on Aenon near Salim:** This quotation derives from Albright, *The Archaeology of Palestine,* p.247.

p.67 **Nudity during baptism:** This was prescribed in Hippolytus' *Apostolic Tradition* XXI, 3, 5, 11, and was required by the Pharisees in their baptism of proselytes and immersion for purification (*Mikwa'ot* 8 and 9; *B. Yebamot* 47b). It is implicit in Paul's reference to 'complete stripping' in Colossians 2: 11. In the earliest Christian art, where Jesus' baptism is a common theme, he is invariably represented as quite naked.

p.67   **'Son of God':** James Mackey, in his *Jesus the Man and the Myth* has pointed out that any Jew '... if unusually faithful to the will of God in this world, could claim to be Son of God in that sense, and have that claim allowed. In the Judaea royal ritual the king was declared son of God on his enthronement' (p.65). For the association of this title with the royal ritual, see 2 Samuel 7 and Psalm 2.

p.68   **Nabi/Nabi'im:** Dr Geza Vermes has pointed out that a technically more correct rendition of the plural is *nebi'im*. *Nabi'im* has however been adopted in order to avoid confusion.

p.68   **King David's adultery:** For biblical references see 2 Samuel, chapters 11 and 12.

p.69   **Feeding of the five thousand:** For Dr John Robinson's observations on this passage, see his *Can we trust the New Testament?*, p.92.

p.69   **That Mark drew on two separate accounts of the feeding of the five thousand:** The Mark gospel author quotes two separate accounts of the feeding of large crowds, one of five thousand (6: 30-44), the other of four thousand (8: 1-10). As pointed out by Dr Vincent Taylor in *The Gospel According to St Mark* (London, 1966), it seems unlikely that these were two separate incidents, particularly since in the second the disciples ask: 'Where could anyone get bread to feed these people in a deserted place like this?', thus apparently ignorant of the first occasion, which they were reported to have witnessed. The sensible explanation is that Mark was working from two slightly different written versions of a single incident. Had his sources been verbal, he would have been more likely to recognize their common origin.

p.71   **Jesus as guerrilla leader:** See S.G.F. Brandon, *Jesus and the Zealots*, Hyam Maccoby, *Revolution in Judaea*, and Joel Carmichael, *The Death of Jesus*.

p.72   **Josephus on the Essenes:** The reference to Essene attitudes to possessions, weapons, footwear, etc. derives from his *Jewish War*, p.133.

p.73   **'Abba':** There are considerable scholarly differences about the significance of Jesus' use of this word. Some have argued it to be the equivalent of our 'Daddy'. Jewish scholars such as Vermes, however, point out that it could be used both formally and as an expression of familiarity. It is to be noted that when Jesus began the so-called 'Lord's Prayer' (Matthew 6: 9-13) with the words 'Our Father in heaven', he was following the pattern of Pharisee prayer which still forms part of the Jewish Daily Prayer Book.

p.73   **'Abba' addressed to God by Honi the Circle Drawer's grandson:**
             See Vermes, *Jesus the Jew,* p.211.

p.73   **Tetragrammaton:** For an introduction to the use of this in early
             manuscripts, see Metzger, *Manuscripts of the Greek Bible,* pp.33-5.

p.73   **Quotation from Prof. Alan Millard:** This derives from a letter by
             Professor Millard, 'Helping to Imagine Jesus' Synagogue' published in
             Biblical Archaeology Review, May/June 1992, p.14.

6

FISHER OF MEN – AND WOMEN

pp.77-8   **Capernaum:** For a useful introductory article with sources, see John
             C.H. Laughlin, 'Capernaum from Jesus' Time and After', *Biblical
             Archaeology Review,* 19, 5, Sept/Oct 1993, p.54 ff.

pp.79-81   **Galilee boat:** See Shelley Wachsmann, 'The Galilee Boat – 2,000-year-
             old hull recovered intact', *Biblical Archaeology Review,* 14, 5, Sept/Oct
             1988, pp.18 ff.

pp.82-4   **Fishing on the Sea of Galilee in Jesus' time:** See Mendel Nun, 'Cast
             your net upon the waters: Fish and Fishermen in Jesus' time', *Biblical
             Archaeology Review,* 19, 6, Nov/Dec 1993, pp.46 ff.

pp.87-8   **Quotation from the 'Gospel of Philip':** See J.M. Robinson, *The Nag
             Hammadi Library,* p.138.

7

MAN OF MAGIC

pp.91-3   **Jesus' reputation as a healer/sorcerer among Jews:** That Jesus''miracles'
             remained in Jewish folk-memory following the crucifixion is indicated
             by several Talmudic passages describing cures performed long after his
             death by means of charms inscribed with his name. See Tosefta, *Hullin*
             II, 22; *B.Av.Zar.* 27b; *Y.Av.Zar.* II, 40d; *Y.Sabb,* XIV, 14d.

p.93   **Quotation from Canon Anthony Harvey:** This derives from his *Jesus
             and the Constraints of History,* p.110.

pp.93-4   **Excavations at the Sheep Pool:** For an excellent, detailed account of
             these, and the literature surrounding the site, see Jack Finegan,
             The Archaeology of the New Testament, pp.142-7. See also J. Jeremias,
             'The Rediscovery of Bethesda'. The names Bethzatha/Bezehta/
             Bethesda, etc., all appear to denote the same site.

p.94   **Quotation from the Bordeaux pilgrim:** This is a translation of the

Latin original published in P. Geyer, *Corpus Scriptorum Ecclesiasticorum Latinorum,* vol. 39 (Vienna, 1889), p.21.

p.94   **Emotional stress as a causative factor in hysterical illnesses:** For a medical appraisal of this, and discussion of the efficacy of hypnosis in the treatment of, for instance, stress-induced skin disorders, see Gordon Ambrose and George Newbold, *Handbook of Medical Hypnosis,* especially chapter 13.

pp.95-7   **Ichthyosis case:** For the detailed medical account of the successful use of hypnosis in this case, see Dr A.A. Mason, 'A Case of Congenital Ichthyosiform Erythrodermia of Brocq treated by Hypnosis', *British Medical Journal,* 23 Aug 1952, pp.422, 423.

p.97   **Professor Lionel Haward and ancient Egyptian use of hypnosis:** See Professor Haward's lecture 'Hypnosis in the service of research', p.2, also F.L. Griffith and H. Thompson, *The Demotic Magical Papyrus of London and Leiden.* According to Professor Haward, this describes self-hypnosis using a light source. British Museum Egyptologists have expressed some doubts over this interpretation, but the controlled induction of a trance-like state, whatever label may be given to it, originates way back in pre-history.

pp.98-9   **Quotation from Professor Oesterreich:** This derives from the English-language edition of his *Possession, Demoniacal and Other,* p.5.

p.99   **Christopher Neil-Smith:** See his *The Exorcist and the Possessed.*

p.99   **West Yorkshire 'possession' case:** For accounts of the trial associated with this, see *The Times,* 22 to 24 April 1975; also *The Yorkshire Post* of the same dates.

pp.99-100   **Multiple personality cases:** There is a growing literature on this subject. Chris Sizemore has written her autobiography under the title *Eve* (see bibliography, Sizemore and Pittillo). US author Daniel Keyes has written an account of the Billy Milligan case in *The Minds of Billy Milligan.* Flora Rheta Schreiber has graphically recreated the problems of a pseudonymous East Coast American art student in *Sybil* (first published in the UK by Allen Lane, 1974).

8

THE ROAD TO JERUSALEM

pp.106-8   **Nahman Avigad's excavations in Old City Jerusalem's Jewish Quarter:** See Nahman Avigad, *Discovering Jerusalem;* Nahman Avigad, *The Herodian Quarter in Jerusalem – Wohl Archaeological Museum;* also a useful introductory aricle by Nitza Rosovsky, 'A Thousand Years of History in Jerusalem's Jewish Quarter', *Biblical Archaeology Review*, 18, 3, May/June 1992, pp.22 ff.

p.108 **Martin Goodman:** See bibliography.

pp.108-9 **Discovery of the Caiaphas Ossuary:** See Zvi Greenhut, 'Burial Cave of the Caiaphas Family', *Biblical Archaeology Review*, 18, 5, Sept/Oct 1992, p.29; also Ronny Reich, 'Caiaphas' name inscribed on Bone Boxes', ibid., pp.38 ff.

pp.109-11 **Reconstruction of Herod's Temple by the Ritmeyers:** See Kathleen & Leen Ritmeyer, 'Reconstructing Herod's Temple Mount in Jerusalem', *Biblical Archaeology Review*, 15, 6, Nov/Dec 1989, pp.23 ff.

p.109 **Alec Garrard's reconstruction of Herod's Temple:** See Kathleen Ritmeyer, 'Herod's Temple in East Anglia', *Biblical Archaeology Review*, 19, 5, Sept/Oct. 1993, pp.62 ff.

pp.111-13 **Temple death penalty notices:** The inscription on these notices reads: 'Let no foreigner enter within the screen and enclosure surrounding the Sanctuary. Whoever is taken doing so will be the cause that death overtakes him.' (Deissmann, *Light from the Ancient East*, p.80).

pp.112-14 **Jesus' entry into Jerusalem:** The interpretation of Jesus' actions in this instance is derived from Canon Anthony Harvey's *Jesus and the Constraints of History*. It is to be acknowledged, however, that this interpretation is regarded with some scepticism by Dr Vermes.

9

THE ROAD TO THE CROSS

p.119 **Pilate dedicatory inscription:** For a full discussion of the inscription, see Carla Brusa Gerra, *Scavi di Caesarea Maritima*, pp.217-20.

p.120 **Solar calendar theory:** See A. Jaubert, *The Date of the Last Supper*.

p.123 **Gethsemane – Jesus' arrest not in a Garden:** See Joan E. Taylor, 'The Garden of Gethsemane: Not the Place of Jesus' Arrest', *Biblical Archaeology Review*, 21, 4, July/Aug 1995, p.26.

p.123 **Josephus on the Essenes' 'weapons to keep off bandits':** See *The Jewish War*, p.133.

p.124 **Dr Frederick Zugibe on haematidrosis:** See his *The Cross and the Shroud*, pp.2-13.

pp.125-8 **Trial of Jesus:** For a Jewish interpretation of this, see Paul Winter's *On the Trial of Jesus*. Classical historians have similarly suggested that

the trial was a mere clandestine interrogation by Temple officials.
Pilate's actions the next day are also regarded as makeshift and informal.
See the report on a Cambridge lecture by F.G.B. Millar in *The Times*,
30 July 1971, p.3.

p.126   **High priest's tearing of his robes:** This appears to be a contemporary
gesture of despair; see also Acts 14: 14. The rending of the veil of the
Temple at Jesus' death (Mark 15: 38) seems to have been injected into
the gospel story as a sign of God's despair at the Jewish establishment's
rejection of Jesus.

p.126   **Chief priests' power of the death penalty:** Worth noting are the words
Josephus attributes to the Roman commander Titus on his reproving
those who participated in the First Jewish Revolt of 66-70 AD: 'You
disgusting people! Didn't you put up that balustrade [on the Temple] to
guard your Holy House? Didn't you at intervals along it place slabs
inscribed in Greek characters and our own forbidding anyone to go
beyond the parapet? And didn't we give you leave to execute anyone
who did go beyond it, even if he was a Roman?' (Josephus, *Jewish War*,
book 6, 136, translation by Williamson, p.347).

p.127   **Josephus on passive resistance:** The quotations derive from *The Jewish
War*, Williamson translation, pp.138-9.

p.131   **Crucifixion victim discovered at Giv'at ha-Mivtar:** See N. Haas,
'Anthrolopological observations on the Skeletal Remains from Giv'at
ha- Mivtar', *Israel Exploration Journal*, 20, 1970, pp.38-59.

p.131   **Dr Yigael Yadin:** For his comments on the Giv'at ha-Mivtar crucifixion
remains, see his article 'Epigraphy and Crucifixion'.

p.131   **Dr Møller-Christenson's reconstruction:** See his article, 'Skeletal
Remains...'.

pp.133-4   **The Turin Shroud:** For the definitive report of the radiocarbon dating,
see P.E. Damon et al., 'Radiocarbon dating of the shroud of Turin',
Nature, v.337, no.6028, 16 February 1989, pp.611-15. Recent
attempts to attribute the Shroud to Leonardo da Vinci (Lynn Picknett
& Clive Prince, *The Turin Shroud: In whose image?*, Bloomsbury,
London, 1994) have been as unconvincing and unworthy as those
attempting to show that the carbon dating was deliberately rigged
(Holger Kersten & Elmar Gruber, *The Jesus Conspiracy*, Element,
Shaftesbury, Dorset, 1994). Whatever the Shroud's true date – and
radiocarbon dating's infallibility is by no means guaranteed – the
Shroud's unmistakably photographic image remains far from
satisfactorily explained.

10

DID JESUS REALLY RISE FROM THE DEAD?

pp.137-8   **Rolling-stone tombs:** For a complete description of 61 rolling-stone tombs, and accompanying discussion of the tomb of Jesus, see Eugenia L. Nitowski, *Reconstructing the Tomb of Christ from Archaeological and Literary Sources* (unpublished doctoral dissertation, University of Notre Dame, 1979).

pp.140-2   **Argument for Jerusalem's Church of the Holy Sepulchre marking the true site of Jesus' tomb:** The definitive report on the excavations carried out at the Church of the Holy Sepulchre is Virgilio C. Corbo, *Il Santo Sepolcro di Gerusalemme*. But for an excellent English-language general introduction, see Dan Bahat, 'Does the Holy Sepulchre Church mark the burial of Jesus?', *Biblical Archaeology Review*, 12, 3, May/June 1986, pp.26 ff.

p.142   **Quotation from Socrates Scholasticus:** This derives from his *History of the Church*, I, 17, English translation by A.C. Zenos, *Nicene and Post-Nicene Christian Fathers*, ser.2, vol.2, (Oxford, 1890).

p.142   **Kathleen Kenyon's excavations:** See her *Jerusalem, Excavating 3,000 Years of History*.

p.146   **The Gallio inscription:** For a full discussion of this, see Deissmann's *St Paul, A Study in Social and Religious History*, Appendix I, pp.244 ff.

p.151   **Strauss' *A New Life of Jesus*:** This was Strauss' second treatise on Jesus, originally published in German under the title *Das Leben Jesu für das deutsche Volk bearbeitet*. The quotation derives from the English ed., vol.I, p.412, published in 1879.

11

A FAITH IS BORN

p.158   **'Gospel of Thomas' reference to James:** 'The disciples said to Jesus, "We know that you will depart from us. Who will be our leader?" Jesus said to them, "Wherever you are, you are to go to James the Righteous …"', J.M. Robinson, *Nag Hammadi Library*, p.119.

p.158   **'Gospel of the Hebrews' reference to Jesus appearing to James:** This is quoted in *St Jerome, De Viris Illustribus*, chapter 2.

pp.160-1   **Hegesippus' references to James:** An extensive extract from Hegesippus' writings on James has been preserved in Eusebius' *History of the Church*, book 2, chapter 23. See Penguin ed., translation by Williamson, pp.99-102.

p.161   **Josephus' reference to James:** This derives from his *Antiquities*, XX, 9, 1.

p.162   **Tacitus:** This reference is from Tacitus, *Annals,* book 15, 44.

p.162   **The fate of Peter:** For authoritative discussion of Peter's likely fate, see John Evangelist Walsh, *The Bones of Peter.*

p.165   **Young woman killed in the house of Kathros:** See Nitza Rosovsky, 'A Thousand Years of History …', p.30.

p.165   **Quotation from Josephus:** From Josephus, *The Jewish War* (VI, 8, 4), translation by G.A. Williamson, p.370.

p.166   **Sarcophagus at Pella:** See Robert Houston Smith, 'A Sarcophagus from Pella', *Archaeology,* 26, pp.250-7.

pp.166-7   **Early Judaeo-Christian Church in Jerusalem:** See Bargil Pixner, 'Church of the Apostles found on Mount Zion', *Biblical Archaeology Review,* 16, 3, May/June 1990, pp.16 ff.

p.167   **Sepphoris pictorial works of art:** See anon., 'Mosaic masterpiece dazzles Sepphoris volunteers', *Biblical Archaeology Review,* 14, 1, Jan/Feb 1988, pp.30-33.

12

THE REAL JESUS

p.175   **Gandhi on Jesus:** 'To me he was one of the greatest teachers humanity has ever had. To his believers he was God's only begotten son. Could the fact that I do or do not accept this belief have any more or less influence in my life? Is all the grandeur of his teaching and his doctrine to be forbidden to me? I cannot believe so … My interpretation … is that Jesus' own life is the key to his nearness to God; that he expressed, as no other could, the spirit and will of God. It is in this sense that I see and recognize him as the son of God.' From Gandhi's *What Jesus means to me,* compiled by R.K. Prabhu (Navajivan Publishing House, Ahmadabad, 1959), pp.9 and 10.

p.175   **Quotation from Helmut Koester:** This is from Koester's 'Historic mistakes haunt the relationship of Chritianity and Judaism', *Biblical Archaeology Review,* 21, 2, Mar/Apr, 1995, p.26.

p.177   **Quotation from Nag Hammadi 'Gospel of Thomas':** This is Logion 65, as published in J.M. Robinson's *The Nag Hammadi Library,* pp.125-6.

p.178   **Quotation from Thomas Keating:** This is from his *The Mystery of Christ* (Amity, New York, 1987), p.17.

p.179   **Quotation from Frances Young:** This derives from her article, 'A Cloud of Witnesses', published in *The Myth of God Incarnate,* ed. John Hick, p.38.

BIBLIOGRAPHY

ALBRIGHT, W.F., *The Archaeology of Palestine* (Penguin Books, Harmondsworth, revised ed., 1956)

ALLEGRO, J., *The Sacred Mushroom and the Cross* (Hodder & Stoughton, London, 1970)

AMBROSE, G., & NEWBOLD, G., *A Handbook of Medical Hypnosis* (Bailliere Tindall & Cassell, London, 1968)

AVIGAD, N., *Discovering Jerusalem* (Thomas Nelson, Nashville TN, 1983)
The Herodian Quarter in Jerusalem – Wohl Archaeological Museum (Keter Publishing House, Jerusalem, 1989)

AVI-YONAH, M., 'A list of Priestly Courses from Caesarea' (*Israel Exploration Journal*, 12, 1962, pp.137-9)

BAHAT, D., 'Does the Holy Sepulchre mark the burial of Jesus?' (*Biblical Archaeology Review*, 12, 3, May/June 1986, pp.26 ff.)

BATEY, R., *Jesus and the Forgotten City* (Baker Book House, Grand Rapids, 1991)
'Sepphoris: An urban portrait of Jesus' (*Biblical Archaeology Review*, 18, 3 May/June, 1992)

BELL, H.I., & SKEAT, T.C., *Fragments of an unknown Gospel* (British Museum, London, 1935)

BENOIT, P., 'Prétoire, Lithostroton et Gabbatha' (*Revue Biblique*, 59, Paris, 1952, pp.531-50)

BOURGUET, P.DU, *Early Christian Art* (Weidenfeld, London, 1971)

BRANDON, S.G.F., *The Fall of Jerusalem and the Christian Church* (SPCK, London, 1951)
'Saint Paul, the problem figure of Christianity' (*History Today*, Oct 1961)
Jesus and the Zealots (Manchester University Press, 1967)
The Trial of Jesus of Nazareth (Batsford, London, 1968)

BRENT, J.T. (ed.), 'Extracts from the Diaries of Dr John Covel 1670-1679', *Early Voyages and Travels in the Levant* (*Hakluyt Society*, 87, 1893, pp.101-287)

BULTMANN, R., *Jesus and the Word* (Scribner, New York, 1958)
The History of the Synoptic Tradition (Oxford University Press, 1963)

BURNEY, C. F., *The Aramaic Origin of the Fourth Gospel* (Clarendon Press, Oxford, 1922)

BURRELL, B., GLEASON, K., & NETZER, E., 'Uncovering Herod's Seaside Palace' (*Biblical Archaeology Review*, 19, 3, May/June 1993, pp.50 ff.)

CARMICHAEL, J., *The Death of Jesus* (Victor Gollancz, London, 1963)

CASE, S.J., *Jesus, A New Biography* (University of Chicago Press, 1927) 'Jesus and Sepphoris' (*Journal of Biblical Literature*, 45, 1926)

CLARK, D., PARKINSON, J., & STEPHENSON, R., 'An Astronomical Re-Appraisal of the Star of Bethlehem. A Nova in 5 BC' (*Quarterly Journal of the Royal Astronomical Society*, 18, 1977, p.443)

CORBO, V., *Il Santo Sepolcro di Gerusalemme, Aspetti arceologici dalle origini al periodo crociato* (parts I-III, Franciscan Printing Press, Jerusalem, 1981-2)

CUPITT, D., & ARMSTRONG, P., *Who was Jesus?* (BBC, London, 1977)

CUPITT, D., *The Debate about Christ* (SCM, London, 1979)

CURZON, R., *A Visit to the Monasteries in the Levant* (reprint with introduction by D.G. Hogarth; Humphrey Milford, London, 1916)

DAMON, P.E., et al., 'Radiocarbon dating of the Shroud of Turin' (*Nature*, v.337, no.6028, 16 Feb 1989, pp.611-15)

DEISSMANN, A., *St Paul, A Study in Social and Religious History* (translation by L.R.M. Strachan; Hodder & Stoughton, London, 1912)

Light from the Ancient East, The New Testament illustrated by recently discovered Texts of the Graeco-Roman World (Hodder & Stoughton, London, 1927)

DEUEL, L., *Testaments of Time. The Search for Lost Manuscripts and Records* (Secker & Warburg, London, 1966)

DODD, C.H., *Historical Tradition in the Fourth Gospel* (Cambridge University Press, 1963)

EISENMAN, R., & WISE, M., *The Dead Sea Scrolls Uncovered* (Element, Shaftesbury, Dorset, 1992)

EUSEBIUS OF CAESAREA, *The History of the Church from Christ to Constantine* (translation by G. A. Williamson; Penguin Books, Harmondsworth, 1965)

FARMER, W. R., *The Synoptic Problem* (Macmillan, London & New York, 1964)

FARRAR, F.W., *The Life of Christ as represented in Art* (A. & C. Black, London, 1901)

FINEGAN, J., *The Archaeology of the New Testament* (Princeton University Press, 1969)

FITZMYER, J.A., 'Did Jesus speak Greek?' (*Biblical Archaeology Review*, 18, 5, Sept/Oct 1992, pp.58 ff.)

FORSYTH, G.H., 'Island of Faith in the Sinai Wilderness' (*National Geographic Magazine*, 125, Jan 1964)

GERRA, C.B., 'Le Inscrizioni', *Scavi di Caesarea Maritima* ('L'Erma' di Bret-schneider, Rome, 1966)

GOLDSTEIN, M., *Jesus in the Jewish Tradition* (Macmillan, New York, 1950)

GOODMAN, M., *The Ruling Class of Judea: The Origins of the Jewish Revolt against Rome* (Cambridge University Press, 1993)

GREENHUT, Z., 'Burial Cave of the Caiaphas Family' (*Biblical Archaeology Review*, 18, 5, Sept/Oct 1992, pp.29 ff.)

GRENFELL, B.P., 'The Oldest Record of Christ. The First Complete Account of the "Sayings of Our Lord"' (Introduction by F.G. Kenyon; *McClure's*, II, 1897, pp.1022-30)

GRENFELL, B.P., & HUNT, A.S., et al., *The Oxyrhynchus Papyri*, vols 1-25 (Egypt Exploration Fund, Graeco-Roman Branch, London, 1898-1959)

GRIFFITH, F.L., & THOMPSON, H., *The Demotic Magical Papyrus of London and Leiden* (Clarendon Press, Oxford, 1921)

GUILDING, A., *The Fourth Gospel and Jewish Worship* (Oxford University Press, 1960)

HAAS, N., 'Anthropological Observations on the Skeletal Remains from Giv'at ha-Mivtar' (*Israel Exploration Journal*, 20, 1970, pp.38-59)

HARVEY, A.E., *Jesus and the Constraints of History*, The Bampton Lectures 1980 (Duckworth, London, 1982)

HAWARD, L.R.C., 'Hypnosis in the Service of Research' (Inaugural Lecture delivered at the University of Surrey, 14 Feb 1979)

HICK, J. (ed.), *The Myth of God Incarnate* (SCM, London, 1977)

HOLUM, K.G., HOHLFELDER, R., BULL, R.J., & RABAN, A., *King Herod's Dream: Caesarea by the Sea* (Norton, New York, 1988)

JAUBERT, A., *The Date of the Last Supper* (translated from French; Alba House, New York, 1965)

JEREMIAS, J., 'The rediscovery of Bethesda', *New Testament Archaeology Monographs*, I (Southern Baptist Theological Seminary, Louisville, KT, 1966)

JONES, A.H.M., *The Herods of Judaea* (Oxford University Press, 1938)

JOSEPHUS, *The Jewish War* (translated by G.A. Williamson, rev. E. Mary Smallwood: Penguin, Harmondsworth, 1981)

The Antiquities of the Jews (translated by H. Thackeray, Loeb Classical Library, 6 vols, London, 1930-65)

KEE, A., *Constantine versus Christ* (SCM, London, 1982)

KENYON, F.G., 'The Text of the Bible, A New Discovery' (*The Times*, 19 Nov 1931, p.13)

The Chester Beatty Biblical Papyri, 8 vols (E. Walker, London, 1933-41)

KENYON, K., *Jerusalem: Excavating 3,000 years of History* (Thames & Hudson, London, 1967)

KHAN, M.F., *Deliverance from the Cross* (The London Mosque, London, 1978)

KLAUSNER, J., *Jesus of Nazareth* (Allen & Unwin, London, 1925)

KOPP, C., *The Holy Places of the Gospels* (translated from German by Ronald Walls; Nelson, London, 1963)

KÜMMEL,W.G., *Introduction to the New Testament* (English translation by A.J. Mattill; London, 1970)

LAUGHLIN, J.C.H., 'Capernaum from Jesus' Time and After' (*Biblical Archaeology Review,* 19, 5, Sept/Oct 1993, pp.54 ff.)

LESSING, G.E. (ed.), *Von dem Zwecke Jesu und seiner Jünger* (G.E. Lessing, Brunswick, 1778)

MACCOBY, H., *Revolution in Judaea, Jesus and the Jewish Resistance* (Ocean Books, London, 1973)

The Sacred Executioner, Human Sacrifice and the Legacy of Guilt (Thames & Hudson, London, 1982)

MACKEY, J.P., *Jesus, the Man and the Myth* (SCM, London, 1979)

MASON, A.A., 'A Case of Congenital Ichthyosiform Erythrodermia of Brocq treated by Hypnosis' (*British Medical Journal,* 23 Aug 1952, pp. 422, 423)

METZGER, B., 'Recently published Greek Papyri of the New Testament' (*Biblical Archaeologist,* 10, 2 May 1947)

Manuscripts of the Greek Bible, An Introduction to Palaeography (Oxford University Press, 1981)

MITCHELL, T.C., *The Bible in the British Museum* (British Museum Press, London, 1988)

MØLLER-CHRISTENSEN, V., 'Skeletal Remains from Giv' at ha-Mivtar' (*Israel Exploration Journal,* 26, 1976, pp.35-8)

MONTEFIORE, H., 'Jesus, the Revelation of God' (*Christ for Us Today,* pp.108-10)

MOULE, C.F.D., *The Birth of the New Testament* (A. & C. Black, London, 1962)

NEILL, S., *The Interpretation of the New Testament 1861-1961* (Oxford University Press, 1964)

NEIL-SMITH, C., *The Exorcist and the Possessed* (James Pike, St Ives, 1974)

NICKELL, J., *Inquest on the Shroud of Turin* (Prometheus, New York, 1983)

NUN, M., 'Cast your Net upon the Waters: Fish and Fishermen in Jesus' Time' (*Biblical Archaeology Review,* 19, 6, Nov/Dec 1993, pp.46 ff.)

OESTERREICH, T.K., *Possession, Demoniacal and Other* (Kegan Paul, London, 1930)

OLMSTEAD, A.T., *Jesus in the Light of History* (Scribner, New York, 1942)

PAGELS, E., *The Gnostic Gospels* (Weidenfeld & Nicolson, London, 1980)

PINES, S., *An Arabic Version of the Testimonium Flavianum and its Implications* (The Israel Academy of Science and Humanities, Jerusalem, 1971)

PIXNER, B., 'Church of the Apostles found on Mount Zion' (*Biblical Archaeology Review,* 16, 3, May/June 1990, pp.16 ff.)

RITMEYER, K., 'Herod's Temple in East Anglia' (*Biblical Archaeology Review,* 19, 5, Sept/Oct 1993, pp.62 ff.)

RITMEYER, K. & L., 'Reconstructing Herod's Temple Mount in Jerusalem' (*Biblical Archaeology Review,* 15, 6, Nov/Dec 1989, pp.23 ff.)

ROBERTS, C.H., *An unpublished Fragment of the Fourth Gospel* (Manchester University Press, 1935)

'An Early Papyrus of the First Gospel' (*Harvard Theological Review,* 46, 1953, pp.233-7)

ROBINSON, J.A.T., *Honest to God* (SCM, London, 1963)

The Human Face of God (SCM, London, 1972)

Redating the New Testament (SCM, London, 1976)

Can we trust the New Testament? (Mowbray, London, 1977)

ROBINSON, J.M. (ed.), *The Nag Hammadi Library* (Harper & Row, New York, 1977)

ROSOVSKY, N., 'A Thousand years of History in Jerusalem's Jewish Quarter' (*Biblical Archaeology Review,* 18, 3, May/June 1992, pp.22 ff.)

SCHOLEM, G., *Major Trends in Jewish Mysticism* (Schocken Books, New York, 1941)

The Messianic Idea in Judaism (Schocken Books, New York, 1971)

SCHONFIELD, H.J., *The Authentic New Testament* (Dennis Dobson, London, 1956)

The Passover Plot (Hutchinson, London, 1965)

Those Incredible Christians, A New Look at the Early Church (Hutchinson, London, 1968)

SCHREIBER, F.R., *Sybil* (Allen Lane, London, 1974)

SCHÜRER, E., *History of the Jewish People in the Age of Jesus Christ* (rev. ed. with new material by G. Vermes and F. Millar; T. & T. Clark, Edinburgh, 1973)

SCHWEITZER, A., *The Quest of the Historical Jesus, A Critical Study of its Progress from Reimarus to Wrede* (translated by W. Montgomery; A. & C. Black, London, 1910)

SHERWIN-WHITE, A.N., *Roman Society and Roman Law in the New Testament* (Clarendon Press, Oxford, 1963)

SIZEMORE, C., & PITTILLO, E.S., *Eve* (Victor Gollancz, London, 1978)

SMITH, J.H., *Constantine the Great* (Hamish Hamilton, London, 1971)

SMITH, M., *Jesus the Magician* (Victor Gollancz, London, 1978)

SMITH, R.H., 'A Sarcophagus from Pella', *Archaeology,* 26, pp.250-57

STRAUSS, D.F., *The Life of Jesus Critically Examined* (translated by G. Eliot; Chapman, London, 1846)

New Life of Jesus (Williams & Norgate, London, 1865)

STREETER, B.H., *The Four Gospels, A Study of Origins* (Macmillan, London, 1927)

SUETONIUS, *The Twelve Caesars* (translated by R. Graves; Penguin Books, Harmondsworth, 1957)

TACITUS, *The Annals of Imperial Rome* (translated by M. Grant; Penguin Books, Harmondsworth, 1956)

TAYLOR, J.E., 'The Garden of Gethsemane: Not the place of Jesus' arrest' (*Biblical Archaeology Review,* 21, 4, July/Aug 1995, pp.26 ff.)

THIEDE, C.P., 'Papyrus Magdalen Greek 17 (Gregory-Aland **p.**64): A Reappraisal', (*Zeitschrift für Papyrologie und Epigraphik,* 105, 1995, pp.13-20)

THROCKMORTON, B.H.(Jr.), *Gospel Parallels: A Synopsis of the First Three Gospels* (Thomas Nelson Inc., New York, 1971)

TISCHENDORF, C. VON, *Codex Sinaiticus, Tischendorf's Story and Argument related by Himself* (Lutterworth Press, London, 1935)

TOYNBEE, A. (ed.), *The Crucible of Christianity* (Thames & Hudson, London, 1969)

TZAFERIS, V., 'Jewish Tombs at and near Giv'at ha-Mivtar' (*Israel Exploration Journal,* 20, 1970, pp.18-32)

VERMES, G., *The Dead Sea Scrolls in English* (Penguin Books, Harmondsworth, 1962)

'Quest for the Historical Jesus' (*Jewish Chronicle Literary Supplement,* 12 Dec 1969)

Jesus the Jew: A Historian's reading of the Gospels (Collins, London, 1973; Fontana, London, 1976: quotations from Fontana ed.)

VINCENT, L.H., 'Le lithostrotos évangélique' (*Revue Biblique,* Paris, 59, 1952, pp.5I3-30)

WACHSMANN, S., 'The Galilee Boat - 2,000-year-old Hull recovered Intact' (*Biblical Archaeology Review,* 14, 5, Sept/Oct 1988, pp.18 ff.)

WALSH, J., *The Bones of St Peter* (Victor Gollancz, London, 1983)

WARNER, M., *Alone of all her Sex: The Myth and Cult of the Virgin Mary* (Weidenfeld & Nicolson, London, 1976)

WELLS, G.A., *The Jesus of the Early Christians* (Pemberton, London, 1971)

The Historical Evidence for Jesus (Prometheus, New York, 1982)

WILSON, I ., *The Turin Shroud* (Victor Gollancz, London, 1978)

WINTER, P., *On the Trial of Jesus* (de Guyter, Berlin, 1961)

YADIN, Y., *Bar-Kokhba* (Weidenfeld & Nicolson, London, 1971)

'Epigraphy and Crucifixion' (*Israel Exploration Journal,* 23, 1973, pp.18-20)

(ed.), *Jerusalem Revealed: Archaeology in the Holy City, 1968-1974* (Yale University Press & Israel Exploration Society, 1976)

ZUGIBE, F., *The Cross and the Shroud* (Angelus Books, New York, 1982)

ACKNOWLEDGEMENTS

Cover: Royal Academy of Arts, London (detail)

Half title: National Gallery, London (detail); frontispiece: British Society for the Turin Shroud; National Gallery: El Greco: *Christ Driving Traders from the Temple*; imprint page: Barrie Schwortz; Contents page chapter headings: 1 John Rylands Library, University of Manchester; 2, Zev Radovan; 3 British Library; 4, 11 British Museum; 5, 6, 7, Weidenfeld & Nicolson Archives; 8 Garo Nalbaldian; 10 National Gallery, London; 9, 12 Israel Antiquities Authority.

Chapter 1: page 10 Werner Braun; pp11, 21 John Rylands Library, University of Manchester: *John Gospel Papyrus P52*; pp15, 18 Ekdotike Athenon, Athens; p20 British Library: *Egerton Papyrus 2*; p23 Magdalen College Oxford/Dr Christine Ferdinand: *Matthew Gospel Magdalen Greek Ms17*.

Chapter 2: pp24, 33 Sonia Halliday; pp25, 37 Zev Radovan; pp34-5 Werner Braun, p35tr Israel Antiquities Authority; p36 Art Resource, New York.

Chapter 3: pp40, 49 Weidenfeld & Nicolson Archives; pp41, 47 British Library *Papyrus 904*; p43 Ny Carlsberg Glyptotek.

Chapter 4: p50 Albatross; pp51, 58 British Museum; p53 Bad Kreuznach Museum; p54 Garo Nalbaldian; p56-7 Ira Block/National Geographic Society; p60t Leen Ritmeyer, b Leen Ritmeyer, after Ehud Netzer; p62 Martha Cooper/National Geographic Society.

Chapter 5: p64 Sonia Halliday; pp65, 69 Weidenfeld & Nicolson Archives; pp66, 74 Zev Radovan; p70 Erich Lessing.

Chapter 6: p76 David Harris; p77, 86 Weidenfeld & Nicolson; p79t Virgilio Corbo, b Garo Nalbaldian; pp 80, 81, 83 Danny Friedman; p82, 89 Zev Radovan; p84 Sonia Halliday; p85 Jo Moore.

Chapter 7: pp90, 91, 100 Weidenfeld & Nicolson Archives; p92 Sonia Halliday; p96 Dr A. A. Mason; p98 Victoria & Albert Museum, London; p99 Garo Nalbaldian.

Chapter 8: p102 Sonia Halliday; pp103, 108 Garo Nalbaldian; p105 Zev Radovan; p107t Israel Museum, b Leen Ritmeyer; p109b Israel Antiquities Authority; pp110-111, 112c Leen Ritmeyer; pp112t (?), b, 113t Zev Radovan; p114 Vatican Grottoes; p117-8 National Gallery, London (as title page).

Chapter 9: pp118, 129b Professor Umberto Fasola; pp119, 126 Israel Antiquities Authority; p128 Zev Radovan; pp120, 121 Weidenfeld & Nicolson Archives; p122 Leen Ritmeyer; p124 Garo Nalbaldian; p130b Israel Antiquities Authority; p131t Erich Lessing; p133 Oxford Research Laboratory; p134 British Society for the Turin Shroud; p135 Barrie Schwortz.

Chapter 10: p136 Silesian Publications; pp137, 147-8, 153 National Gallery, London: Orcagna: *Jesus Appearing to Mary Magdalen*; p138 Israel Antiquities Authority; p139 Sonia Halliday; p140t Carta Jerusalem; p141 Garo Nalbaldian; p144-5 Hershel Shanks; p.145 David Willis.

Chapter 11: pp154, 161, 162, Weidenfeld & Nicolson Archives; pp155, 169 British Museum; p163 Ian Wilson; p165 Zev Radovan; p166t Hershel Shanks, b Louis Hugues Vincent; p167 Joint Sepphoris Project, Duke University & Hebrew University.

Chapter 12: pp170, 177 Ian Wilson; pp171, 176 Israel Antiquities Authority; p172 Weidenfeld & Nicolson Archives.

INDEX

Page numbers in *italics* denote illustrations or charts

criteria for the selection and use of visuals in instruction

a workbook

Educational Technology Publications
Englewood Cliffs, New Jersey 07632

George L. Gropper

Zita Glasgow

Jean Klingensmith

FOREWORD

This WORKBOOK is one part of a training program developed for personnel serving training or audio-visual functions. The program has been designed to train them in the preparation, selection, and use of visuals in instruction. It is intended for use by personnel who have had some prior training in the application of behavioral principles to the preparation of instructional materials.

The HANDBOOK is designed to assist the learner in solving practice problems. Accordingly, the learner should read each section of the handbook, and whenever directed to do so by instructions in the handbook, he should proceed to relevant practice exercises in this workbook. It is recommended that the learner not merely read the handbook; he should engage in the practice exercises specifically prepared to accompany it.

The learner may refer back to the handbook as needed while working on the practice problems appearing in this workbook.

Each exercise or sub-exercise appears on a left-hand page. Answers to exercise problems appear on a right-hand page.

Each exercise or sub-exercise contains multiple problems. In obtaining feedback from the answer pages about correctness of his answers, the learner may proceed in one of two ways: (1) he may do all the problems on the page and then look at the answers; or (2) he may do each problem and then look up the answer to it. The former strategy is recommended as long as the learner feels confident about his answers and is not experiencing any difficulty. If he is uncertain about answers, he may wish to check the answers to individual problems before going on to the next problem. Since answers to some types of problems depend on judgment, the second strategy may be more appropriate.

In order to preclude the opportunity to see answers before doing the problems, which would rob problem-solving of its usefulness, the following recommendations are made: (1) if all problems are done before looking up answers, the learner should fold back the answer page while doing the problems; (2) if answers are consulted after each problem, the learner should use a mask on the answer page to cover the answers to the remaining problems.

It is probably preferable that the learner use Strategy #2: getting feedback after each problem.

ACKNOWLEDGMENTS

This volume was prepared by the American Institutes for Research, Pittsburgh, Pennsylvania for the Bureau of Naval Personnel under Contract No. N00022-68-C-0106. It was developed in the conduct of a project, under the direction of Dr. George L. Gropper, the principal aim of which was to develop guide lines for decisions about the use of film or instructional television in instruction.

The reproduction of this volume was heavily dependent on the skill of Miss Kathleen Gubala in preparing the manuscript.

PART I

EXERCISES
1 - 13

EXERCISE #1

I. Recognize

A. Classify the following types of visuals by checking the appropriate column.

Visual	Realistic	Reproduced	Fabricated
1. Chart showing net corporate earnings for twelve-month period			
2. Scale model of car			
3. Cartoons			
4. Airplane panel			
5. Flight simulator panel			
6. Outboard motor			
7. Job study diagram			
8. Automobile coming off assembly line			
9. Photograph of a computer keyboard			
10. Spare automobile parts			

SEE ANSWERS

EXERCISE #1

I. Recognize

A. Classify the following types of visuals by checking the appropriate column.

Visual	Realistic	Reproduced	Fabricated
1. Chart showing net corporate earnings for twelve-month period			✓
2. Scale model of car		✓	
3. Cartoons			✓
4. Airplane panel	✓		
5. Flight simulator panel		✓	
6. Outboard motor	✓		
7. Job study diagram			✓
8. Automobile coming off assembly line	✓		
9. Photograph of a computer keyboard		✓	
10. Spare automobile parts	✓		

II. Produce

A. Give two specific examples of each of the three kinds of visuals. (If possible, use examples from jobs you are currently dealing with.)

REALISTIC: 1. _____

2. _____

REPRODUCED: 1. _____

2. _____

FABRICATED: 1. _____

2. _____

SEE ANSWERS

EXERCISE #1

II. Produce

A. Give two specific examples of each of the three kinds of visuals. (If possible, use examples from jobs you are currently dealing with.)

REALISTIC: 1. *wrench*

              2. *carburetor*

REPRODUCED: 1. *film of rocket launch*

              2. *TV tape of a play*

FABRICATED: 1. *sketch of an airplane*

              2. *pie chart showing disposition of income*

RESUME READING ON PAGE 1.9
IN THE HANDBOOK.

EXERCISE #2

I. Recognize

A. Classify the following types of outputs as visual or non-visual by
    checking the appropriate column.

Job - Output	Visual	Non-Visual
1. Lecturer - a talk		
2. Copywriter - text of a TV commercial		
3. Dentist - a filling		
4. Sign painter - name on a door		
5. Janitor - waxed floor		
6. Woodcarver - a wall plaque		
7. Waiter - total of dinner tab		
8. Draftsman - a circle drawn with a compass		
9. Audio technician - setting of volume level on a numerical dial		
10. Waitress - filled cup of coffee		

SEE ANSWERS

EXERCISE #2

I. Recognize

A. Classify the following types of outputs as visual or non-visual by checking the appropriate column.

Job - Output	Visual	Non-Visual
1. Lecturer - a talk		✓
2. Copywriter - text of a TV commercial		✓
3. Dentist - a filling	✓	
4. Sign painter - name on a door		✓
5. Janitor - waxed floor	✓	
6. Woodcarver - a wall plaque	✓	
7. Waiter - total of dinner tab		✓
8. Draftsman - a circle drawn with a compass	✓	
9. Audio-technician - setting of volume level on a numerical dial		✓
10. Waitress - filled cup of coffee	✓	

EXERCISE #2

I. Recognize

B. For each of the jobs below, select the output (A or B) that HAS relevant visual display characteristics.

JOB	OUTPUT A	OUTPUT B	A	B	BOTH
Lumberjack cutting tree down with ax	Direction in which tree falls	Impact of ax on tree			
Carpenter tightening screws with screwdriver	Closeness of screw to surface	Tightness of screw			
Golfer	Follow through on swing	Trajectory of ball			
Gardener watering lawn with a hose	Horizontal distance of spray	Wetness of area covered			
Carpenter drilling holes in wood	Size of hole drilled	Resistance to drill			

SEE ANSWERS

1.8

EXERCISE #2

I. Recognize

B. For each of the jobs below, select the output (A or B) that HAS relevant visual display characteristics.

JOB	OUTPUT A	OUTPUT B	A	B	BOTH
Lumberjack cutting tree down with ax	Direction in which tree falls	Impact of ax on tree	X		
Carpenter tightening screws with screwdriver	Closeness of screw to surface	Tightness of screw	X		
Golfer	Follow through on swing	Trajectory of ball		X	
Gardener watering lawn with a hose	Horizontal distance of spray	Wetness of area covered			X
Carpenter drilling holes in wood	Size of hole drilled	Resistance to drill	X		

EXERCISE #2

I. Recognize

C. Classify the following outputs as having or not having relevant visual display characteristics.

   If they do have relevant visual display characteristics, write what they are in the last column.

JOB - OUTPUT	HAS	HAS NOT	VISUAL CHARACTERISTICS
1. Seaman - deck cleaned of rust			
2. Baseball player - follow through on swing			
3. Jockey - pace of horse nearing finish line			
4. Book binder - holes punched on one side of paper			
5. Carpet installer - carpet abutting wall			
6. Dishwasher - dish			
7. Football player - impact of tackle			
8. Bricklayer - brick wall			
9. Truck driver - change in speed as a result of gearing down			
10. Electronics repairman - soldered leads			

1.10

SEE ANSWERS

EXERCISE #2

I. Recognize

C. Classify the following outputs as <u>having</u> or <u>not having</u> relevant visual display characteristics.

   If they <u>do have</u> relevant visual display characteristics, write what they are in the last column.

JOB - OUTPUT	HAS	HAS NOT	VISUAL CHARACTERISTICS
1. Seaman - deck cleaned of rust	✓		*absence of rust*
2. Baseball player - follow through on swing		✓	
3. Jockey - pace of horse nearing finish line		✓	
4. Book binder - holes punched on one side of paper	✓		*closeness to margin*
5. Carpet installer - carpet abutting wall	✓		*closeness to wall or evenness*
6. Dishwasher - dish	✓		*cleanness*
7. Football player - impact of tackle		✓	
8. Bricklayer - brick wall	✓		*even rows, smooth rows of cement, etc.*
9. Truck driver - change in speed as a result of gearing down		✓	
10. Electronics repairman - soldered leads	✓		*completeness or intactness of solder*

RESUME READING ON PAGE 1.18 IN THE HANDBOOK.

EXERCISE #3

I. Recognize

A. Classify the following types of inputs by checking the appropriate column.

Job - Input	Visual	Non-Visual
1. Telephone operator - beep tone		
2. Building contractor - blueprints		
3. Proofreader - galley proofs		
4. Batter - fast ball		
5. Artist - paints and canvas		
6. Bill collector - list of overdue accounts		
7. Telephone installer - color-coded lines		
8. Maintenance mechanic - maintenance checklist		
9. Naval officer - position of enemy vessel		
10. Bus driver - yellow curb		

SEE ANSWERS

EXERCISE #3

<u>I. Recognize</u>

A. Classify the following types of inputs by checking the appropriate column.

Job - Input	Visual	Non-Visual
1. Telephone operator - beep tone		✓
2. Building contractor - blueprints	✓	
3. Proofreader - galley proofs		✓
4. Batter - fast ball	✓	
5. Artist - paints and canvas	✓	
6. Bill collector - list of overdue accounts		✓
7. Telephone installer - color-coded lines	✓	
8. Maintenance mechanic - maintenance checklist		✓
9. Naval officer - position of enemy vessel	✓	
10. Bus driver - yellow curb	✓	

RESUME READING ON PAGE 1.22 IN THE HANDBOOK.

EXERCISE #4

I. Recognize

A. Classify the visual actions in the jobs below as (A) identifies visual characteristics of inputs,
   (B) alters visual characteristics of inputs, or (C) produces a visual output.

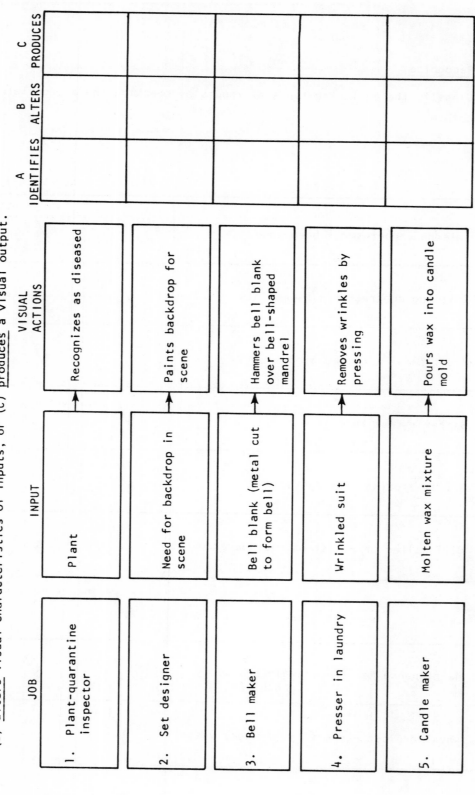

JOB	INPUT	VISUAL ACTIONS	A IDENTIFIES	B ALTERS	C PRODUCES
1. Plant-quarantine inspector	Plant	Recognizes as diseased			
2. Set designer	Need for backdrop in scene	Paints backdrop for scene			
3. Bell maker	Bell blank (metal cut to form bell)	Hammers bell blank over bell-shaped mandrel			
4. Presser in laundry	Wrinkled suit	Removes wrinkles by pressing			
5. Candle maker	Molten wax mixture	Pours wax into candle mold			

SEE ANSWERS

1.14

EXERCISE #4

1. Recognize

A. Classify the visual actions in the jobs below as (A) identifies visual characteristics of inputs,
   (B) alters visual characteristics of inputs, or (C) produces a visual output.

JOB	INPUT	VISUAL ACTIONS	A IDENTIFIES	B ALTERS	C PRODUCES
1. Plant-quarantine inspector	Plant	Recognizes as diseased	X		
2. Set designer	Need for backdrop in scene	Paints backdrop for scene			X
3. Bell maker	Bell blank (metal cut to form bell)	Hammers bell blank over bell-shaped material		X	
4. Presser in laundry	Wrinkled suit	Removes wrinkles by pressing		X	
5. Candle maker	Molten wax mixture	Pours wax into candle mixture		X	

EXERCISE #4

I. Recognize

A. Classify the visual actions in the jobs below as (A) identifies visual characteristics of inputs,
   (B) alters visual characteristics of inputs, or (C) produces a visual output.

JOB	INPUT	VISUAL ACTIONS	A IDENTIFIES	B ALTERS	C PRODUCES
6. Florist	Pile of cut flowers	Arranges flowers			
7. Fingerprint expert	Two sets of finger-prints	Matches fingerprints			
8. Winemaker	New wine	Inspects clarity of wine			
9. Graphics specialist	Verbal instructions	Draws graph			
10. Foreman	Assembly line	Observes movement of products			

SEE ANSWERS

EXERCISE #4

I. Recognize

A. Classify the visual actions in the jobs below as (A) _identifies_ visual characteristics of inputs,
   (B) _alters_ visual characteristics of inputs, or (C) _produces_ a visual output.

JOB	INPUT	VISUAL ACTIONS	A IDENTIFIES	B ALTERS	C PRODUCES
6. Florist	Pile of cut flowers	Arranges flowers		X	
7. Fingerprint expert	Two sets of finger-prints	Matches fingerprints	X		
8. Winemaker	New wine	Inspects clarity of wine	X		
9. Graphics specialist	Verbal instructions	Draws graph			X
10. Foreman	Assembly line	Observes movement of products	X		

1.17

EXERCISE #4

II. Recognize

A. For each of the jobs below, select the action (A or B) which is VISUAL.

JOB	ACTION A	ACTION B	A	B
1. Driver	Makes a right-hand turn	Turns on his right-hand blinker		
2. Pin boy	Picks up fallen pins	Spots pins on pegs in floor		
3. Fan blade aliner	Places blade assembly on spindle	Sights across blade and bends until in contact with gage pin		
4. Petroleum geologist	Prepares surface and subsurface maps	Estimates oil reserves		
5. Candy maker	Spreads candy onto cooling slab until filled to edges	Tastes product to evaluate flavor		

SEE ANSWERS

1.18

EXERCISE #4

II. Recognize

A. For each of the jobs below, select the action (A or B) which is VISUAL.

JOB	ACTION A	ACTION B	A	B
1. Driver	Makes a right-hand turn	Turns on his right-hand blinker		X
2. Pin boy	Picks up fallen pins	Spots pins on pegs in floor		X
3. Fan blade aliner	Places blade assembly on spindle	Sights across blade and bends until in contact with gage pin		X
4. Petroleum geologist	Prepares surface and subsurface maps	Estimates oil reserves	X	
5. Candy maker	Spreads candy onto cooling slab until filled to edges	Tastes product to evaluate flavor	X	

II. Recognize

B. Classify the following types of actions as <u>visual</u> or <u>non-visual</u> by checking the appropriate column.

If the action is visual, indicate in the last column the type of visual action.

	JOB	ACTION	VISUAL	NON-VISUAL	TYPE OF VISUAL ACTION
1.	Claims adjustor	Writes accident report			
2.	Barber	Evens off both sideburns			
3.	Cigar maker	Assesses firmness of cigar			
4.	Florist	Arranges flowers into a corsage			
5.	Nurse	Reads thermometer			
6.	Linoleum examiner	Examines linoleum for defects			
7.	Umpire	Calls balls and strikes			
8.	Map maker	Makes maps			
9.	Accountant	Calculates payroll			
10.	Stonegrader	Inspects quarried stone for size and quality			

SEE ANSWERS

II. Recognize

B. Classify the following types of actions as <u>visual</u> or <u>non-visual</u> by checking the appropriate column.

If the action is visual, indicate in the last column the type of visual action.

JOB	ACTION	VISUAL	NON-VISUAL	TYPE OF VISUAL ACTION
1. Claims adjustor	Writes accident report		X	
2. Barber	Evens off both sideburns	X		*Alters*
3. Cigar maker	Assesses firmness of cigar		X	
4. Florist	Arranges flowers into a corsage	X		*Alters*
5. Nurse	Reads thermometer		X	
6. Linoleum examiner	Examines linoleum for defects	X		*Identifies*
7. Umpire	Calls balls and strikes	X		*Identifies*
8. Map maker	Makes maps	X		*Produces*
9. Accountant	Calculates payroll		X	
10. Stonegrader	Inspects quarried stone for size and quality	X		*Identifies*

EXERCISE #4

III. Edit

A. Each of the visual actions below has been _incorrectly_ labeled. Correct the labels.

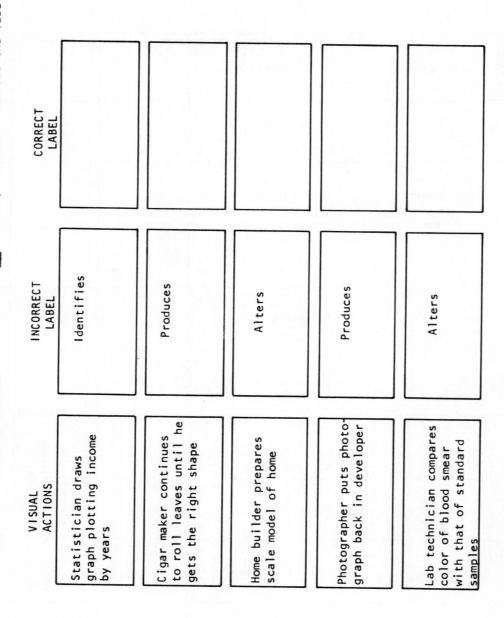

VISUAL ACTIONS	INCORRECT LABEL	CORRECT LABEL
Statistician draws graph plotting income by years	Identifies	
Cigar maker continues to roll leaves until he gets the right shape	Produces	
Home builder prepares scale model of home	Alters	
Photographer puts photograph back in developer	Produces	
Lab technician compares color of blood smear with that of standard samples	Alters	

SEE ANSWERS

1.22

EXERCISE #4

III. Edit

A. Each of the visual actions below has been _incorrectly_ labeled. Correct the label.

VISUAL ACTIONS	INCORRECT LABEL	CORRECT LABEL
Statistician draws graph plotting income by years	Identifies	*Produces*
Cigar maker continues to roll leaves until he gets the right shape	Produces	*Alters*
Home builder prepares scale model of home	Alters	*Produces*
Photographer puts photograph back in developer	Produces	*Alters*
Lab technician compares color of blood smear with that of standard samples	Alters	*Identifies*

RESUME READING ON PAGE 1.29 IN THE HANDBOOK.

EXERCISE #5

I. Produce

A. For the jobs below, indicate what confusion the job holder might have if he were unable to discriminate between outputs.

JOB	DISCRIMINATION FAILURE	CONFUSION
1. Rifleman cleans rifle bore	Cannot discriminate between properly and improperly cleaned bore	
2. TV repairman makes adjustments in TV image	Cannot discriminate between properly and improperly adjusted image	
3. Hi-fi repairman using oscilloscope to align a tuner	Cannot discriminate between properly and improperly aligned tuner	
4. Mechanic adjusting positions of parts to be joined together	Cannot discriminate between correct and incorrect positioning	
5. Sales clerk attempting to calm down irate customer	Cannot discriminate between satisfied and unsatisfied customer	

SEE ANSWERS

EXERCISE #5

I. Produce

A. For the jobs below, indicate what confusion the job holder might have if he were unable to discriminate between outputs.

JOB	DISCRIMINATION FAILURE	CONFUSION
1. Rifleman cleans rifle bore	Cannot discriminate between properly and improperly cleaned bore	*May consider an improperly cleaned bore as being properly cleaned and vice versa*
2. TV repairman makes adjustments in TV image	Cannot discriminate between properly and improperly adjusted image	*May consider an improper adjustment to be a proper adjustment and vice versa*
3. Hi-fi repairman using oscilloscope to align a tuner	Cannot discriminate between properly and improperly aligned tuner	*May consider an improper alignment as a proper alignment and vice versa*
4. Mechanic adjusting positions of parts to be joined together	Cannot discriminate between correct and incorrect positioning	*May consider incorrect position as being correct and vice versa*
5. Sales clerk attempting to calm down irate customer	Cannot discriminate between satisfied and unsatisfied customer	*May consider an unsatisfied customer as satisfied and vice versa*

1.25

EXERCISE #5

II. Recognize

A. For the jobs below, identify the consequences likely to occur if the job holder fails to discriminate between correct and incorrect visual outputs. (Check the appropriate column.)

JOB	FAILS TO DISCRIMINATE BETWEEN OUTPUTS		CONSEQUENCES STOPS TOO SOON	CONTINUES TOO LONG	EITHER
1. Rifleman cleans rifle bore	Properly cleaned bore	Improperly cleaned bore			
2. TV repairman makes adjustments in TV image	Properly adjusted image	Improperly adjusted image			
3. Hi-fi repairman using oscilloscope to align a tuner	Pattern for a properly aligned tuner	Pattern for an improperly aligned tuner			
4. Mechanic adjusting positions of parts to be joined together	Correct positioning (orientation) of parts	Incorrect positioning (orientation) of parts			
5. Sales clerk attempting to calm down irate customer	Customer satisfied with explanation	Customer dissatisfied with explanation			

SEE ANSWERS

1.26

EXERCISE #5

II. Recognize

A. For the jobs below, identify the consequences likely to occur if the job holder fails to discriminate between correct and incorrect visual outputs. (Check the appropriate column.)

JOB	FAILS TO DISCRIMINATE BETWEEN OUTPUTS		CONSEQUENCES		
			STOPS TOO SOON	CONTINUES TOO LONG	EITHER
1. Rifleman cleans rifle bore	Properly cleaned bore	Improperly cleaned bore			X
2. TV repairman makes adjustments in TV image	Properly adjusted image	Improperly adjusted image			X
3. Hi-fi repairman using oscilloscope to align a tuner	Pattern for a properly aligned tuner	Pattern for an improperly aligned tuner			X
4. Mechanic adjusting positions of parts to be joined together	Correct positioning (orientation) of parts	Incorrect positioning (orientation) of parts			X
5. Sales clerk attempting to calm down irate customer	Customer satisfied with explanation	Customer dissatisfied with explanation			X

EXERCISE #5

III. Produce

A. For the jobs below, in your own words create examples of what the job holder might do wrong if he were unable to discriminate between outputs. (Fill in as many columns as are applicable.)

JOB	OUTPUTS		STOPS TOO SOON	CONTINUES TOO LONG	FAILS TO CORRECT ERRORS
1. Rifleman cleaning gun	Properly cleaned gun	Improperly cleaned gun			
2. TV repairman	Adjusted image	Over-adjusted image			
3. Hi-fi repairman aligning tuner	Aligned tuner	Mal-aligned tuner			
4. Mechanic positioning parts	Correct position	Incorrect position			
5. Sales clerk calming customer	Calmed customer	Uncalmed customer			

SEE ANSWERS

EXERCISE #5

III. Produce

A. For the jobs below, in your own words create examples of what the job holder might do wrong if he were unable to discriminate between outputs. (Fill in as many columns as are applicable.)

	JOB	OUTPUTS		STOPS TOO SOON	CONTINUES TOO LONG	FAILS TO CORRECT ERRORS
1.	Rifleman cleaning gun	Properly cleaned gun	Improperly cleaned gun	*Would stop too soon, leaving dirt in*		
2.	TV repairman	Adjusted image	Overadjusted image		*Would continue to make adjustment although he had actually achieved a good adjustment*	*Would fail to go back to the correct adjustment*
3.	Hi-fi repairman aligning tuner	Aligned tuner	Malaligned tuner	*Would stop aligning tuner before it was properly aligned*	*Would continue making adjustments past a proper aligning*	*Would fail to correct his overadjustment*
4.	Mechanic positioning parts	Correct position	Incorrect position	*Would stop short of a correct position*	*Would go past a correct position*	*Would fail to reposition an improperly positioned part*
5.	Sales clerk calming customer	Calmed customer	Uncalmed customer	*Would stop talking too soon*	*Would talk too long*	*Would fail to make further amends*

1.29

EXERCISE #5

III. Produce

B. In order to prevent the job holder either from stopping too soon, continuing too long, or failing to correct errors, for each of the jobs below, indicate between what types of outputs the job holder should have practice making discriminations.

JOBS	OUTPUT 1	OUTPUT 2
1. Seamstress positioning sleeves she will sew onto dress.		
2. Furniture sander sands and polishes wood until it reaches a specified sheen.		
3. Medical aide applies bandage to wounds.		
4. Carpenter making picture frames has to fit edges together in a miter joint.		
5. Secretary applies thin film of corrective fluid to stencil to delete typing error.		
6. Clerk obtains fingerprints free of smudges.		
7. Gardener waters plants which must have ground saturated.		
8. Etcher applies acid to non-printing areas until printing depth is attained.		
9. Soldier folds flag according to regulations.		
10. Pile driver activates power hammer which drives piles to required depth.		

SEE ANSWERS

III. Produce

B. In order to prevent the job holder either from stopping too soon, continuing too long, or failing to correct errors, for each of the jobs below, indicate between what types of outputs the job holder should have practice making discriminations.

JOBS	OUTPUT 1	OUTPUT 2
1. Seamstress positioning sleeves she will sew onto dress.	*Correctly oriented sleeves*	*Incorrectly oriented sleeves*
2. Furniture sander sands and polishes wood until it reaches a specified sheen.	*Presence of sheen*	*Absence of sheen*
3. Medical aide applies bandage to wounds.	*Acceptable bandage*	*Unacceptable bandage*
4. Carpenter making picture frames has to fit edges together in a miter joint.	*Correctly mitered joint*	*Incorrectly mitered joint*
5. Secretary applies thin film of corrective fluid to stencil to delete typing error.	*Correct amount applied*	*Too much fluid applied*
6. Clerk obtains fingerprints free of smudges.	*Fingerprints free of smudges*	*Smudged fingerprints*
7. Gardener waters plants which must have ground saturated.	*Saturated ground*	*Too little water*
8. Etcher applies acid to non-printing areas until printing depth is attained.	*Sufficient depth*	*Insufficient depth*
9. Soldier folds flag according to regulations.	*Correctly folded flag*	*Incorrectly folded flag*
10. Pile driver activates power hammer which drives piles to required depth.	*Piles at correct depth*	*Piles at incorrect depth*

RESUME READING ON PAGE 1.32 IN THE HANDBOOK.

EXERCISE #6

I. Produce

A. For the jobs below, indicate what <u>confusion</u> might occur if the job holder were unable to <u>generalize</u> across <u>outputs.</u>

JOB	GENERALIZATION FAILURE	CONFUSION
1. Clerk wrapping gifts in department store	Cannot generalize across examples of slightly different but acceptable bows	
2. Textile worker pours compound on fabric and spreads it	Cannot generalize across <u>varied</u> examples of <u>improperly</u> spread compound	
3. Painter cutting in paint where wall meets ceiling	Cannot generalize across <u>varied</u> examples of acceptably straight lines	
4. Pizza maker measuring out dough by sight	Cannot generalize across <u>varied</u> examples of a correct amount of dough	
5. Manager trying to calm subordinate who appears upset	Cannot generalize across <u>varied</u> examples of upset employees	

SEE ANSWERS

1.32

I. Produce

A. For the jobs below, indicate what confusion might occur if the job holder were unable to generalize across outputs.

JOB	GENERALIZATION FAILURE	CONFUSION
1. Clerk wrapping gifts in department store	Cannot generalize across examples of slightly different but acceptable bows	*May confuse an acceptable bow for an unacceptable bow*
2. Textile worker pours compound on fabric and spreads it	Cannot generalize across varied examples of improperly spread compound	*May confuse an improper spread for a proper one*
3. Painter cutting in paint where wall meets ceiling	Cannot generalize across varied examples of acceptably straight lines	*May confuse an acceptably straight line for an unacceptable line*
4. Pizza maker measuring out dough by sight	Cannot generalize across varied examples of a correct amount of dough	*May confuse a correct amount of dough for an incorrect amount*
5. Manager trying to calm subordinate who appears upset	Cannot generalize across varied examples of upset employees	*May confuse a (still) upset employee for a calm one*

EXERCISE #6

II. Recognize

A. For the jobs below, identify the consequences likely to occur if the job holder fails to <u>generalize</u> <u>across outputs</u> and he has produced output B. (Check the appropriate column.)

JOB	FAILS TO GENERALIZE ACROSS OUTPUTS A.	B.	CONSEQUENCES STOPS TOO SOON	CONTINUES TOO LONG	EITHER
Clerk wrapping gifts in department store	An ideal bow	An acceptable bow (but not ideal)			
Textile worker pours compound on fabric and spreads it	Obvious case of improperly spread compound	Less obvious case of improperly spread compound			
Painter cutting in paint where wall meets ceiling	Acceptable line	Another line, slightly less good, but acceptable			
Pizza maker measuring out (by sight) dough	Ideal amount of dough	More than ideal amount but acceptable			
Manager trying to calm subordinate who <u>appears</u> upset	Obvious look of upset employee	Subtle look of upset employee			

SEE ANSWERS

1.34

EXERCISE #6

II. Recognize

A. For the jobs below, identify the consequences likely to occur if the job holder fails to generalize across outputs and he has produced output B. (Check the appropriate column.)

JOB	FAILS TO GENERALIZE ACROSS OUTPUTS A.	B.	CONSEQUENCES STOPS TOO SOON	CONTINUES TOO LONG	EITHER
Clerk wrapping gifts in department store	An ideal bow	An acceptable bow (but not ideal)		X	
Textile worker pours compound on fabric and spreads it	Obvious case of improperly spread compound	Less obvious case of improperly spread compound	X		
Painter cutting in paint where wall meets ceiling	Acceptable line	Another line, slightly less good, but acceptable		X	
Pizza maker measuring out (by sight) dough	Ideal amount of dough	More than ideal amount but acceptable		X	
Manager trying to calm subordinate who appears upset	Obvious look of upset employee	Subtle look of upset employee	X		

1.35

III. Produce

A. For the jobs below, create examples of what the job holder might do if he were unable to __generalize__ across visual outputs.

JOB	OUTPUTS		STOPS TOO SOON	CONTINUES TOO LONG	FAILS TO CORRECT ERRORS
Rust removal before painting	Tolerable amount of rust	Another tolerable amount of rust			
Adjusting TV color	Unacceptable blue	Another unacceptable blue			
Slicing potatoes	Potato slice A (too big)	Potato slice B (too big)			
Designing Roman-style letters	Contrast A between lines tolerable	Contrast B between lines tolerable			
Balancing coal on barge	Uneven distribution of coal	Another uneven distribution of coal			

SEE ANSWERS

III. Produce

A. For the jobs below, create examples of what the job holder might do if he were unable to generalize across visual outputs.

JOB	OUTPUTS		STOPS TOO SOON	CONTINUES TOO LONG	FAILS TO CORRECT ERRORS
Rust removal before painting	Tolerable amount of rust	Another tolerable amount of rust		*May spend too much time trying to remove more rust*	
Adjusting TV color	Unacceptable blue	Another unacceptable blue	*May stop adjusting before an acceptable blue is reached*		
Slicing potatoes	Potato slice A (too big)	Potato slice B (too big)			*May fail to trim down the potato slices*
Designing Roman-style letters	Contrast A between lines tolerable	Contrast B between lines tolerable		*May spend too much time trying to get exact amount of contrast in every letter*	
Balancing coal distribution on barge	Uneven distribution of coal	Another uneven distribution of coal			*May fail to distribute coal evenly*

EXERCISE #6

III. Produce

B. In order to prevent the job holder either from stopping too soon,
continuing too long, or failing to correct errors, for each of the
jobs below, indicate across what types of visual outputs the job
holder should have practice generalizing.

VISUAL OUTPUTS

1. Chef broiling "rare" steaks			
2. Pilot banking plane			
3. TV repairman making "vertical" adjustment			
4. Man grinding edge of glass until smooth			
5. Photographer developing picture			
6. Sailor steering small boat in narrow inlet			
7. Welder welding two plates together			
8. Bricklayer spreading mortar			
9. Tennis player hitting a deep lob			
10. Artist stretching canvas over frame until canvas is taut			

SEE ANSWERS

EXERCISE #6

III. Produce

B. In order to prevent the job holder either from stopping too soon,
continuing too long, or failing to correct errors, for each of the
jobs below, indicate across what types of <u>visual outputs</u> the job
holder should have practice.

VISUAL OUTPUTS

1. Chef broiling "rare" steaks	*Red steak*	*Blood red steak*	
2. Pilot banking plane	*Acceptable bank*	*Other acceptable bank*	
3. TV repairman making "vertical" adjustment	*Image does not roll up and down*	*Image fills top and bottom of screen*	*Space between lines even*
4. Man grinding edge of glass until smooth	*Acceptable degree of smoothness*	*Another acceptable degree of smoothness*	
5. Photographer developing picture	*One end of acceptable range*	*Other end of acceptable range*	
6. Sailor steering small boat in narrow inlet	*Acceptable closeness to sides*	*Another degree of acceptable closeness*	
7. Welder welding two plates together	*Acceptable welding job*	*Another different but acceptable job*	
8. Bricklayer spreading mortar	*Acceptable degree of thickness*	*Another acceptable degree of thickness*	
9. Tennis player hitting a deep lob	*Lob with one degree of depth*	*Lob with different degree of depth*	
10. Artist stretching canvas over frame until canvas is taut	*One degree of tautness*	*Another acceptable degree of tautness*	

RESUME READING ON PAGE 1.34 IN THE HANDBOOK.

EXERCISE #7

I. Produce

A. For the jobs below, write in examples of <u>visual inputs</u> between which the
    job holder must be able to <u>discriminate</u> if he is to be able to take the
    right action.

JOBS	INPUTS		
1. A cosmetician recommends face powders based on hair coloring.			
2. Farmer schedules harvesting based on the crop involved.			
3. Egg candler packs eggs according to size.			
4. Butcher packages and labels cuts of meat for retail.			
5. Confectionery factory sorter separates candy according to type.			
6. Stage door man controls entry back stage based on authorization to enter.			
7. Refuse collector sorts refuse according to ability to burn it.			
8. Art dealer labels paintings according to medium used.			
9. Dressmaker selects fasteners from varied types available.			
10. Floor installer selects coverings for kitchen floors from varied types available.			

SEE ANSWERS

I. Produce

A. For the jobs below, write in examples of <u>visual inputs</u> between which the
job holder must be able to <u>discriminate</u> if he is to be able to take the
right action.

JOBS	INPUTS		
1. A cosmetician recommends face powders based on hair coloring.	*redhead*	*brunette*	*blonde*
2. Farmer schedules harvesting based on the crop involved.	*grain*	*citrus fruit*	*tobacco*
3. Egg candler packs eggs according to size.	*Grade A eggs*	*Grade B eggs*	*Grade C eggs*
4. Butcher packages and labels cuts of meat for retail.	*roasts*	*chops*	*steaks*
5. Confectionery factory sorter separates candy according to type.	*chocolates*	*hard candy*	*caramels*
6. Stage door man controls entry back stage based on authorization to enter.	*cast members*	*unauthorized persons*	*stagehands*
7. Refuse collector sorts refuse according to ability to burn it.	*combustible refuse*		*non-combustible refuse*
8. Art dealer labels paintings according to medium used.	*oil*	*water*	*ink*
9. Dressmaker selects fasteners from varied types available.	*zippers*	*buttons*	*snaps*
10. Floor installer selects coverings for kitchen floors from varied types available.	*linoleum*	*tile block*	*indoor-outdoor carpeting*

EXERCISE #7

I. Produce

B. In column A, write in examples of visual inputs that must be discriminated. In column B, write in examples of what can go wrong if the job holder is unable to make the necessary discrimination.

JOB	A. VISUAL INPUTS TO BE DISCRIMINATED	B. WHAT CAN GO WRONG
1. Soldier on scouting patrol		
2. Cosmetic clerk custom mixes powder according to coloring of customer's hair		
3. Glassware inspector inspects glasses for perfects and salable seconds		
4. Aerial photographer photographs military installations camouflaged by trees		
5. Supermarket bag packer packs non-fragile and fragile items		

SEE ANSWERS

1.42

EXERCISE #7

I. Produce

B. In column A, write in examples of visual inputs that must be discriminated. In column B, write in examples of what can go wrong if the job holder is unable to make the necessary discrimination.

JOB	A. VISUAL INPUTS TO BE DISCRIMINATED	B. WHAT CAN GO WRONG
1. Soldier on scouting patrol	Friendly forces vs. enemy forces	Mistake friend for foe and shoot
2. Cosmetic clerk custom mixes powder according to coloring of customer's hair	Redhead, brunette, blonde	Confuses one type of hair color for another and advises inappropriate powder
3. Glassware inspector inspects glasses for perfects and salable seconds	First quality glass vs. slightly flawed glass	Mistakes some first quality glass as flawed and vice versa
4. Aerial photographer photographs military installations camouflaged by trees	Camouflaged military installations vs. ordinary wooded area	Confuses ordinary and camouflaged areas and makes wrong report
5. Supermarket bag packer packs non-fragile and fragile items	Fragile items vs. non-fragile items	Confuses fragile and non-fragile items and packs in the wrong part of the bag

1.43

EXERCISE #7

I. Produce

B. In column A, write in examples of visual inputs that must be discriminated. In column B, write in examples of what can go wrong if the job holder is unable to make the necessary discriminations.

JOB	A. VISUAL INPUTS TO BE DISCRIMINATED	B. WHAT CAN GO WRONG
6. Art museum curator places paintings in rooms according to period and nationality		
7. Gunner estimates range and speed of tank		
8. Buyer for business men and college age suits selects merchandise for season		
9. Lab technician examines blood samples for traces of leukemia		
10. Film editor inspects for quality of film after usage		

SEE ANSWERS

1.44

EXERCISE #7

I. Produce

B. In column A, write in examples of visual inputs that must be discriminated. In column B, write in examples of what can go wrong if the job holder is unable to make the necessary discriminations.

JOB	A. VISUAL INPUTS TO BE DISCRIMINATED	B. WHAT CAN GO WRONG
6. Art museum curator places paintings in rooms according to period and nationality	Flemish vs. French, Renaissance vs. Modern	May mistake Flemish for French painting and put in wrong room
7. Gunner estimates range and speed of tank	Fast vs. slow, near vs. far	Mistakes speed and makes poor allowance
8. Buyer for business men and college age suits selects merchandise for season	Young college suits vs. business men's suits	May confuse college clothing and business men's clothing
9. Lab technician examines blood samples for traces of leukemia	Blood sample with traces of leukemia vs. normal blood sample	Mistakes blood sample with traces of leukemia for normal blood sample and advises physician wrongly
10. Film editor inspects for quality of film after usage	Film O.K. for further use vs. film not O.K. for further use	Mistakes O.K. and not O.K. film and sends either out for further use

1.45

EXERCISE #7

11. Produce

A. For the jobs below, indicate the confusion that might occur if the job holder cannot discriminate among visual inputs.

JOB	DISCRIMINATION FAILURE	CONFUSION
1. Inspector grading meat	Cannot discriminate between the look of choice and prime meat	
2. Seaman identifying ships	Cannot discriminate between allied and enemy ships	
3. Sandwich maker	Cannot discriminate between rye bread and whole wheat bread	
4. Roofer repairing roof	Cannot discriminate between the look of a slate roof and a shingle roof	
5. Tree surgeon	Cannot discriminate between tree with only dead branches and completely dead tree	

SEE ANSWERS

EXERCISE #7

II. Produce

A. For the jobs below, indicate the confusion that might occur if the job holder cannot discriminate among visual inputs.

JOB	DISCRIMINATION FAILURE	CONFUSION
1. Inspector grading meat	Cannot discriminate between the look of choice and prime meat	May confuse choice with prime and vice versa
2. Seaman identifying ships	Cannot discriminate between allied and enemy ships	May confuse allied ships and enemy ships and vice versa
3. Sandwich maker	Cannot discriminate between rye bread and whole wheat bread	May confuse whole wheat with rye and vice versa
4. Roofer repairing roof	Cannot discriminate the look of a slate roof and a shingle roof	May confuse slate with shingle and vice versa
5. Tree surgeon	Cannot discriminate between tree with only dead branches and completely dead tree	May confuse dead tree with tree with dead branches only and vice versa

RESUME READING ON PAGE 1.36 IN THE HANDBOOK.

EXERCISE #8

1. Produce

A. For the jobs below, indicate what confusion might occur if the job holder were unable to generalize across inputs.

JOB	GENERALIZATION FAILURE	CONFUSION
1. Geologist identify-ing rocks	Failure to generalize across all varieties of crystalline rock (rock crystal, yellow quartz, etc.)	
2. Watchmaker inspect-ing watch dials for defects	Failure to generalize across varied types of defects (scratches, dirty, uncentered cannon, etc.)	
3. Aerial observer on lookout for enemy planes	Failure to generalize across varied types of enemy bombers	
4. Baseball player swinging at pitched balls	Failure to generalize across varied examples of "fast" pitches	
5. TV repairman	Failure to generalize across varied symptoms all indicative of "horizontal" problems	

SEE ANSWERS

1.48

EXERCISE #8

I. Produce

A. For the jobs below, indicate what confusion might occur if the job holder were unable to generalize across inputs.

JOB	GENERALIZATION FAILURE	CONFUSION
1. Geologist identifying rocks	Failure to generalize across all varieties of crystalline rock (rock crystal, yellow quartz, etc.)	May confuse some types of crystalline for non-crystalline rocks
2. Watchmaker inspecting watch dials for defects	Failure to generalize across varied types of defects (scratches, dirty, uncentered cannon, etc.)	May mistake a defective dial for a good dial
3. Aerial observer on lookout for enemy planes	Failure to generalize across varied types of enemy bombers	May mistake an enemy bomber for a friendly one
4. Baseball player swinging at pitched balls	Failure to generalize across varied examples of "fast" pitches	May mistake some moderately fast pitches for slow pitches and swing too late
5. TV repairman	Failure to generalize across varied symptoms all indicative of "horizontal" problems	May mistake some of the symptoms as indicative of other types of problems (automatic gain control, horizontal)

1.49

EXERCISE #8

I. Produce

B. For the jobs below, write in examples of visual inputs across which the
    job holder must generalize if he is to be able to take the right action.

Jobs	Visual Inputs		
1. Lifeguard watching swimmers in pool for varied signals of distress			
2. Truck driver must slow down under various hazardous conditions			
3. TV repairman makes repair in vertical circuit based on varied symptoms			
4. Man operating IBM card sorter on the lookout for signs of equipment failure			
5. Skier watching for various types of dangers on slope			
6. Ambassador must use appropriate title in greeting various types of generals			
7. Jewelry designer looking for precious stone to use as center of necklace			
8. Teacher trying to identify children who are uncertain about assignment			
9. Decorator looking for suitable instrument to cut picture wire before hanging picture			
10. Teacher diagnoses child as having vision problem on basis of various types of symptoms			

SEE ANSWERS

EXERCISE #8

I. Produce

B. For the jobs below, write in examples of <u>visual inputs</u> across which the
    job holder must <u>generalize</u> if he is to be able to take the right action.

	Jobs	Visual Inputs		
1.	Lifeguard watching swimmers in pool for varied signals of distress	*swimmer goes under water*	*swimmer gasping for air*	*swimmer strokes frantically*
2.	Truck driver must slow down under various hazardous conditions	*steep hill*	*wet road*	*sharp curve*
3.	TV repairman makes repair in vertical circuit based on varied symptoms	*picture slips up or down*	*picture narrows at top and bottom*	*horizontal line through picture*
4.	Man operating IBM card sorter on the lookout for signs of equipment failure	*cards being bent*	*cards not falling in slots*	*cards not going into different bins*
5.	Skier watching for various types of dangers on slope	*icy spot*	*bare spot*	*skiers coming downhill from above*
6.	Ambassador must use appropriate title in greeting various types of generals	*4 star general*	*3 star general*	*2 star general*
7.	Jewelry designer looking for precious stone to use as center of necklace	*diamond*	*emerald*	*pearl*
8.	Teacher trying to identify children who are uncertain about assignment	*student raises hand*	*looking at page number of surrounding students*	*student beckoning to teacher*
9.	Decorator looking for suitable instrument to cut picture wire before hanging picture	*scissors*	*pliers*	*wirecutters*
10.	Teacher diagnoses child as having vision problem on basis of <u>various</u> types of symptoms	*child squints*	*child blinks often*	*child's eyes water*

1.51

EXERCISE #8

I. Produce

C. In column A, write examples of visual inputs that must be generalized. In column B, write in examples of what can go wrong if the job holder is unable to make the necessary generalizations.

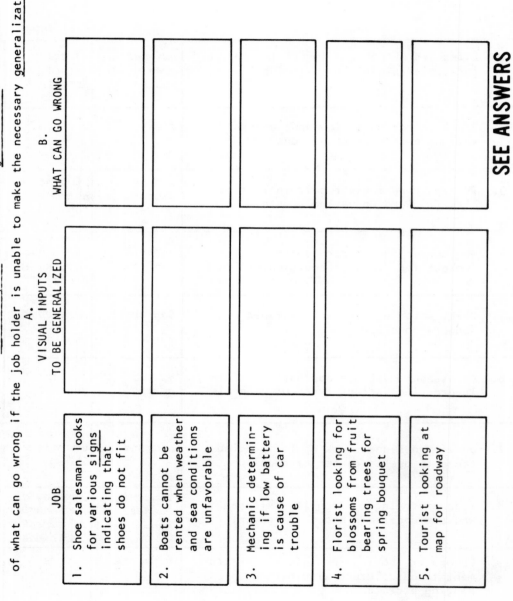

JOB	A. VISUAL INPUTS TO BE GENERALIZED	B. WHAT CAN GO WRONG
1. Shoe salesman looks for various signs indicating that shoes do not fit		
2. Boats cannot be rented when weather and sea conditions are unfavorable		
3. Mechanic determining if low battery is cause of car trouble		
4. Florist looking for blossoms from fruit bearing trees for spring bouquet		
5. Tourist looking at map for roadway		

SEE ANSWERS

1.52

EXERCISE #8

I. Produce

C. In column A, write examples of visual inputs that must be generalized. In column B, write in examples of what can go wrong if the job holder is unable to make the necessary generalizations.

JOB	A. VISUAL INPUTS TO BE GENERALIZED	B. WHAT CAN GO WRONG
1. Shoe salesman looks for various signs indicating that shoes do not fit	Toes touch front of shoe; arch puffs out over vamp; laces have side separation over tongue	Salesman may ignore one or more of these signs and advise customer to buy shoes
2. Boats cannot be rented when weather and sea conditions are unfavorable	High waves, dark skies, strong winds	May confuse some conditions for O.K. days
3. Mechanic determining if low battery is cause of car trouble	Dim lights, mild battery, slow windshield wipers	Ignores one or more of these indications of low battery
4. Florist looking for blossoms from fruit bearing trees for spring bouquet	Apple blossoms, orange blossoms, peach blossoms	Passes by these blossoms when actually all would make floral bouquet
5. Tourist looking at map for roadway	Various red and black lines indicate roadway	May miss roadway indication

RESUME READING ON PAGE 1.38 IN THE HANDBOOK.

1.53

EXERCISE #9

I. Produce

A. For the jobs below, indicate what confusion might occur if the job holder were unable to associate the correct visual action with the appropriate input.

JOB	ASSOCIATION FAILURE	CONFUSION
1. Film projectionist turns knob to raise or lower image on screen	For the input "image too low" does not associate "turn knob clockwise" (action)	
2. Man hunting with bow and arrow	For the input "animal far away" does not associate "aim high" (action)	
3. Gardener keeping ground at desirable (water) saturation level	For the input "newly planted grass" does not associate "daily watering" (action)	
4. Man fishing for trout has to keep line at appropriate degree of tautness	For the input "bobbin moving" does not associate "slacken line" (action)	
5. Golfer adjusts his stance according to type of club he is using	For the input "short iron" does not associate "take narrowest stance" (action)	

SEE ANSWERS

1.54

EXERCISE #9

I. Produce

A. For the jobs below, indicate what confusion might occur if the job holder were unable to associate the correct visual action with the appropriate input.

JOB	ASSOCIATION FAILURE	CONFUSION
1. Film projectionist turns knob to raise or lower image on screen	For the input "image too low" does not associate "turn knob clockwise" (action)	*May instead turn the knob counterclockwise and raise the image*
2. Man hunting with bow and arrow	For the input "animal far away" does not associate "aim high" (action)	*May instead aim too low and miss target*
3. Gardener keeping ground at desirable (water) saturation level	For the input "newly planted grass" does not associate "daily watering" (action)	*May instead water it less frequently and ground will be too dry*
4. Man fishing for trout has to keep line at appropriate degree of tautness	For the input "bobbin moving" does not associate "slacken line" (action)	*May instead reel in line making it too taut*
5. Golfer adjusts his stance according to type of club he is using	For the input "short iron" does not associate "take narrowest stance" (action)	*May instead take a medium or wide stance*

RESUME READING ON
PAGE 1.40 IN THE HANDBOOK.

1.55

EXERCISE #10

I. Recognize

A. Check one column indicating the type of failure the job holder is exhibiting for each of the wrong
actions taken.

PROBABLE FAILURE

JOB TASK	SITUATION	WRONG ACTION	DISCRIMI-NATION	GENERAL-IZATION	ASSOCI-ATION
1. Cook must produce sauce with correct degree of thickness	Recognizes sauce as being thick	Adds thickening agent instead of adding water			
2. Highway patrolman tagging speeders	Car moving at 60 mph and another at 70 mph in a 60 mph zone	Chases man going 60 mph			
3. Turn boat so wake of passing ship will not capsize it	Sees large wake from ship	Changes course so that boat is parallel to wake instead of taking perpendicular course			
4. Examiner of fingerprints	Compares two sets of fingerprints	Incorrectly identifies them as being the same			
5. Pet store owner selling dogs	In addition to other breeds has varied types of spaniels on hand including cocker spaniel, springer spaniel, and water spaniel	Fails to show a water spaniel to customer asking to see all the types of spaniels on hand			

SEE ANSWERS

1.56

EXERCISE #10

I. Recognize

A. Check one column indicating the type of failure the job holder is exhibiting for each of the wrong actions taken.

JOB TASK	SITUATION	WRONG ACTION	DISCRIMINATION	GENERALIZATION	ASSOCIATION
1. Cook must produce sauce with correct degree of thickness	Recognizes sauce as being thick	Adds thickening agent instead of adding water			✓
2. Highway patrolman tagging speeders	Car moving at 60 mph and another at 70 mph in a 60 mph zone	Chases man going 60 mph	✓		
3. Turn boat so wake of passing ship will not capsize it	Sees large wake from ship	Changes course so that boat is parallel to wake instead of taking perpendicular course			✓
4. Examiner of fingerprints	Compares two sets of fingerprints	Incorrectly identifies them as being the same	✓		
5. Pet store owner selling dogs	In addition to other breeds has varied types of spaniels on hand including cocker spaniel, spimper spaniel, and water spaniel	Fails to show a water spaniel to customer asking to see all the types of spaniels on hand		✓	

EXERCISE #10

I. Recognize

A. Check one column indicating the type of failure the job holder is exhibiting for each of the wrong actions taken.

JOB TASK	SITUATION	WRONG ACTION	DISCRIMI- NATION	GENERAL- IZATION	ASSOCI- ATION
6. Driver has to park car in space big enough for his car	Parking space too small for car	Attempts to park in space			
7. Steering outboard motorboat by turn-ing rudder in di-rection opposite to one you want	Bend in waterway toward right	Turns rudder to right			
8. Nurse weighing patient on scale	Indicator is as follows	Moves the weight to the right			
9. Surfer looking for good wave to ride on	Series of acceptable waves	Passes up one of the waves			
10. Identifying resistance of color-coded resistors	Has to figure out resistance of a resis-tor based on colors	Arrives at wrong value			

SEE ANSWERS

1.58

I. Recognize

A. Check one column indicating the type of failure the job holder is exhibiting for each of the wrong actions taken.

JOB TASK	SITUATION	WRONG ACTION	DISCRIMINATION	GENERALIZATION	ASSOCIATION
6. Driver has to park car in space big enough for his car	Parking space too small for car	Attempts to park in space	X		
7. Steering outboard motorboat by turning rudder in direction opposite to one you want	Bend in waterway toward right	Turns rudder to right			X
8. Nurse weighing patient on scale	Indicator is as follows	Moves the weight to the right			X
9. Surfer looking for good wave to ride on	Series of _acceptable_ waves	Passes up one of the waves		X	
10. Identifying resistance of color-coded resistors	Has to figure out resistance of a resistor based on colors	Arrives at wrong value			X

1.59

EXERCISE #10

II. Produce

A. The job holder may take the wrong action for any of three reasons. For each of the jobs below, write in examples in each column (if appropriate) illustrating what might go wrong.

JOB	INPUT	ACTION	DISCRIMINATIONS BETWEEN INPUTS	GENERALIZATIONS ACROSS INPUTS	ASSOCIATING INPUTS AND ACTIONS
electronic maintenance man	color-coded resistors (ten colors)	interprets resistance values			
American teacher new in Orient	faces of Oriental children	calls them by name			
American teacher	faces of American children	calls them by name			
baseball player	pitch coming toward plate	takes appropriate type swing			
painter	oil and water-based paint (unlabeled)	uses thinner or water to thin paint			

SEE ANSWERS

1.60

EXERCISE #10

II. Produce

A. The job holder may take the wrong action for any of three reasons. For each of the jobs below, write in examples in each column (if appropriate) illustrating what might go wrong.

JOB	INPUT	ACTION	DISCRIMINATIONS BETWEEN INPUTS	GENERALIZATIONS ACROSS INPUTS	ASSOCIATING INPUTS AND ACTIONS
electronic maintenance man	color-coded resistors (ten colors)	interprets resistance values	May be unable to see difference between colors	May confuse possible variations in one color as constituting the same color	May fail to associate proper numerical value (0-9) with appropriate color
American teacher new in Orient	faces of Oriental children	calls them by name	May be unable to see difference in appearance		May fail to associate names and students
American teacher	faces of American children	calls them by name	May be unable to see difference in appearance		May fail to associate names and students
baseball player	pitch coming toward plate	takes appropriate type swing	May be unable to see difference between slow and fast ball or between straight and curve ball	May be unable to see similarity among various types of curve ball	May fail to associate type of swing with type of pitch
painter	oil and water-based paint (unlabeled)	uses thinner or water to thin paint	May fail to discriminate between oil and water-based paints	May fail to generalize across varied examples of oil or varied examples of water-based paints	May fail to associate appropriate actions (thin with water instead of with thinner and converse)

1.61

EXERCISE #10

II. Produce

B. Below are the answers to the previous exercise. For each of the jobs below, put an X through the one failure out of the three that is the most likely to occur.

JOB	INPUT	ACTION	DISCRIMINATIONS BETWEEN INPUTS	GENERALIZATIONS ACROSS INPUTS	ASSOCIATING INPUTS AND ACTIONS
electronic maintenance man	color-coded resistors (ten colors)	interprets resistance values	May be unable to see difference between colors	May confuse possible variations in one color as constituting the same color	May fail to associate proper numerical value (0-9) with appropriate color
American teacher new in Orient	faces of Oriental children	calls them by name	May be unable to see difference in appearance		May fail to associate names and students
American teacher	faces of American children	calls them by name	May be unable to see difference in appearance		May fail to associate names and students
baseball player	pitch coming toward plate	takes appropriate type swing	May be unable to see difference between slow and fast ball or between straight and curve ball	May be unable to see similarity among various types of curve ball	May fail to associate type of swing with type of pitch
painter	oil and water-based paint (unlabeled)	uses thinner or water to thin paint	May fail to discriminate between oil and water-based paints	May fail to generalize across varied examples of oil or varied examples of water-based paints	May fail to associate appropriate actions (thin with water instead of with thinner and converse)

SEE ANSWERS

1.62

EXERCISE #10

II. Produce

B. Below are the answers to the previous exercise. For each of the jobs below, put an X through the one failure out of the three that is the most likely to occur.

JOB	INPUT	ACTION	DISCRIMINATIONS BETWEEN INPUTS	GENERALIZATIONS ACROSS INPUTS	ASSOCIATING INPUTS AND ACTIONS
electronic maintenance man	color-coded resistors (ten colors)	interprets resistance values	May be unable to see difference between colors	May confuse possible variations in one color as constituting the same color	May fail to associate proper numerical value (0-9) with appropriate color [X]
American teacher new in Orient	faces of Oriental children	calls them by name	May be unable to see difference in appearance [X]		May fail to associate names and students
American teacher	faces of American children	calls them by name	May be unable to see difference in appearance		May fail to associate names and students [X]
baseball player	pitch coming toward plate	takes appropriate type swing	May be unable to see difference between slow and fast ball or between straight and curve ball [X]	May be unable to see similarity among various types of curve ball	May fail to associate type of swing with type of pitch
painter	oil and water-based paint (unlabeled)	uses thinner or water to thin paint	May fail to discriminate between oil and water-based paints [X]	May fail to generalize across varied examples of oil or dried examples of water-based paints [X]	May fail to associate appropriate actions (thin with water instead of with thinner and converse)

RESUME READING ON PAGE 1.43 IN THE HANDBOOK.

EXERCISE #11

I. Recognize

A. Identify the criterion visuals involved in each of the jobs below by checking as many of the cells as are appropriate.

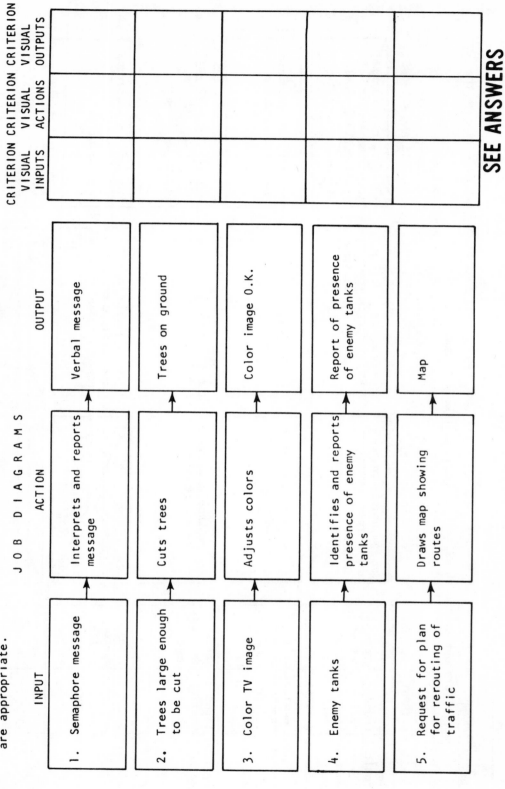

JOB DIAGRAMS

	INPUT	ACTION	OUTPUT		CRITERION VISUAL INPUTS	CRITERION VISUAL ACTIONS	CRITERION VISUAL OUTPUTS
1.	Semaphore message	Interprets and reports message	Verbal message				
2.	Trees large enough to be cut	Cuts trees	Trees on ground				
3.	Color TV image	Adjusts colors	Color image O.K.				
4.	Enemy tanks	Identifies and reports presence of enemy tanks	Report of presence of enemy tanks				
5.	Request for plan for rerouting of traffic	Draws map showing routes	Map				

SEE ANSWERS

1.64

EXERCISE #11

I. Recognize

A. Identify the criterion visuals involved in each of the jobs below by checking as many of the cells as are appropriate.

JOB DIAGRAMS

	INPUT	ACTION	OUTPUT	CRITERION VISUAL INPUTS	CRITERION VISUAL ACTIONS	CRITERION VISUAL OUTPUTS
1.	Semaphore message	Interprets and reports message	Verbal message	X		
2.	Trees large enough to be cut	Cuts trees	Trees on ground	X		
3.	Color TV image	Adjusts colors	Color image O.K.	X	X	X
4.	Enemy tanks	Identifies and reports presence of enemy tanks	Report of presence of enemy tanks	X	X	
5.	Request for plan for rerouting of traffic	Draws map showing routes	Map	X	X	X

EXERCISE #11

I. Recognize

B. Classify the visuals below as examples of <u>presentation</u> or <u>representation</u>. Check the appropriate column.

Visual Used in Instruction	Presentation	Representation
1. Photographs of cloud formations used to instruct pilot		
2. A camera lens used to instruct photographer		
3. Film of opposing team used to instruct football player		
4. Blueprint used to instruct carpenter how to construct door frame		
5. A piece of marble used to instruct sculptor		
6. A simulator used to instruct tractor trailer driver		
7. Developed photographs used to train photographer		
8. Actual paints and brushes used to instruct artist		
9. Balloon covered with shaving cream used to instruct barber		
10. Balsa wood and mat knife used to instruct model builder		

1.66

SEE ANSWERS

EXERCISE #11

I. Recognize

B. Classify the visuals below as examples of <u>presentation</u> or <u>representation</u>. Check the appropriate column.

Visual Used in Instruction	Presentation	Representation
1. Photographs of cloud formations used to instruct pilot		X
2. A camera lens used to instruct photographer	X	
3. Film of opposing team used to instruct football player		X
4. Blueprint used to instruct carpenter how to construct door frame		X
5. A piece of marble used to instruct sculptor	X	
6. A simulator used to instruct tractor trailer driver		X
7. Developed photographs used to train photographer	X	
8. Actual paints and brushes used to instruct artist	X	
9. Balloon covered with shaving cream used to instruct barber		X
10. Balsa wood and mat knife used to instruct model builder	X	

RESUME READING ON PAGE 1.47 IN THE HANDBOOK.

EXERCISE #12

I. Recognize

A. Classify the referents below as objects or abstractions. Then indicate how they can be visually presented or represented.

Referent To Be Presented or Represented	Type of Referent		Can Be Represented Only	Can Be Presented or Represented
	Object	Abstraction		
1. Tape spliced				
2. How wood is dove-tailed				
3. Concept of "justice"				
4. An airfoil being lifted by air				
5. Light refracted by water				
6. Drawing power of a shopping center				
7. Items moving on an assembly line				
8. Eighteen-button telephone				
9. Source of funds for a community project				
10. Movement of tides				

SEE ANSWERS

EXERCISE #12

I. Recognize

A. Classify the referents below as objects or abstractions. Then indicate how they can be visually presented or represented.

Referent To Be Presented or Represented	Type of Referent Object	Type of Referent Abstraction	Can Be Represented Only	Can Be Presented or Represented
1. Tape spliced	X			X
2. How wood is dove-tailed	X			X
3. Concept of "justice"		X	X	
4. An airfoil being lifted by air	X			X
5. Light refracted by water	X			X
6. Drawing power of a shopping center		X	X	
7. Items moving on an assembly line	X			X
8. Eighteen-button telephone	X			X
9. Source of funds for a community project		X	X	
10. Movement of tides	X			X

EXERCISE #12

I. Recognize

B. In the examples below, the same referent is presented or represented by
different media. Classify the media as to their degree of fidelity to the
referent. Put an X in the appropriate column for each of the media.

| | DEGREES OF FIDELITY | | | |
MEDIA	VERY HIGH	HIGH	MODERATE	LOW
1a. Blueprint of a cultural center				
1b. Stylized painting of a cultural center				
1c. An actual cultural center				
1d. Model of a cultural center				
2a. Film of dancers going through steps				
2b. Diagram of dance steps				
3a. An actual customer for fitting dress				
3b. A dress form to customer's measurement for fitting dress				
4a. A film showing pole vaulter jumping				
4b. A dotted line showing path of pole vaulter				

1.70

SEE ANSWERS

EXERCISE #12

I. Recognize

B. In the examples below, the same referent is presented or represented by different media. Classify the media as to their degree of fidelity to the referent. Put an X in the appropriate column for each of the media.

DEGREES OF FIDELITY

MEDIA	VERY HIGH	HIGH	MODERATE	LOW
1a. Blueprint of a cultural center				X
1b. Stylized painting of a cultural center			X	
1c. An actual cultural center	X			
1d. Model of a cultural center		X		
2a. Film of dancers going through steps		X		
2b. Diagram of dance steps				X
3a. An actual customer for fitting dress	X			
3b. A dress form to customer's measurement for fitting dress		X		
4a. A film showing pole vaulter jumping		X		
4b. A dotted line showing path of pole vaulter				X

RESUME READING ON PAGE 1.58 IN THE HANDBOOK.

1.71

EXERCISE #13

<u>1.</u> <u>Recognize</u>

A. Classify the representational <u>directness</u> of the visuals below by checking
    the appropriate column.

Concept	Visual	Direct	Indirect	Analogous
1. Anxiety	Child chewing hair			
2. Vertebrates	Horse			
3. Color theory	Chart showing three primary colors as source of all color			
4. Force of gravity	Person standing on scale (weight = force of gravity			
5. Law enforcement	Policeman giving traffic ticket			
6. Reflection of light	Arrow hitting object and bending			
7. Evaluation of a system	Flow chart showing steps			
8. Surface tension of water	A razor blade floating on water			
9. Training	Man demonstrating how to assemble a rifle			
10. Force of air	Sailboat moving			

1.72

SEE ANSWERS

EXERCISE #13

I. Recognize

A. Classify the representational <u>directness</u> of the visuals below by checking
    the appropriate column.

Concept	Visual	Direct	Indirect	Analogous
1. Anxiety	Child chewing hair		X	
2. Vertebrates	Horse	X		
3. Color theory	Chart showing three primary colors as source of all color			X
4. Force of gravity	Person standing on scale (weight = force of gravity)		X	
5. Law enforcement	Policeman giving traffic ticket	X		
6. Reflection of light	Arrow hitting object and bending			X
7. Evaluation of a system	Flow chart showing steps			X
8. Surface tension of water	A razor blade floating on water		X	
9. Training	Man demonstrating how to assemble a rifle	X		
10. Force of air	Sailboat moving		X	

RESUME READING ON
PAGE <u>II.1</u> IN THE HANDBOOK.

PART II

EXERCISES
14 - 18

EXERCISE #14

1. Recognize

A. Identify the criterion visuals involved in each of the jobs below by checking as many of the cells as are appropriate.

JOB DIAGRAMS

INPUT	ACTION	OUTPUT
1. Semaphore message	Interprets and reports message	Verbal message
2. Trees large enough to be cut	Cuts trees	Trees on ground
3. Color TV image	Adjusts colors	Color image O.K.
4. Enemy tanks	Identifies and reports presence of enemy tanks	Report of presence of enemy tanks
5. Request for plan for rerouting of traffic	Draws map showing routes	Map

CRITERION VISUAL INPUTS	CRITERION VISUAL ACTIONS	CRITERION VISUAL OUTPUTS

SEE ANSWERS

II.2

EXERCISE #14

I. Recognize

A. Identify the criterion visuals involved in each of the jobs below by checking as many of the cells as are appropriate.

JOB DIAGRAMS

INPUT	ACTION	OUTPUT	CRITERION VISUAL INPUTS	CRITERION VISUAL ACTIONS	CRITERION VISUAL OUTPUTS
1. Semaphore message	Interprets and reports message	Verbal message	X		
2. Trees large enough to be cut	Cuts trees	Trees on ground	X	X	X
3. Color TV image	Adjusts colors	Color image O.K.	X	X	X
4. Enemy tanks	Identifies and reports presence of enemy tanks	Report of presence of enemy tanks	X	X	
5. Request for plan for rerouting of traffic	Draws map showing routes	Map		X	X

EXERCISE #14

I. Recognize

B. Identify the types of VISUAL practice required for each of the jobs below by checking as many of the cells as are appropriate.

INPUT	ACTION	OUTPUT	DISCRIMI-NATING BETWEEN VISUAL INPUTS	GENERAL-IZING ACROSS VISUAL INPUTS	ASSOCIATING VISUAL ACTIONS AND INPUTS
1. Chart indicating medication to be administered	Measures out appropriate liquid volume	Correct dosage			
2. Moving object (to be photographed)	Sets wide lens opening (according to speed)	Unblurred photograph			
3. Lamp cue on telephone switch-board flashing	Answers flashing cue	Answered call			
4. Man to be finger-printed	Applies ink to fingers and records	Clearly defined fingerprint			
5. Blonde	Mixes face powder according to hair coloring	Mixed face powder matches standard			

SEE ANSWERS

11.4

EXERCISE #14

I. Recognize

B. Identify the types of VISUAL practice required for each of the jobs below by checking as many of the cells as are appropriate.

	INPUT	ACTION	OUTPUT	DISCRIMINATING BETWEEN VISUAL INPUTS	GENERALIZING ACROSS VISUAL INPUTS	ASSOCIATING VISUAL ACTIONS AND INPUTS
1.	Chart indicating medication to be administered	Measures out appropriate liquid volume	Correct dosage		X	X
2.	Moving object (to be photographed)	Sets wide lens opening (according to speed)	Unblurred photograph	X	X	X
3.	Lamp cue on telephone switchboard flashing	Answers flashing cue	Answered call	X		
4.	Man to be fingerprinted	Applies ink to fingers and records	Clearly defined fingerprint	X	X	X
5.	Blonde	Mixes face powder according to hair coloring	Mixed face powder matches standard	X	X	X

EXERCISE #14

II. Produce

A. For the jobs below, write in examples of the types of VISUAL practice the job diagrams indicate are necessary.

			PRACTICE WITH INPUTS	PRACTICE WITH ACTIONS	PRACTICE WITH OUTPUTS
INPUT	ACTION	OUTPUT			
defective toys: scratch, loose screw, unbent tab	paint scratch, tighten screw, tab down	repaired toy			
clothes with even and uneven colors	puts uneven colors back in dye vat	desired color on fabric			
various examples of fast pitches	swing same for all	hit or strike			
soft stage and liquid stage candy	spread evenly on cooling slab or pour in mold	evenly spread candy and filled mold			
flushed, glassy-eyed, listless child	recog-nize as ill	report to doctor			

SEE ANSWERS

11.6

EXERCISE #14

II. Produce

A. For the jobs below, write in examples of the types of VISUAL practice the job diagrams indicate are necessary.

INPUT	ACTION	OUTPUT	PRACTICE WITH INPUTS	PRACTICE WITH ACTIONS	PRACTICE WITH OUTPUTS
defective toys: scratch, loose screw, unbent tab	paint scratch, tighten screw, tab down	repaired toy	discriminating among various types of defects	associating the correct repair action with each input	discriminating between repaired and unrepaired toys
clothes with even and uneven colors	puts uneven colors back in dye vat	desired color on fabric	discriminating between even and uneven colors	associating required corrective action with the right input	same as for inputs
various examples of fast pitches	swing same for all	hit or strike	generalizing across various examples of fast pitches		
soft stage and liquid stage candy	spread evenly on cooling slab or pour in mold	evenly spread candy and filled mold	discriminating between soft stage and liquid stage candy	associating correct action with each input	discriminating and generalizing about evenly spread candy
flushed, glassy-eyed, listless child	recognize as ill	report to doctor	generalizing across various signs of illness	associating correct identification with inputs	

RESUME READING ON PAGE 11.15 IN THE HANDBOOK.

EXERCISE #15

I. Recognize

A. Identify the kind of skill that was learned from the kind of practice
    offered in each of the training situations below. If the skill had to
    be generalized, indicate in the last column what the job holder has to
    be able to do on the job.

Training Situation	Specific Skill	General-izable Skill	What Must Job Holder Be Able To Do?
1. Attendant parks cars driven by restaurant customers. He received his training with 1967 Fords, Jaguars, and Oldsmobiles.			
2. Teacher has to call each child by name. She practiced calling each child by name.			
3. Part-time secretary works for different organizations each day. In training, she practiced on IBM electric typewriter and IBM manual typewriter.			
4. Receptionist answers incoming call indicated by slow flashing light and identifies fast flashing light as line busy. In training, she practiced doing each.			
5. Deaf man communicates with hand signs. In training, he practiced each of the various hand signs.			
6. Shoemaker resoles shoes. In training, he practiced on women's sandles, pumps, and men's loafers.			
7. Technologist must classify unrefined wool as first clip, hog wool, taglocks, or pulled wool. He practiced classifying wool of each type.			
8. Inspector must identify acceptable solder jobs. In training, he practiced identifying least acceptable solder jobs and most acceptable solder jobs.			
9. Veterinarian diagnoses rabies in animals brought into clinic. In training, he practiced recognizing rabies in cats and dogs.			
10. Mechanic tunes carburetors of cars brought into his shop. In training, he practiced on Chevy's, Cadillacs, and Volkswagons.			

11.8

SEE ANSWERS

EXERCISE #15

I. Recognize

A. Identify the kind of skill that was learned from the kind of practice offered in each of the training situations below. If the skill had to be generalized, indicate in the last column what the job holder has to be able to do on the job.

Training Situation	Specific Skill	General-izable Skill	What Must Job Holder Be Able To Do?
1. Attendant parks cars driven by restaurant customers. He received his training with 1967 Fords, Jaguars, and Oldsmobiles.		X	Park all brands and models of cars
2. Teacher has to call each child by name. She practiced calling each child by name.	X		
3. Part-time secretary works for different organizations each day. In training, she practiced on IBM electric typewriter and IBM manual typewriter.		X	Use all or any model typewriter
4. Receptionist answers incoming call indicated by slow flashing light and identifies fast flashing light as line busy. In training, she practiced doing each.	X		
5. Deaf man communicates with hand signs. In training, he practiced each of the various hand signs.	X		
6. Shoemaker resoles shoes. In training, he practiced on women's sandles, pumps, and men's loafers.		X	Resole any kind of shoe
7. Technologist must classify unrefined wool as first clip, hog wool, taglocks, or pulled wool. He practiced classifying wool of each type.	X		
8. Inspector must identify acceptable solder jobs. In training, he practiced identifying least acceptable solder jobs and most acceptable solder jobs.		X	Identify complete range of acceptable solder jobs
9. Veterinarian diagnoses rabies in animals brought into clinic. In training, he practiced recognizing rabies in cats and dogs.		X	Diagnose rabies in all animals
10. Mechanic tunes carburetors of cars brought into his shop. In training, he practiced on Chevy's, Cadillacs, and Volkswagons		X	Tune carburetor on all or any cars

11.9

I. Recognize

B. Classify the failures in columns A and B as being failures in acquisition, retention, or transfer by putting the letters A and B in the appropriate spaces.

	FAILURE IN		
	ACQUISITION	RETENTION	TRANSFER

	A	B
Projectionist practices threading a Bell & Howell projector and making film loops of appropriate size	Later in school setting makes incorrect loops on RCA projector	On a training test, makes incorrect loops on Bell & Howell
Pilot practices taking corrective action based on panel indicator reading	A week after training, he fails to take corrective action in same kind of situation	During evaluation at end of training, he fails to take corrective action in same situation
Two decorators practice identifying dense acoustical materials: ceiling tile, and carpeting	On the job, one decorator fails to consider carpeting as a noise abater	On the job, the other man fails to recognize dense wall tile as acoustical
Teacher practices identifying child's intense laughter before a test and during recitation as a sign of tension	On training test, she fails to identify intense laughter as a sign of tension	Later she fails to recognize child's intense laughter when classmate is hurt as a sign of tension
Music student practices reading notes above and below scale on sheet music	During rehearsal for recital, he incorrectly identifies key of G above scale as key of A	During training test, he incorrectly identifies key of G above scale as key of A

SEE ANSWERS

EXERCISE #15

I. Recognize

B. Classify the failures in columns A and B as being failures in acquisition, retention, or transfer by putting the letters A and B in the appropriate spaces.

| | A | B | FAILURE IN | | |
			ACQUI-SITION	RETEN-TION	TRANSFER
Projectionist practices threading a Bell & Howell projector and making film loops of appropriate size	Later in school setting makes incorrect loops on RCA projector	On a training test, makes incorrect loops on Bell & Howell	B		A
Pilot practices taking corrective action based on panel indicator reading	A week after training, he fails to take corrective action in same kind of situation	During evaluation at end of training, he fails to take corrective action in same situation			
Two decorators practice identifying dense acoustical materials: ceiling tile, and carpeting	On the job, one decorator fails to consider carpeting as a noise abater	On the job, the other man fails to recognize dense wall tile as acoustical	B	A	B
Teacher practices identifying child's intense laughter before a test and during recitation as a sign of tension	On training test, she fails to identify intense laughter as a sign of tension	Later she fails to recognize child's intense laughter when classmate is hurt as a sign of tension	A	A	B
Music student practices reading notes above and below scale on sheet music	During rehearsal for recital, he incorrectly identifies key of G above scale as key of A	During training test, he incorrectly identifies key of G above scale as key of A	B	A	

RESUME READING ON PAGE II.25 IN THE HANDBOOK.

EXERCISE #16

I. Recognize

A. Check the one kind of learning failure most likely to occur as a result of the training provided.

In the blank space, write in the probable cause of the failure.

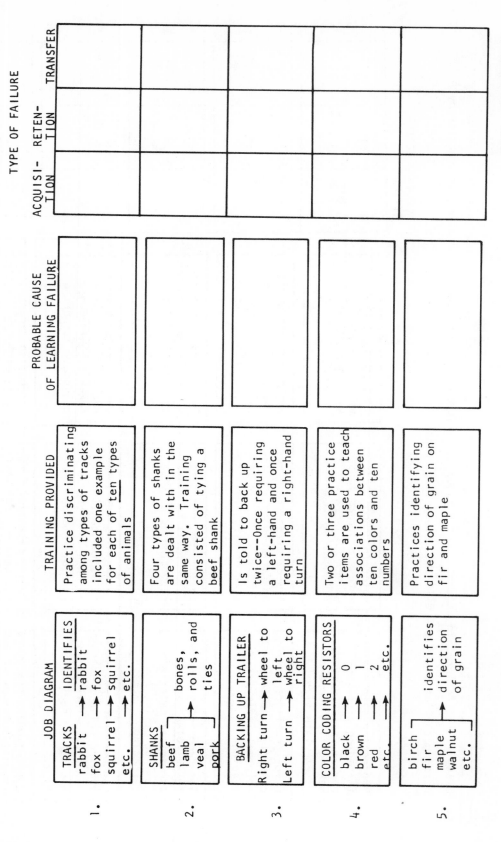

	PROBABLE CAUSE OF LEARNING FAILURE	TYPE OF FAILURE		
		ACQUISI-TION	RETEN-TION	TRANSFER
1. JOB DIAGRAM TRACKS → IDENTIFIES rabbit → rabbit fox → fox squirrel → squirrel etc. TRAINING PROVIDED: Practice discriminating among types of tracks included one example for each of ten types of animals				
2. SHANKS beef, lamb, veal, pork → bones, rolls, and ties TRAINING PROVIDED: Four types of shanks are dealt with in the same way. Training consisted of tying a beef shank				
3. BACKING UP TRAILER Right turn → wheel to left Left turn → wheel to right TRAINING PROVIDED: Is told to back up twice--Once requiring a left-hand and once requiring a right-hand turn				
4. COLOR CODING RESISTORS black → 0 brown → 1 red → 2 etc. TRAINING PROVIDED: Two or three practice items are used to teach associations between ten colors and ten numbers				
5. birch, fir, maple, walnut, etc. → identifies direction of grain TRAINING PROVIDED: Practices identifying direction of grain on fir and maple				

SEE ANSWERS

1. Recognize

A. Check the one kind of learning failure most likely to occur as a result of the training provided.

   In the blank space, write in the probable cause of the failure.

TYPE OF FAILURE

	JOB DIAGRAM	TRAINING PROVIDED	PROBABLE CAUSE OF LEARNING FAILURE	ACQUISITION	RETENTION	TRANSFER
1.	TRACKS → IDENTIFIES: rabbit → rabbit, fox → fox, squirrel → squirrel, etc. → etc.	Practice discriminating among types of tracks included one example for each of ten types of animals	An insufficient number of examples for each type of animal	X		
2.	SHANKS: beef, lamb, veal, pork → bones, rolls, and ties	Four types of shanks are dealt with in the same way. Training consisted of tying a beef shank	An insufficient sample of other shanks that have to be dealt with in the same way			X
3.	BACKING UP TRAILER: Right turn → wheel to left; Left turn → wheel to right	Is told to back up twice—Once requiring a left-hand and once requiring a right-hand turn	An insufficient number of practice opportunities associating direction of trailer turn and wheel turn	X		
4.	COLOR CODING RESISTORS: black → 0, brown → 1, red → 2, etc. → etc.	Two or three practice items are used to teach associations between ten colors and ten numbers	An insufficient number of practice opportunities for a difficult association problem		X	
5.	birch, fir, maple, walnut, etc. → identifies direction of grain	Practices identifying direction of grain on fir and maple	An insufficient sample of types of wood used			X

EXERCISE #16

II. Produce

A. For each of the following problems based on the job diagram on the opposite page, describe the kind of practice that is required to avoid the problems listed below.

*	INPUTS	ACTIONS	To Avoid a Problem in ACQUISITION	To Avoid a Problem in RETENTION	To Avoid a Problem in TRANSFER
1. generalization	A₁ A₂ A₃ →		Two or more practice items identifying each of three types of materials requiring latex house paint	Additional practice items identifying each of the three types of materials	All three types of materials should be represented in practice
2. discrimination	A → C → E →		Two or more examples from each of the three categories, providing opportunities to practice discriminations between types	Additional practice items including examples from each of the three categories	
3. association	C₁ C₂ C₃ C₄ →	D₁	Two or more examples of each of the four types; practice associating examples of material and type of paint	Additional practice items providing association practice	A variety of examples of each of the four types of materials
4. generalization	E₁ E₂ →		Two or more examples for brick and for stucco; practice identifying each as belonging to same category (re-quiring masonry paint)	Additional examples	Both major types should be represented; a variety of subtypes within each major type should be sampled
5. association	A → B C → D E → F		Two or more examples of each association should be used in practice	More examples of the associations	

RESUME READING ON PAGE II.39 IN THE HANDBOOK.

✱ Letters on this page correspond to the letters in the job diagram on the previous page.

II.17

I. __Recognize__

A. For the following jobs, check the type of transfer problem that is likely to result from the kind of practice provided in training: (1) Transfer from training to job, and (2) Generalization from practiced to unpracticed situation.

INPUTS	ACTIONS	TYPE OF PRACTICE RECEIVED	POTENTIAL PROBLEM		
			(1) TRANSFER	(2) GENERALIZATION	NONE
1. Angry customers	Clerk deals with their problems	Practice involves paper-and-pencil verbal case studies			
2. Fingers to be fingerprinted	Policeman makes fingerprints	Practice involves a large sample of __actual__ people			
3. All brands of __TV__ sets	Repairman repairs malfunctions	Practice on actual TV set: Zenith			
4. Pitched baseballs	Batter takes appropriate swing	Practices with mechanical pitching machine			
5. Computer keyboard	Presses appropriate keys	Practices with a drawing of a keyboard			

SEE ANSWERS

EXERCISE #17

I. Recognize

A. For the following jobs, check the type of transfer problem that is likely to result from the kind of practice provided in training: (1) Transfer from training to job, and (2) Generalization from practiced to unpracticed situation.

INPUTS	ACTIONS	TYPE OF PRACTICE RECEIVED	POTENTIAL PROBLEM		
			(1) TRANSFER	(2) GENERALIZATION	NONE
1. Angry customers	Clerk deals with their problems	Practice involves paper-and-pencil verbal case studies	X		
2. Fingers to be fingerprinted	Policeman makes fingerprints	Practice involves a large sample of actual people			X
3. All brands of TV sets	Repairman repairs malfunctions	Practice on actual TV set: Zenith		X	
4. Pitched baseballs	Batter takes appropriate swing	Practices with mechanical pitching machine	X		
5. Computer keyboard	Presses appropriate keys	Practices with a drawing of a keyboard	X		

11.19

EXERCISE #17

II. Produce

A. For each of the job tasks below, describe the type of practice you would design to avoid: (1) problems in transfer, and (2) problems in generalization.

		JOB TASK FOR WHICH TRAINING IS REQUIRED	TO AVOID PROBLEMS IN TRANSFER FROM TRAINING TO JOB	TO AVOID PROBLEMS IN TRANSFER TO JOB	TO AVOID PROBLEMS IN GENERALIZATION
	INPUT · ACTION · OUTPUT				
1.	first quality glass — identify as firsts; slightly flawed glass — identify as seconds	To identify what is first quality and what is salable seconds and the limits of each category			
2.	marked worn spot — identify and splice out of reel; poor splice — intact audio tape	To identify all types of tape flaws that have to be spliced out			
3.	narrow TV image — adjust hori-zontal hold; jagged diagonal lines — proper TV image	To alter the TV image, i.e., make a horizon-tal adjustment			
4.	unclean rifle bore — clean bore — O.K. clean / not O.K. clean	To alter the cleanness of a rifle bore and identify whether it is acceptably clean			
5.	good prospects — sales pitch #1; poor sales prospects — sales pitch #2	To identify sales prospects on the basis of facial expressions			

SEE ANSWERS

EXERCISE #17

II. Produce

A. For each of the job tasks below, describe the type of practice you would design to avoid: (1) problems in transfer, and (2) problems in generalization.

	INPUT	ACTION	OUTPUT	JOB TASK FOR WHICH TRAINING IS REQUIRED	TO AVOID PROBLEMS IN TRANSFER FROM TRAINING TO JOB	TO AVOID PROBLEMS IN GENERALIZATION
1.	first quality glass / slightly flawed glass	identify as firsts / identify as seconds		To identify what is first quality and what is salable seconds and the limits of each category	Provide actual glassware and have learner practice identifying quality of glass	Provide a large sample of glassware in each category
2.	marked worn spot / poor splice	identify and splice out of reel	intact audio tape	To identify all types of tape flaws that have to be spliced out	Provide actual tapes and have learner practice identifying tape flaws that need to be spliced out	Provide a sample of all the conditions that require splicing out
3.	narrow TV image / jagged diagonal lines	adjust horizontal hold	proper TV image	To alter the TV image, i.e., make a horizontal adjustment	Provide horizontal hold problems on actual TV set and require learner to make actual adjustments	Provide a sample of all conditions requiring a horizontal hold adjustment
4.	unclean rifle bore	clean bore	O.K. clean / not O.K. clean	To alter the cleanness of a rifle bore and identify whether it is acceptably clean	Provide practice in actually cleaning an actual rifle and in identifying what is and is not acceptably clean	Provide a sample of the range of acceptably and not acceptably clean rifles
5.	good prospects / poor sales prospects	sales pitch #1 / sales pitch #2		To identify sales prospects on the basis of facial expressions	Have actual people (or role-playing people) and have learner practice on them	Provide a range of types within each category

RESUME READING ON PAGE II.49 IN THE HANDBOOK.

EXERCISE #18

I. Recognize

A. For each of the following jobs, training will include criterion visual
inputs. Put an X through the appropriate media display requirements.

	CRITERION VISUAL INPUTS	MEDIA DISPLAY REQUIREMENTS IN TRAINING		
1.	Furrier has to discriminate among pelts of differing quality	fur pelts	photographs of pelts	sketches of pelts
2.	TV director has to discriminate between televised scenes differing in effectiveness for desired audience impact	whole scene in studio	scene appearing on TV monitor	artist's sketch of scene
3.	Civil engineer has to evaluate (discriminate adequate from inadequate) maps of underground utilities	all utility ducts (on location)	photographs of utility ducts	maps of utility ducts
4.	Planner produces charts showing distribution of dilapidated housing in differing metropolitan areas	areas of city (on location)	aerial photographs of areas	charts
5.	Electronic maintenance man has to discriminate among parts and among locations in complex equipment	parts to be repaired	photographs of parts and locations	diagrams of part locations

SEE ANSWERS

EXERCISE #18

I. Recognize

A. For each of the following jobs, training will include criterion visual inputs. Put an X through the appropriate media display requirements.

CRITERION VISUAL INPUTS

MEDIA DISPLAY REQUIREMENTS IN TRAINING

CRITERION VISUAL INPUTS	MEDIA DISPLAY REQUIREMENTS IN TRAINING		
1. Furrier has to discriminate among pelts of differing quality	fur pelts ✗	photographs of pelts	sketches of pelts
2. TV director has to discriminate between televised scenes differing in effective-ness for desired audience impact	whole scene in studio	scene appearing on TV monitor ✗	artist's sketch of scene
3. Civil engineer has to evaluate (discrimi-nate adequate from inadequate) maps of underground utilities	all utility ducts (on location)	photographs of utility ducts	maps of utility ducts ✗
4. Planner produces charts showing distri-bution of dilapidated housing in differ-ing metropolitan areas	areas of city (on location)	aerial photographs of areas	charts ✗
5. Electronic maintenance man has to dis-criminate among parts and among locations in complex equipment	parts to be repaired ✗	photographs of parts and loca-tions	diagrams of part locations

EXERCISE #18

I. Recognize

B. For each of the following jobs, training will include criterion visual
actions. Put an X through the appropriate practice requirements.

CRITERION VISUAL ACTIONS	PRACTICE REQUIREMENTS IN TRAINING		
1. Glass artist paints design (produces visual outputs) on glass	draws designs on glass	draws designs on paper	draws sketches of design on glass
2. Judge in beauty contest evaluates contestants (identification of visual inputs)	girls plus score cards	photographs plus score cards	TV tape plus score cards
3. Dentist smooths out existing filling (alteration of visual inputs)	filling; smooths out	dummy filling; smooths out	photograph; selects smooth one
4. Umpire calls balls and strikes (identification of visual inputs)	pitches; makes mental note	film of pitches; calls out	pitches; calls out
5. Botanist classifies specimens (identification of visual inputs)	leaves put in piles	photographs put in piles	sketches put in piles
6. Man forms cement sidewalks (produces visual output)	raw materials; describes actions	raw materials; forms sidewalk	raw materials; instructs another
7. Mechanic rotates distributor in car to correct timing of engine (alteration of visual input)	distributor; says what to do	distributor; points out direction of turn	distributor; turns to correct position
8. Airplane spotter reports enemy planes (identifies visual inputs)	planes; checks list	planes; reports in	planes; compares with photograph
9. Stage director repositions actors on stage (altering visual inputs)	players on stage; makes notes	players on stage; directs moves	players on stage; players decide
10. Pilot tests wing flaps (altering visual inputs)	equipment; moves flaps	mock-up; moves flaps	photographs; select right positions

SEE ANSWERS

EXERCISE #18

I. Recognize

B. For each of the following jobs, training will include criterion visual
    actions. Put an X through the appropriate practice requirements.

	CRITERION VISUAL ACTIONS	PRACTICE REQUIREMENTS IN TRAINING		
1.	Glass artist paints design (produces visual outputs) on glass	~~draws designs on glass~~	draws designs on paper	draws sketches of design on glass
2.	Judge in beauty contest evaluates contestants (identification of visual inputs)	~~girls plus score cards~~	photographs plus score cards	TV tape plus score cards
3.	Dentist smooths out existing filling (alteration of visual inputs)	~~filling; smooths out~~	dummy filling; smooths out	photograph; selects smooth one
4.	Umpire calls balls and strikes (identification of visual inputs)	pitches; makes mental note	film of pitches; calls out	~~pitches; calls out~~
5.	Botanist classifies specimens (identification of visual inputs)	~~leaves put in piles~~	photographs put in piles	sketches put in piles
6.	Man forms cement sidewalks (produces visual outputs)	raw materials; describes actions	~~raw materials; forms sidewalk~~	raw materials; instructs another
7.	Mechanic rotates distributor in car to correct timing of engine (alteration of visual input)	distributor; says what to do	distributor; points out direction of turn	~~distributor; turns to correct position~~
8.	Airplane spotter reports enemy planes (identifies visual inputs)	planes; checks list	~~planes; reports in~~	planes; compares with photograph
9.	Stage director repositions actors on stage (altering visual inputs)	players on stage; makes notes	~~players on stage; directs moves~~	players on stage; players decide
10.	Pilot tests wing flaps (altering visual inputs)	~~equipment; moves flaps~~	mock-up; moves flaps	photographs; selects right positions

II. Produce

A. For the following jobs involving CRITERION VISUALS, describe the MEDIA display requirements and the MEDIA practice requirements if CRITERION VISUALS are used in training.

	INPUTS	ACTIONS	OUTPUTS	MEDIA DISPLAY REQUIREMENTS	MEDIA PRACTICE REQUIREMENTS
1.	printing rollers	spread ink on rollers	surface properly covered		
2.	spoiled and unspoiled drugs	identify condition based on color	categorized drug samples		
3.	auto tires	adds air if needed	properly inflated tires		
4.	aerial photographs	identifies location of gun emplacements	location marked		
5.	human model	produces sculpture	sculptured figure		

SEE ANSWERS

RESUME READING ON PAGE III.1 IN THE HANDBOOK.

EXERCISE #18

II. Produce

A. For the following jobs involving CRITERION VISUALS, describe the MEDIA display requirements and the MEDIA practice requirements if CRITERION VISUALS are used in training.

	INPUTS	ACTIONS	OUTPUTS	MEDIA DISPLAY REQUIREMENTS	MEDIA PRACTICE REQUIREMENTS
1.	printing rollers	spread ink on rollers	surface properly covered	printing rollers	ink and tools to mix and spread it; practice spreading ink
2.	spoiled and unspoiled drugs	identify condition based on color	categorized drug samples	samples of spoiled and unspoiled drugs	sorts samples into two categories
3.	auto tires	adds air if needed	properly inflated tires	sample of tires with varying need for air	air hose and gauges; fills tires with air and measures adequacy
4.	aerial photographs	identifies location of gun emplacements	location marked	photographs with (and without) gun emplacements	marks gun emplacements on photographs
5.	human model	produces sculpture	sculptured figure	human model	raw materials (clay, metal, or marble) and tools; practices producing figures

11.27

PART III

EXERCISES
19 - 25

I. Recognize

A. Check as many columns as are appropriate identifying the types of
    problems of most concern if criterion visuals were used in each of
    the <u>training</u> situations described below.

CONDITIONS	DOWN TIME	COST OR DANGER	SAMPLING OR STANDARDIZATION
1. Intern practices making diagnoses based on physical examination of patient in out-patient department			
2. Electronic maintenance man practices troubleshooting circuits in a large electronic computer			
3. Upholsterer practices installing padding before furniture proceeds to next department			
4. Operator practices handling long distance, transatlantic, ship-to-shore calls, etc.			
5. Fireman practices combatting different types of fires with appropriate chemicals			
6. Claim adjuster practices filling out various forms based on type and cost of accident			
7. Gift wrapper in department store practices wrapping gifts while customers wait			
8. Watchmaker on an assembly line practices smoothing edges and sets width of main-spring to be used in manufacture of watches			
9. Directory assistance operator practices finding numbers for various residential, business, and government requests			
10. Infantryman practices using rifle to kill enemy			

SEE ANSWERS

EXERCISE #19

I. Recognize

A. Check as many columns as are appropriate identifying the types of
    problems of most concern if criterion visuals were used in each of
    the training situations described below.

CONDITIONS	DOWN TIME	COST OR DANGER	SAMPLING OR STANDARDIZATION
1. Intern practices making diagnoses based on physical examination of patient in out-patient department		X	X
2. Electronic maintenance man practices troubleshooting circuits in a large electronic computer	X	X	X
3. Upholsterer practices installing padding before furniture proceeds to next department	X		
4. Operator practices handling long distance, transatlantic, ship-to-shore calls, etc.		X	X
5. Fireman practices combatting different types of fires with appropriate chemicals	X	X	X
6. Claim adjuster practices filling out various forms based on type and cost of accident			X
7. Gift wrapper in department store practices wrapping gifts while customers wait		X	
8. Watchmaker on an assembly line practices smoothing edges and sets width of main-spring to be used in manufacture of watches	X		
9. Directory assistance operator practices finding numbers for various residential, business, and government requests			X
10. Infantryman practices using rifle to kill enemy		X	

EXERCISE #19

I. Recognize

B. The criterion visuals described below **are** to be used in training. On
each of the three listed criteria, rate the degree of seriousness of
using them (S = serious; A = average; N = negligible).

	CRITERIA								
CRITERION VISUALS USED IN TRAINING	DOWN TIME			COST OR DANGER			SAMPLING OR STANDARDIZATION		
	S	A	N	S	A	N	S	A	N
1. Dental student practices filling cavities on patients									
2. Gift wrapper practices tying two types of bow (no customer waiting)									
3. Boat handler practices docking boat in heavily trafficked docking area									
4. Teacher practices identifying problem children and referring those who need professional help									
5. Repairman practices diagnosing and repairing faulty (gas-burning) hot water heater in customer's home									
6. The highway patrolman practices spotting and ticketing speeding or safety violations									
7. Printer practices operating one of two machines in a company printing department (that turns out daily market advice)									
8. Gardener in a nursery practices transplanting a common type seedling									
9. Diamond cutter practices splitting diamonds into smaller sizes									
10. Air traffic controller practices interpreting radar patterns and radioing instructions									

III.4

SEE ANSWERS

EXERCISE #19

I. Recognize

B. The criterion visuals described below are to be used in training. On each of the three listed criteria, rate the degree of seriousness of using them (S = serious; A = average; N = negligible).

| | C R I T E R I A | | | | | | | | |
| | DOWN TIME | | | COST OR DANGER | | | SAMPLING OR STANDARDIZATION | | |
CRITERION VISUALS USED IN TRAINING	S	A	N	S	A	N	S	A	N
1. Dental student practices filling cavities on patients			X	X			X		
2. Gift wrapper practices tying two types of bow (no customer waiting)			X		X				X
3. Boat handler practices docking boat in heavily trafficked docking area		X		X					X
4. Teacher practices identifying problem children and referring those who need professional help			X	X			X		
5. Repairman practices diagnosing and repairing faulty (gas-burning) hot water heater in customer's home		X		X				X	
6. The highway patrolman practices spotting and ticketing speeding or safety violations			X	X			X		
7. Printer practices operating one of two machines in a company printing department (that turns out daily market advice)	X				X				X
8. Gardener in a nursery practices transplanting a common type seedling			X		X				X
9. Diamond cutter practices splitting diamonds into smaller sizes			X	X			X		
10. Air traffic controller practices interpreting radar patterns and radioing instructions	X			X			X		

I. Recognize

C. Below are the ratings of the seriousness of using criterion visuals
(from the previous problem). For each situation, write in whether you
would use criterion visuals, use _either_ criterion or simulated visuals,
or use simulated visuals.

CRITERION VISUALS USED IN TRAINING	DOWN TIME			COST OR DANGER			SAMPLING OR STANDARDIZATION		
	S	A	N	S	A	N	S	A	N
1. Dental student practices filling cavities on patients			X	X			X		
2. Gift wrapper practices tying two types of bow (no customer waiting)			X		X				X
3. Boat handler practices docking boat in heavily trafficked docking area		X		X					X
4. Teacher practices identifying problem children and referring those who need professional help			X	X			X		
5. Repairman practices diagnosing and repairing faulty (gas-burning) hot water heater in customer's home		X		X				X	
6. The highway patrolman practices spotting and ticketing speeding or safety violations			X	X			X		
7. Printer practices operating one of two machines in a company printing department (that turns out daily market advice)	X				X				X
8. Gardener in a nursery practices transplanting a common type seedling			X		X				X
9. Diamond cutter practices splitting diamonds into smaller sizes			X	X			X		
10. Air traffic controller practices interpreting radar patterns and radioing instructions	X			X			X		

SEE ANSWERS

I. Recognize

C. Below are the ratings of the seriousness of using criterion visuals (from the previous problem). For each situation, write in whether you would use criterion visuals, use _either_ criterion or simulated visuals, or use simulated visuals.

	CRITERIA								
	DOWN TIME			COST OR DANGER			SAMPLING OR STANDARDIZATION		
CRITERION VISUALS USED IN TRAINING	S	A	N	S	A	N	S	A	N
1. Dental student practices filling cavities on patients			X	X _simulation_			X		
2. Gift wrapper practices tying two types of bow (no customer waiting)			X			X _criterion_			X
3. Boat handler practices docking boat in heavily trafficked docking area		X			X _criterion or simulation_				X
4. Teacher practices identifying problem children and referring those who need professional help			X	X _simulation_			X		
5. Repairman practices diagnosing and repairing faulty (gas-burning) hot water heater in customer's home		X			X _criterion or simulation_			X	
6. The highway patrolman practices spotting and ticketing speeding or safety violations			X		X _simulation_		X		
7. Printer practices operating one or two machines in a company printing department (that turns out daily market advice)	X					X _simulation_			X
8. Gardener in a nursery practices transplanting a common type seedling			X			X _criterion_			X
9. Diamond cutter practices splitting diamonds into smaller sizes			X	X _simulation_			X		
10. Air traffic controller practices interpreting radar patterns and radioing instructions	X			X _simulation_			X		

RESUME READING ON PAGE III.17 IN THE HANDBOOK.

EXERCISE #20

I. Produce

A. For each of the jobs below, design three types of simulation that might be used in training using: realistic visuals, reproductions, and fabrications.

JOB	INPUT	ACTION	SIMULATED BY REALISTIC VISUALS	SIMULATED BY REPRODUCTIONS	SIMULATED BY FABRICATIONS
1. matches powder to hair color of customer	red, brunette, blond coloring; customers	identifies coloring; selects powder			
2. arranges furniture in homes	sofas, arm chairs, etc.	arranges groupings			
3. clothes buyer in store	dresses, suits, skirts	selects models for purchase			
4. inspects missile for leaks	missile leak sites	inspects for leaks			
5. visually observes performance of subordinates	subordinate performance	rates			

SEE ANSWERS

III.8

I. Produce

A. For each of the jobs below, design three types of simulation that might be used in training using: realistic visuals, reproductions, and fabrications.

	JOB	INPUT	ACTION	SIMULATED BY REALISTIC VISUALS	SIMULATED BY REPRODUCTIONS	SIMULATED BY FABRICATIONS
1.	matches powder to hair color of customer	red, brunette, blond coloring of customers	identifies coloring; selects powder	Actors or other students for practice identifying hair color	Wigs or colored photographs for practice identifying hair color	Rectangular color samples; colored pictures of hair
2.	arranges furniture in homes	sofas, arm chairs, etc.	arranges groupings	Uses folding chairs and arranges them in groupings	Small scale models of furniture; arranges them in groupings	Learner draws floor plan of furniture arrangement
3.	clothes buyer in store	dresses, suits, skirts	selects models for purchase	Sees one style of dress; practices selecting other versions of same just from swatches of cloth	Photographs of clothing are used in practice	Clothes sketches are used in training
4.	inspects missile leak for leaks	missile leak for sites	inspects for leaks	Training missile; looks for leaks	Mock-up missile; looks for leaks	Missile blueprint; (marks where he would look for leaks)
5.	visually observes performance of subordinates	subordinate performance	rates	Role play of subordinate performance	Film of subordinate performance	Animation of subordinate performance

I. Produce

B. For each of the jobs below, design three types of simulation that might be used in training to simulate actions.

JOB	INPUT	ACTION	SIMULATION BY RECOGNITION PRACTICE	SIMULATION BY EDITING PRACTICE	SIMULATION BY PRODUCTION PRACTICE
1. matches powder to hair color of customer	red, brunette, blond coloring; customer	identifies selects powder			
2. arranges furniture in homes	sofas, arm chairs, etc.	arranges groupings			
3. clothes buyer in suits, store	dresses, suits, skirts	selects models for purchase			
4. inspects missile for leaks	missile leak sites	inspects for leaks			
5. visually observes performance of subordinates	subordinate performance	rates subordinates			

SEE ANSWERS

EXERCISE #20

I. Produce

B. For each of the jobs below, design three types of simulation that might be used in training to simulate actions.

	JOB	INPUT	ACTION	SIMULATION BY RECOGNITION PRACTICE	SIMULATION BY EDITING PRACTICE	SIMULATION BY PRODUCTION PRACTICE
1.	matches powder to hair color of customer	red, brunette, blond customers	identifies coloring; selects powder	*Selects from options powder for appropriate given hair color*	*Corrects (selects another) poor choice of powder for given hair color*	*Obtains a ready-mixed powder (instead of mixing it) for a given coloring*
2.	arranges furniture in homes	sofas, arm chairs, etc.	arranges groupings	*Selects an arrangement from alternative arrangements*	*Changes a poor pattern into an improved one*	*Produces an arrangement or grouping (on paper, with models, etc.)*
3.	clothes buyer in store	dresses, suits, skirts	selects models for purchase	*Presented with choices (e.g., good and bad buys) selects what he considers a good buy*	*Presented with an example of a poor buy, indicates what he would buy instead*	*Draws examples of clothes he would like to buy*
4.	inspects missile for leaks	missile leak sites	inspects for leaks	*Presented with examples of leak and no leak conditions, selects the one with a leak*	*A leak is incorrectly identified as a non-leak (or the converse) and the learner changes the diagnosis*	*May be required to create a condition (on a mock-up) that would indicate a leak to him*
5.	visually observes performance of subordinates	subordinate performance	rates	*Presented with alternative performances, selects the best or identifies the worst*	*Presented with an evaluation of a performance, changes the evaluation (and makes it correct or better)*	

RESUME READING ON PAGE III.35 IN THE HANDBOOK.

EXERCISE #21

I. Recognize

A. For the jobs below, check the example of visual simulation which bears the greatest similarity to criterion visuals found on the job.

	INPUT	ACTION	OUTPUT	EXAMPLE #1	EXAMPLE #2	EXAMPLE #3
1.	customer to be measured for suit	takes measurements	measurements recorded	Life-size silhouette of man which student measures	A dummy which student measures	Photographs of man student measures
2.	window glass to be replaced	measures for correct size	correct size selected	Wooden mock-up of window frame	Paper-and-pencil exercise giving practice in measuring areas	Editing film of glass being measured
3.	steep hill and runaway truck	gear down and looks for exit	truck safely stopped	Film showing driver handling runaway truck	Driver simulator with all conditions represented	Driver simulator with some of the conditions represented
4.	TV monitor for traffic control	identifies trouble spots	alarm	TV tape of typical traffic problems	Film of typical traffic problems	Photographs of typical traffic problems
5.	child seeks attention	teacher ignores behavior	behavior weakened	Animated cartoon of child seeking attention; teacher reacts to cartoon	Case studies with still photos of situation; teacher writes out her action	Actors role playing situation; teacher reacts to actors

SEE ANSWERS

EXERCISE #21

I. Recognize

A. For the jobs below, check the example of visual simulation which bears the greatest similarity to criterion visuals found on the job.

	INPUT	ACTION	OUTPUT	EXAMPLE #1	EXAMPLE #2	EXAMPLE #3
1.	customer to be measured for suit	takes measure- ments	measure- ments recorded	Life-size silhouette of man which student measures	A dummy which student measures ⊠	Photographs of man student measures
2.	window glass to be replaced	measures for correct size	correct size selected	Wooden mock-up of window frame ⊠	Paper-and-pencil exer- cise giving practice in measuring areas	Editing film of glass being measured
3.	steep hill and runaway truck	gear down and looks for exit	truck safely stopped	Film showing driver handling runaway truck	Driver simulator with all conditions repre- sented ⊠	Driver simulator with some of the conditions represented
4.	TV monitor for traffic control	identi- fies trouble spots	alarm	TV tape of typical traffic problems ⊠	Film of typical traffic problems	Photographs of typical traffic problems
5.	child seeks atten- tion	teacher ignores behavior	behavior weakened	Animated cartoon of child seeking atten- tion; teacher reacts to cartoon	Case studies with still photos of situation; teacher writes out her action	Actors role playing situation; teacher reacts to actors ⊠

EXERCISE #21

I. Recognize

B. For each of the jobs below, check the example of non-visual simulation (#1 or #2) which bears the closer similarity to the criterion visuals found on the job.

	JOB DIAGRAM			VERBAL PRACTICE PROBLEM IN TRAINING	NON-VISUAL SIMULATION	
	INPUT	ACTION	OUTPUT		EXAMPLE #1	EXAMPLE #2
1.	dissatisfied customer	tries to satisfy customer	satisfied customer	How would you handle the following customer?	While returning merchandise, customer is in tears	While returning merchandise, customer is upset
2.	outdoor lighting	sets camera openings	lens set to correct opening	What setting would you use in the following situation?	A sunny day	A sunny day--at noon
3.	light	sets camera lens opening	correct opening	Which setting would you use in taking pictures on a very bright day?	1/250 or 1/60	The more the light, -The smaller the opening vs. -The bigger the opening
4.	load	sets fulcrum on lever	fulcrum positioned	Where would you put the fulcrum in the following situation in order to make your job easier?	The distance between the fulcrum and the load should be -smaller -larger	It will be easier to lift a load when the distance between the load and fulcrum is -6 feet -10 feet
5.	colors	mixes them	new colors	Solve the following problem in color mixing.	How do you produce a secondary color?	What colors do you mix to get purple?

SEE ANSWERS

111.14

EXERCISE #21

I. Recognize

B. For each of the jobs below, check the example of non-visual simulation (#1 or #2) which bears the closer similarity to the criterion visuals found on the job.

NON-VISUAL SIMULATION

JOB DIAGRAM INPUT	ACTION	OUTPUT	VERBAL PRACTICE PROBLEM IN TRAINING	EXAMPLE #1	EXAMPLE #2
1. dissatisfied customer	tries to satisfy customer	satisfied customer	How would you handle the following customer?	While returning merchandise, customer is in tears	While returning merchandise, customer is upset
2. outdoor lighting	sets camera openings	lens set to correct opening	What setting would you use in the following situation?	A sunny day	A sunny day--at noon
3. light	sets camera lens opening	correct opening	Which setting would you use in taking pictures on a very bright day?	1/250 or 1/60	The more the light, -The smaller the opening vs. -The bigger the opening
4. load	sets fulcrum on lever	fulcrum positioned	Where would you put the fulcrum in the following situation in order to make your job easier?	The distance between the fulcrum and the load should be -smaller -larger	It will be easier to lift a load when the distance between the load and fulcrum is -6 feet -10 feet
5. colors	mixes them	new colors	Solve the following problem in color mixing.	How do you produce a secondary color?	What colors do you mix to get purple?

EXERCISE #21

I. Recognize

C. For each of the job tasks below, rank the three examples of simulation for their similarity to the criterion visuals involved: 1 = highest similarity; 2 = middle; 3 = lowest similarity.

VISUAL INPUT	VISUAL ACTION	VISUAL OUTPUT	EXAMPLE #1	EXAMPLE #2	EXAMPLE #3
1. orbits of planets			Drawing showing relative sizes and distances of planets — Rank ___	Mobile using spheres of varying sizes and distances from one another; spheres circle the center sphere — Rank ___	Stationary version of mobile in example #2 — Rank ___
2. texture of lunar surface			Desert (landscaped to look like lunar surface) — Rank ___	Photograph of desert (landscaped to look like lunar surface) — Rank ___	Detailed concrete: verbal description of actual lunar surface — Rank ___
3.	draws blueprints		States principles about how to draw blueprints — Rank ___	States concrete details about how to draw blueprints — Rank ___	States principles about drawings in general — Rank ___
4. cooking sauce			Color photograph of sauce — Rank ___	Black and white photographs of sauce — Rank ___	Mock sauce with full visual properties — Rank ___
5. shape of diamonds			Glass cut like diamonds — Rank ___	Opaque model of diamonds — Rank ___	Photographs of diamonds — Rank ___

SEE ANSWERS

EXERCISE #21

1. Recognize

C. For each of the job tasks below, rank the three examples of simulation for their similarity to the criterion visuals involved: 1 = highest similarity; 2 = middle; 3 = lowest similarity.

VISUAL INPUT	VISUAL ACTION	VISUAL OUTPUT	EXAMPLE #1	EXAMPLE #2	EXAMPLE #3
1. orbits of planets			Drawing showing relative sizes and distances of planets Rank 3	Mobile using spheres of varying sizes and distances from one another; spheres circle the center sphere Rank 1	Stationary version of mobile in example #2 Rank 2
2. texture of lunar surface			Desert (landscaped to look like lunar surface) Rank 1	Photograph of desert (landscaped to look like lunar surface) Rank 2	Detailed concrete: verbal description of actual lunar surface Rank 3
3.	draws blueprints		States principles about how to draw blueprints Rank 2	States concrete details about how to draw blueprints Rank 1	States principles about drawings in general Rank 3
4. cooking sauce			Color photographs of sauce Rank 2	Black and white photographs of sauce Rank 3	Mock sauce with full visual properties Rank 1
5. shape of diamonds			Glass cut like diamonds Rank 1	Opaque model of diamonds Rank 2	Photographs of diamonds Rank 3

EXERCISE #21

I. Recognize

C. (Continued) For each of the job tasks below, rank the three examples of simulation for their similarity to the criterion visuals involved: 1 = highest similarity; 2 = middle; 3 = lowest similarity.

	EXAMPLE #1	EXAMPLE #2	EXAMPLE #3
VISUAL INPUT 6. anatomy of eye	Cutaway drawing of eye showing interior and exterior parts Rank ___	Detailed verbal description of parts of the eye Rank ___	Transparent plastic eye showing exterior and interior parts Rank ___
VISUAL OUTPUT 7. adjusted TV image	Picture of properly adjusted image (spacing of horizontal lines) Rank ___	Drawing of properly adjusted image (spacing of horizontal lines) Rank ___	Detailed verbal description of proper amount of spacing of horizontal lines in properly adjusted image Rank ___
VISUAL ACTION 8. rotates distributor to adjust engine timing	Corrects rotation of a mock-up distributor Rank ___	Indicates whether a distributor is correctly rotated Rank ___	Rotates mock-up distributor Rank ___
VISUAL ACTION 9. smiles and acts friendly to customer	Verbal case study: indicates verbally what he would do Rank ___	Verbal case study: verbally edits or corrects a wrong action Rank ___	Verbal case study: selects from verbal options what he would do Rank ___
VISUAL INPUT 10. movement of bull in bull-fight	Film of bull from point of view of bullfighter Rank ___	Young bull in ring Rank ___	Series of still photographs showing changes in movement Rank ___

SEE ANSWERS

I. Recognize

C. (Continued) For each of the job tasks below, rank the three examples of simulation for their similarity to the criterion visuals involved: 1 = highest similarity; 2 = middle; 3 = lowest similarity.

	VISUAL INPUT	VISUAL ACTION	VISUAL OUTPUT	EXAMPLE #1	EXAMPLE #2	EXAMPLE #3
6.	anatomy of eye			Cutaway drawing of eye showing interior and exterior parts — Rank 2	Detailed verbal description of parts of the eye — Rank 3	Transparent plastic eye showing exterior and interior parts — Rank 1
7.			adjusted TV image	Picture of properly adjusted image (spacing of horizontal lines) — Rank 1	Drawing of properly adjusted image (spacing of horizontal lines) — Rank 2	Detailed verbal description of proper amount of spacing of horizontal lines in properly adjusted image — Rank 3
8.		rotates distributor to adjust engine timing		Corrects rotation of a mock-up distributor — Rank 2	Indicates whether a distributor is correctly rotated — Rank 3	Rotates mock-up distributor — Rank 1
9.		smiles and acts friendly to customer		Verbal case study: indicates verbally what he would do — Rank 1	Verbal case study: verbally edits or corrects a wrong action — Rank 3	Verbal case study: selects from verbal options what he would do — Rank 2
10.	movement of bull in bullfight			Film of bull from point of view of bullfighter — Rank 2	Young bull in ring — Rank 1	Series of still photographs showing changes in movement — Rank 3

I. Recognize

D. For each learning problem identified below, put an X through the one
property of the criterion visual you would most want to simulate with
the highest degree of similarity to the criterion.

LEARNING PROBLEM	MOST IMPORTANT PROPERTY TO SIMULATE		
	#1	#2	#3
1. Jeweler has to discriminate between various types of cracks in diamonds that influence their value. *Property of visual inputs to be simulated:*	brilliance	shape	cracks
2. Physics student has to associate the "application of heat" and "molecular movement." *Property of visual inputs to be simulated:*	speed of molecules	molecule arrangements	molecule size
3. Life guard has to associate condition of drowning swimmer and type of rescue action to take in water (e.g., rescue hold to use). *Property of visual inputs to be simulated:*	color of victim's face	thrashing about or unconscious	male or female
4. Baseball umpire has to discriminate between "balls" and "strikes." *Property of visual inputs to be simulated:*	speed of pitch	path: curve, slider, etc.	height of pitch
5. Baseball batter has to associate the timing of his swing and the type of pitch. *Property of visual inputs to be simulated:*	speed of pitch	path: curve, slider, etc.	height of pitch
6. Third base coach has to discriminate between hits to the outfield that allow the runner to score from second base and those that do not. *Property of visual inputs to be simulated:*	distance of ball from home plate	hit to left field or right field (direction)	number of outs
7. Rifleman has to learn to assemble a rifle. *Property of visual actions to be simulated:*	opportunity to recognize correct sequence	opportunity to produce correct sequence	opportunity to state what a correct sequence is
8. Flight controller has to learn to interpret radar patterns. *Property of visual actions to be simulated:*	opportunity to sketch patterns	opportunity to describe patterns	opportunity to identify patterns
9. Electronics maintenance man has to learn to repair malfunctions (leading to normal oscilloscope reading). *Property of visual actions to be simulated:*	opportunity to replace components	opportunity to state cause of malfunction	opportunity to select from alternative repair decisions
10. Window display man has to arrange props in window leading to a pleasing advertisement. *Summary of visual actions to be simulated.*	opportunity to select objects to arrange	opportunity to criticise his own arrangements	opportunity to arrange objects

SEE ANSWERS

EXERCISE #21

I. **Recognize**

D. For each learning problem identified below, put an X through the one
property of the criterion visual you would most want to simulate with
the highest degree of similarity to the criterion.

	LEARNING PROBLEM	MOST IMPORTANT PROPERTY TO SIMULATE		
		#1	#2	#3
1.	Jeweler has to discriminate between various types of cracks in diamonds that influence their value. *Property of visual inputs to be simulated:*	brilliance	shape	cracks ✗
2.	Physics student has to associate the "application of heat" and "molecular movement." *Property of visual inputs to be simulated:*	speed of molecules ✗	molecule arrangements	molecule size
3.	Life guard has to associate condition of drowning swimmer and type of rescue action to take in water (e.g., rescue hold to use). *Property of visual inputs to be simulated:*	color of victim's face	thrashing about or unconscious ✗	male or female
4.	Baseball umpire has to discriminate between "balls" and "strikes." *Property of visual inputs to be simulated:*	speed of pitch	path: curve, slider, etc.	height of pitch ✗
5.	Baseball batter has to associate the timing of his swing and the type of pitch. *Property of visual inputs to be simulated:*	speed of pitch ✗	path: curve, slider, etc.	height of pitch
6.	Third base coach has to discriminate between hits to the outfield that allow the runner to score from second base and those that do not. *Property of visual inputs to be discriminated.*	distance of ball from home plate ✗	hit to left field or right field (direction)	number of outs
7.	Rifleman has to learn to assemble a rifle. *Property of visual actions to be simulated:*	opportunity to recognize correct sequence	opportunity to produce correct sequence ✗	opportunity to state what a correct sequence is
8.	Flight controller has to learn to interpret radar patterns. *Property of visual actions to be simulated:*	opportunity to sketch patterns	opportunity to describe patterns	opportunity to identify patterns ✗
9.	Electronics maintenance man has to learn to repair malfunctions (leading to normal oscilloscope reading). *Property of visual actions to be simulated:*	opportunity to replace components ✗	opportunity to state cause of malfunction	opportunity to select from alternative repair decisions
10.	Window display man has to arrange props in window leading to a pleasing advertisement. *Summary of visual actions to be simulated.*	opportunity to select objects to arrange	opportunity to criticise his own arrangements	opportunity to arrange objects ✗

EXERCISE #21

II. Edit

A. For each of the job tasks below, devise a type of simulated practice which you feel is better than the one given and will make transfer easier.

	INPUT	ACTION	OUTPUT	LESS DESIRABLE SIMULATION	MORE DESIRABLE SIMULATION
1.	stag, doe, or fawn tracks	identify shape and depth of tracks	weight of deer identi- fied	Opportunity to identify tracks from photographs with dark and light areas providing clues about depth of tracks	
2.	bleeding vein	locate pressure point	identi- fied pressure point	Locating pressure spot on anatomical diagram	
3.	narrow steel girder 40' up in air	walks across in care- ful short steps	girder crossed	Practice walking quickly on narrow white line drawn on ground	
4.	types of damaged hair	identi- fies and treats for type of damage	treated hair	From photographs of types of damage, states verbally how to treat hair	
5.	TV trans- mitter parts	assem- bles parts	trans- mitter assembled	Critiques and edits (verbally) assembly seen on film	

SEE ANSWERS

III.22

II. Edit

A. For each of the job tasks below, devise a type of simulated practice which you feel is <u>better</u> than the one given and will make transfer easier.

	INPUT	ACTION	OUTPUT	LESS DESIRABLE SIMULATION	MORE DESIRABLE SIMULATION
1.	stag, doe, or fawn tracks	identify shape and depth of tracks	weight of deer identified	Opportunity to identify tracks from photographs with dark and light areas providing clues about depth of tracks	Opportunity to identify tracks from cast of mold showing depth and shape of track
2.	bleeding vein	locate pressure point	identified pressure point	Locating pressure spot on anatomical diagram	Locating pressure spot on human model or on dummy
3.	narrow steel girder 40' up in air	walks across in careful short steps	girder crossed	Practice walking quickly on narrow white line drawn on ground	Opportunity to practice short, careful steps on girder safe distance above ground
4.	types of damaged hair	identifies and treats for type of damage	treated hair	From photographs of types of damage, states verbally how to treat hair	Applies treatment to wig on dummy (that represents a type of problem)
5.	TV transmitter parts	assembles parts	transmitter assembled	Critiques and edits (verbally) assembly seen on film	Assembles mock-up parts

III. Produce

A. For each job task below, devise the type of simulation you feel will make transfer most likely to occur. SIMULATE ONLY THAT PART OF THE JOB DIAGRAM THAT IS CAPITALIZED (e.g., only the INPUT or only the ACTION).

	INPUT	ACTION	OUTPUT	RECOMMENDED SIMULATION
1.	ENEMY RUNNING ACROSS FIELD	Aims rifle ahead according to speed	Hit (or miss)	
2.	MERCHANDISE	Arranges in showcase	Display of merchandise	
3.	Take-off of missile	TRACKS ACTUAL FLIGHT VISUALLY	Tracking report	
4.	TYPE OF STUDENT BEHAVIOR PROBLEMS	Does or says appropriate thing	Stops problem temporarily	
5.	DISASSEMBLED CARBURETOR	Assembles carburetor	Assembled carburetor	
6.	Airport landing strip	Steers plane for landing	Plane correctly positioned for landing	
7.	RAW MATERIAL	Forms cement and lays sidewalk	Sidewalk completed	
8.	INSTRUMENT PANEL (DIALS, KNOBS, ETC.)	Obtain readings from dials	Report of equipment condition	
9.	COMPLAINTS SUBORDINATES	Takes appropriate action	Problem solved	
10.	Scene to be filmed	Set up shot and shoot scene	Scene on film	

SEE ANSWERS

EXERCISE #21

III. Produce

   A. For each job task below, devise the type of <u>simulation</u> you feel will
       make <u>transfer</u> most likely to occur. SIMULATE ONLY THAT PART OF THE
       JOB DIAGRAM THAT IS CAPITALIZED (e.g., only the INPUT or only the
       ACTION).

	INPUT	ACTION	OUTPUT	RECOMMENDED SIMULATION
1.	ENEMY RUNNING ACROSS FIELD	Aims rifle ahead according to speed	Hit (or miss)	*Moving target on a track that can go at different speeds.*
2.	MERCHANDISE	Arranges in showcase	Display of merchandise	*Dummy packages can be used to arrange showcase display.*
3.	Take-off of missile	TRACKS ACTUAL FLIGHT VISUALLY	Tracking report	*Film of actual flight (taken from ground level and from point of view of tracker). Tracks flight and makes report.*
4.	TYPE OF STUDENT BEHAVIOR PROBLEMS	Does or says appropriate thing	Stops problem temporarily	*Film of behavior problem showing relevant symptoms calling for particular actions. Teacher may say out loud what she would say to student.*
5.	DISASSEMBLED CARBURETOR	Assembles carburetor	Assembled carburetor	*All parts simulated by mock-up (to scale). Mechanic assembles parts.*
6.	Airport landing strip	Steers plane for landing	Plane correctly positioned for landing	*Airplane trainer uses actual landing strip or simulator with filmed view of landing strip. Trainee manipulates controls to bring plane into correct position.*
7.	RAW MATERIAL	Forms cement and lays sidewalk	Sidewalk completed	*Sand could be used to simulate cement and sidewalk formed from it.*
8.	INSTRUMENT PANEL (DIALS, KNOBS, ETC.)	Obtain readings from dials	Report of equipment condition	*Full mock-up of instrument panel; all dials present and functioning.*
9.	COMPLAINTS SUBORDINATES	Takes appropriate action	Problem solved	*Actors or fellow trainees role-play complaint behavior; or film of actual complaining subordinate. Trainee practices saying or doing appropriate thing.*
10.	Scene to be filmed	Set up shot and shot scene	Scene on film	*Dry-run practice with actual scene (but no film in camera).*

RESUME READING ON PAGE
III.55 IN THE HANDBOOK.

EXERCISE #22

1. Recognize

A. Put an X through the simulated INPUT (or OUTPUT) which is the best candidate for use in training from an __instructional__ point of view.

	INPUT	ACTION	OUTPUT	#1	#2	#3
1.	rust on bridge	remove rust before painting	TOLERABLE AMOUNT OF RUST	Photographs showing range of tolerable amounts of rust	Pieces of metal showing range of tolerable amounts of rust	Verbal description of what is a tolerable amount of rust
2.	FLOWERS AND PLANTS	identify best temperature and soil conditions	conditions and temperature identified	Drawings of plants	Artificial plants	Photographs of plants
3.	VICTIM WITH BROKEN LEG	apply splint and wrap	splint correctly applied	Person acting as victim	Film of accident showing leg to be treated	A wooden figure serving as the victim
4.	CLOUD FORMATIONS	predict weather based on clouds	prediction made	Drawing of clouds	Detailed, concrete description of clouds	Photographs of clouds
5.	CUSTOMER ROUTES IN SUPERMARKET	identifies traffic flow pattern	flow patterns identified	Maps of store showing routes and flow patterns	Frequency tabulations for traffic volume in each aisle	Description of flow patterns and traffic volume

SEE ANSWERS

EXERCISE #22

I. Recognize

A. Put an X through the simulated INPUT (or OUTPUT) which is the __best__ candidate for use in training from an __instructional__ point of view.

	INPUT	ACTION	OUTPUT	#1	#2	#3
1.	rust on bridge	remove rust before painting	TOLERABLE AMOUNT OF RUST	Photographs showing range of tolerable amounts of rust	Pieces of metal showing range of tolerable amounts of rust ⊠	Verbal description of what is a tolerable amount of rust
2.	FLOWERS AND PLANTS	identify best temperature and soil conditions	conditions and temperature identified	Drawings of plants	Artificial plants ⊠	Photographs of plants
3.	VICTIM WITH BROKEN LEG	apply splint and wrap	splint correctly applied	Person acting as victim ⊠	Film of accident showing leg to be treated	A wooden figure serving as the victim
4.	CLOUD FORMA-TIONS	predict weather based on clouds	predic-tion made	Drawing of clouds	Detailed, concrete description of clouds	Photographs of clouds ⊠
5.	CUSTOMER ROUTES IN SUPER-MARKET	identi-fies traffic flow pattern	flow patterns identi-fied	Maps of store showing routes and flow patterns ⊠	Frequency tabulations for traffic volume in each aisle	Description of flow patterns and traffic volume

I. Recognize

B. Put an X through the simulated ACTION which is the best candidate (from the three classes offered) for use in training from an instructional point of view.

	INPUT	ACTION	OUTPUT	#1	#2	#3
1.	rifle parts	ASSEMBLES RIFLE IN CORRECT SEQUENCE	assembled rifle	Verbally states the order in which he would assemble parts	Points to parts in the order in which he would assemble them	From options presented him, selects parts next in the assembly sequence
2.	faulty TV image	ADJUSTS IMAGE	correct image	On simulated TV console turns knobs that produce a correct image	Indicates whether a TV image is adjusted or non-adjusted	Selects from multiple options the best adjusted TV image
3.	malfunction indicated by oscilloscope	LOCATES MALFUNCTION IN EQUIPMENT	malfunction identified	Verbal description of symptoms; learner selects from verbal options what circuits he would investigate	Verbal description of symptoms; learner circles circuits he would investigate on circuit diagram	Verbal description of symptoms; learner selects one of two circuits as the one to investigate
4.	cooking sauce	ADDS LIQUIDS TO THIN SAUCE	thinned sauce	States verbally how much liquid he would add (for given initial thickness of sauces)	Edits (verbally) an incorrectly selected amount of liquid to be added	Selects from verbal options the amount of liquid to select
5.	traffic hazards	AVOIDS HAZARDS	safe driving	In auto simulator, presses buttons when a hazard is spotted	In auto simulator, calls out what he would do	In auto simulator, turns wheel away from site of hazard

SEE ANSWERS

EXERCISE #22

I. Recognize

B. Put an X through the simulated ACTION which is the best candidate (from the three classes offered) for use in training from an <u>instructional</u> point of view.

	INPUT	ACTION	OUTPUT	#1	#2	#3
1.	rifle parts	ASSEMBLES RIFLE IN CORRECT SEQUENCE	assembled rifle	Verbally states the order in which he would assemble parts	Points to parts in the order in which he would assemble them (X)	From options presented him, selects parts next in the assembly sequence
2.	faulty TV image	ADJUSTS IMAGE	correct image	On simulated TV console turns knobs that produce a correct image (X)	Indicates whether a TV image is adjusted or non-adjusted	Selects from multiple options the best adjusted TV image
3.	malfunction indicated by oscilloscope	LOCATES MALFUNCTION IN EQUIPMENT	malfunction identified	Verbal description of symptoms; learner selects from verbal options what circuits he would investigate	Verbal description of symptoms; learner circles circuits he would investigate on circuit diagram (X)	Verbal description of symptoms; learner selects one of two circuits as the one to investigate
4.	cooking sauce	ADDS LIQUIDS TO THIN SAUCE	thinned sauce	States verbally how much liquid he would add (for given initial thickness of sauces) (X)	Edits (verbally) an incorrectly selected amount of liquid to be added	Selects from verbal options the amount of liquid to select
5.	traffic hazards	AVOIDS HAZARDS	safe driving	In auto simulator, presses buttons when a hazard is spotted	In auto simulator, calls out what he would do	In auto simulator, turns wheel away from site of hazard (X)

RESUME READING ON PAGE III.65 IN THE HANDBOOK.

EXERCISE #23

I. Recognize

A. Put an X through the type of simulation which would be the most desirable from a <u>logistical</u> point (i.e., the <u>smallest logistical burden</u> would be involved).

TYPES OF SIMULATION

	JOB	INPUT	ACTION			
1.	agriculture expert	damaged corn, wheat, soybeans	identifies insect responsible for damage	Training samples of actual damaged crops	Enlarged photographs of damaged crops	Verbal descriptions of what damaged crops look like
2.	doctor	patient with skin condition	diagnoses problem	Color photographs	Color motion picture film	Black and white photographs
3.	electronics maintenance man	electronic malfunction symptoms	locates malfunction in circuit	Printed descriptions of symptoms	Photographs of symptoms	Three-dimensional mock-up with symptoms displayed
4.	rating building foundation for soundness	sound, cracked, or sagging foundation	evaluates soundness	Training samples (actual houses)	Three-dimensional small scale models	Photographs of foundations
5.	maintain washing machine	damaged valve in washing machine	disassemble machine and replace valve	Three-dimensional functioning mock-up of machine	Diagram showing location of parts of machine	Film of assembly and disassembly of machine

SEE ANSWERS

EXERCISE #23

I. Recognize

A. Put an X through the type of simulation which would be the most desirable from a logistical point (i.e., the smallest logistical burden would be involved).

TYPES OF SIMULATION

	JOB	INPUT	ACTION			
1.	agriculture expert	damaged corn, wheat, soybeans	identifies insect responsible for damage	Training samples of actual damaged crops	Enlarged photographs of damaged crops	Verbal descriptions of what damaged crops look like [X]
2.	doctor	patient with skin condition	diagnoses problem	Color photographs	Color motion picture film	Black and white photographs [X]
3.	electronics maintenance man	electronic malfunction symptoms	locates malfunction in circuit	Printed descriptions of symptoms [X]	Photographs of symptoms	Three-dimensional mock-up with symptoms displayed
4.	rating building foundation for soundness	sound, cracked, or sagging foundation	evaluates soundness	Training samples (actual houses)	Three-dimensional small scale models	Photographs of foundations [X]
5.	maintain washing machine	damaged valve in washing machine	disassemble machine and replace valve	Three dimensional functioning mock-up of machine	Diagram showing location of parts of machine [X]	Film of assembly and disassembly of machine

RESUME READING ON PAGE III.71 IN THE HANDBOOK.

II. Produce

A. For the examples below, create an example of simulated practice which you feel is a good compromise between what is offered as "best" from an instructional and from a logistical point of view. Keep in mind other properties of inputs or actions that should be simulated.

	INPUT	ACTION	OUTPUT	BEST INSTRUCTIONAL	BEST LOGISTICAL	COMPROMISE
1.	facial expression of customer	clerk deals with customer accordingly	best customer treatment	An actor simulating the role, customers with which clerk practices correct action	Concrete, verbally described situation, and clerk produces correct action in writing	
2.	medieval and renaissance baroque paintings	analyze on difference in treatments of light	paintings analyzed	Full color printed high quality reproductions	Black and white reproductions from textbooks shown with aid of overhead projector	
3.	patient with broken arm to be X-rayed	position arm on bed and operate controls	patient X-rayed	Training model of machine with working controls and someone acting as patient; learner produces actions	Drawing of controls and correct and incorrect positioning of arm; learner verbalizes and identifies correct actions	
4.	TV monitor showing tunnel traffic problems	identify and report troubles	problems reported	TV tape showing typical traffic problems (e.g., length of backup)	Schematic sketch of traffic problems	
5.	moving blip on radar screen	identify position and distance as blip moves	position and distance identified	Film of blip moving across radar screen	Drawing of blip "path"	

SEE ANSWERS

EXERCISE #24

II. Produce

A. For the examples below, create an example of simulated practice which you feel is a good compromise between what is offered as "best" from an instructional and from a logistical point of view. Keep in mind other properties of inputs or actions that should be simulated.

	INPUT	ACTION	OUTPUT	BEST INSTRUCTIONAL	BEST LOGISTICAL	COMPROMISE
1.	facial expression of customer	clerk deals with customer accordingly	best customer treatment	An actor simulating the role, customers with which clerk practices correct action	Concrete, verbally described situation, and clerk produces correct action in writing	*Photographs of facial expressions showing mood of customer to which clerk responds accordingly*
2.	medieval and renaissance baroque paintings	analyze on difference in treatment of light	paintings analyzed	Full color printed high quality reproductions	Black and white reproductions from textbooks shown with aid of overhead projector	*Colored slides of painting*
3.	patient with broken arm to be X-rayed	position arm on bed and operate controls	patient X-rayed	Training model of machine with working controls and someone acting as patient; learner produces actions	Drawing of controls and correct and incorrect positioning of arm; learner verbalizes and identifies correct actions	*Mock-up of machine with non-functioning controls and someone acting as patient; learner simulates setting controls on mock-up*
4.	TV monitor showing tunnel traffic problems	identify show and report troubles	problems reported	TV tape showing typical traffic problems (e.g., length of backup)	Schematic sketch of traffic problems	*Photographs of backed-up traffic*
5.	moving blip on radar screen	identify position and distance as blip moves	position and distance identified	Film of blip moving across radar screen	Drawing of blip "path"	*Mechanical model with hand-operated discs showing moving blips*

RESUME READING ON PAGE III.77 IN THE HANDBOOK.

III.33

EXERCISE #25

I. Produce

A. For each of the following job tasks, describe in Column A the best <u>simulation</u> from an <u>instructional</u> point of view you would recommend. Simulate either inputs or actions as identified in the problem. In Column B, describe the media requirements appropriate to the simulation you have designed.

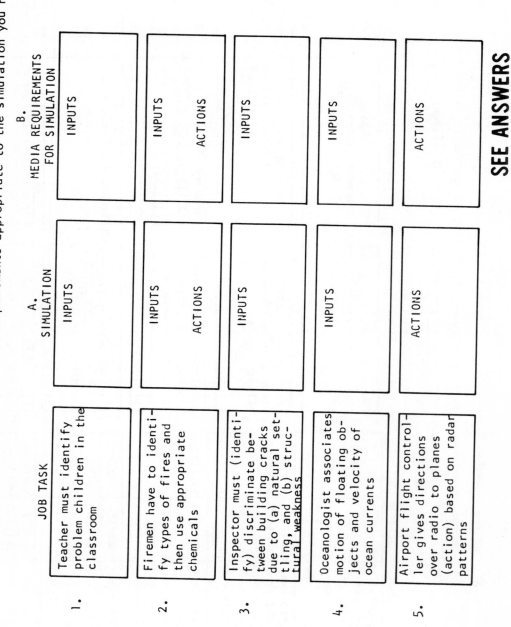

JOB TASK	A. SIMULATION	B. MEDIA REQUIREMENTS FOR SIMULATION
1. Teacher must identify problem children in the classroom	INPUTS	INPUTS
2. Firemen have to identify types of fires and then use appropriate chemicals	INPUTS / ACTIONS	INPUTS / ACTIONS
3. Inspector must (identify) discriminate between building cracks due to (a) natural settling, and (b) structural weakness	INPUTS	INPUTS
4. Oceanologist associates motion of floating objects and velocity of ocean currents	INPUTS	INPUTS
5. Airport flight controller gives directions over radio to planes (action) based on radar patterns	ACTIONS	ACTIONS

SEE ANSWERS

EXERCISE #25

I. Produce

A. For each of the following job tasks, describe in Column A the best simulation from an instructional point of view you would recommend. Simulate either inputs or actions as identified in the problem. In Column B, describe the media requirements appropriate to the simulation you have designed.

JOB TASK	A. SIMULATION	B. MEDIA REQUIREMENTS FOR SIMULATION
1. Teacher must identify problem children in the classroom	INPUTS *(a) actors role-playing; or (b) film of actors or of actual problem children*	INPUTS *(a) realistic visuals: actual human beings; or (b) reproductions: films*
2. Firemen have to identify types of fires and then use appropriate chemicals	INPUTS *film or photographs* ACTIONS *verbal answers on paper*	INPUTS *reproductions: film or photographs* ACTIONS *paper and pencil*
3. Inspector must (identify) discriminate between building cracks due to (a) natural settling, and (b) structural weakness	INPUTS *(a) photographs; (b) models*	INPUTS *reproductions: photographs or models*
4. Oceanologist associates motion of floating objects and velocity of ocean currents	INPUTS *(a) film of moving objects; (b) tank of water simulating currents and objects floating*	INPUTS *(a) reproduction: film; or (b) realistic: tank of water*
5. Airport flight controller gives directions over radio to planes (action) based on radar patterns	ACTIONS *talks with microphone*	ACTIONS *realistic visual: actual object (microphone)*

RESUME READING ON PAGE IV.1 IN THE HANDBOOK.

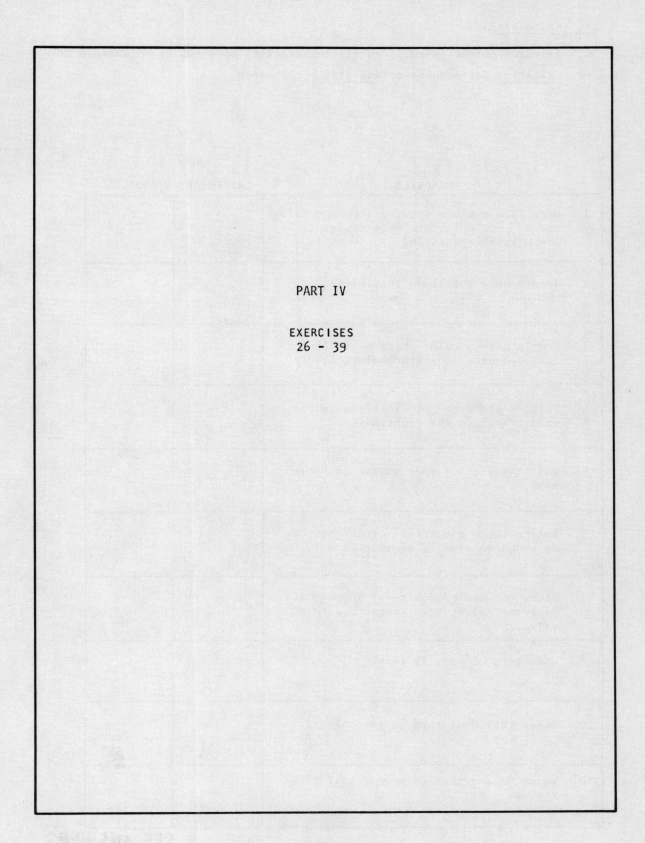

PART IV

EXERCISES
26 - 39

EXERCISE #26

I. Recognize

A. In the problems below, identify the practice obtained as an example of
criterion performance or assisted performance.

PRACTICE	CRITERION	ASSISTED
1. Here is a picture showing a Chippendale chair. Now which of these tables is in the Chippendale style?		
2. Disassemble and clean this rifle.		
3. Complete this color wheel by filling in the secondary and intermediate colors.		
4. This is the wrong way to tie a square knot. What is the right way?		
5. Weld these steel rods to form a table base.		
6. Splice these electrical wires together as shown on page 72 of your manual.		
7. Study the exploded view of an automatic diverter valve; then reassemble this valve.		
8. What type of wool is this?		
9. Steer this boat through the channel.		
10. Watch me and then grip your golf club the way I do.		

SEE ANSWERS

EXERCISE #26

I. Recognize

A. In the problems below, identify the practice obtained as an example of criterion performance or assisted performance.

PRACTICE		CRITERION	ASSISTED
1.	Here is a picture showing a Chippendale chair. Now which of these tables is in the Chippendale style?		X
2.	Disassemble and clean this rifle.	X	
3.	Complete this color wheel by filling in the secondary and intermediate colors.		X
4.	This is the wrong way to tie a square knot. What is the right way?	X	
5.	Weld these steel rods to form a table base.	X	
6.	Splice these electrical wires together as shown on page 72 of your manual.		X
7.	Study the exploded view of an automatic diverter valve; then reassemble this valve.		X
8.	What type of wool is this?	X	
9.	Steer this boat through the channel.	X	
10.	Watch me and then grip your golf club the way I do.		X

RESUME READING ON PAGE IV.13 IN THE HANDBOOK.

EXERCISE #27

I. Recognize

A. Put an X through the situation in which assistance in discriminating among inputs is _more_ likely
   to be necessary. In the last column, tell why.

	SITUATION #1	SITUATION #2	WHY?
1.	A judge has to rank the performance of five gymnasts	A judge has to rank the performance of fifteen gymnasts	
2.	A watch inspector uses a standard for comparison. Parts are coming out 1/64 of an inch different	A watch inspector uses a standard for comparison. Parts are coming out 1/100 of an inch different	
3.	Typing Persian rugs on the basis of the number of borders and color	Typing Persian rugs on the basis of the number of borders	
4.	Having to mix a low intensity blue and a high intensity yellow	Having to mix a low intensity blue and a high intensity blue	
5.	Distinguishing such mammals as horses, cows, and pigs from such reptiles as snakes and alligators	Distinguishing such mammals as whales and porpoises from such reptiles as crocodiles and alligators	

SEE ANSWERS

IV.4

EXERCISE #27

I. Recognize

A. Put an X through the situation in which assistance in discriminating among inputs is more likely
   to be necessary. In the last column, tell why.

	SITUATION #1	SITUATION #2	WHY?
1.	A judge has to rank the performance of five gymnasts.	A judge has to rank the performance of fifteen gymnasts.	Having to rank more people makes seeing the differences harder.
2.	A watch inspector uses a standard for comparison. Parts are coming out 1/64 of an inch different.	A watch inspector uses a standard for comparison. Parts are coming out 1/100 of an inch different.	The less deviation from the standard, the harder the discrimination.
3.	Typing Persian rugs on the basis of the number of borders and color.	Typing Persian rugs on the basis of the number of borders.	There are more things to be attended to and thus harder to tell apart.
4.	Having to mix a low intensity blue and a high intensity yellow.	Having to mix a low intensity blue and a high intensity blue.	The more similar colors are, the harder it is to tell them apart.
5.	Distinguishing such mammals as horses, cows, and pigs from such reptiles as snakes and alligators.	Distinguishing such mammals as whales and porpoises from such reptiles as crocodiles and alligators.	They all live in water (have similarities) and therefore can become confused.

EXERCISE # 27

I. Recognize

B. Put an X through the situation in which assistance in generalizing across inputs is likely to be necessary. In the last column, tell why.

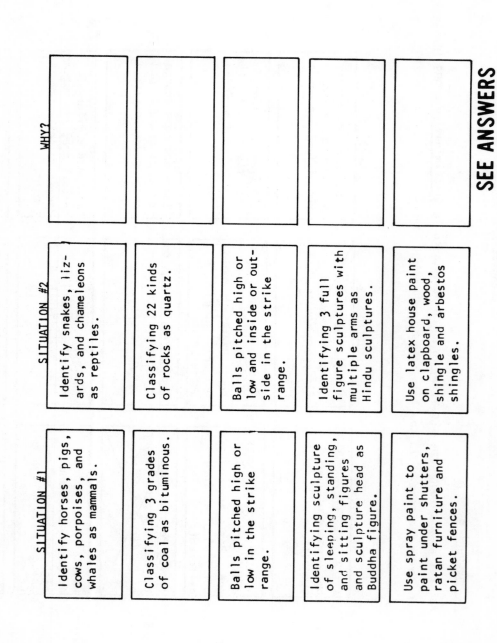

SITUATION #1	SITUATION #2	WHY?
Identify horses, pigs, cows, porpoises, and whales as mammals.	Identify snakes, lizards, and chameleons as reptiles.	
Classifying 3 grades of coal as bituminous.	Classifying 22 kinds of rocks as quartz.	
Balls pitched high or low in the strike range.	Balls pitched high or low and inside or outside in the strike range.	
Identifying sculpture of sleeping, standing, and sitting figures and sculpture head as Buddha figure.	Identifying 3 full figure sculptures with multiple arms as Hindu sculptures.	
Use spray paint to paint under shutters, ratan furniture and picket fences.	Use latex house paint on clapboard, wood, shingle and arbestos shingles.	

SEE ANSWERS

IV.6

EXERCISE # 27

I. Recognize

B. Put an X through the situation in which assistance in generalizing across inputs is likely to be necessary. In the last column, tell why.

SITUATION #1	SITUATION #2	WHY?
~~Identify horses, pigs, cows, porpoises, and whales as mammals.~~	Identify snakes, lizards, and chameleons as repitiles.	Because whales and porpoises appear dissimilar to horses, pigs, and cows.
Classifying 3 grades of coal as bituminous.	~~Classifying 22 kinds of rocks as quartz.~~	Harder to see 22 inputs as belonging to same class than 3 inputs.
Balls pitched high or low in the strike range.	~~Balls pitched high or low and inside or outside in the strike range.~~	With more situations to be attended to it is harder to see the similarity among balls in the strike range.
~~Identifying sculpture of sleeping, standing, and sitting figures and sculpture head as Buddha figure.~~	Identifying 3 full figure sculptures with multiple arms as Hindu sculptures.	The apparent dissimilarity of the sculpture makes it harder to see them all as Buddha figures.
~~Use spray paint to paint under shutters ratan furniture and picket fences.~~	Use latex house paint on clapboard, wood, shingle and arbestos shingles.	The greater apparent dissimilarity makes it harder to see their similarity.

EXERCISE #27

I. Recognize

C. Put an X through the situation in which assistance in associating (or chaining) input and action
   is likely to be necessary. In the last column tell why.

	SITUATION #1	SITUATION #2	WHY?
1.	Loading a movie camera by threading the film	Loading a snap in cartridge type movie camera	
2.	Associating twenty paintings with twenty art students	Associating five paintings with five art students	
3.	Associating ten faces and ten names	Associating twelve faces and twelve names	
4.	Taking apart electronic equipment, piece by piece, replacing faulty component and assembling	Replacing intact modules on a piece of electronic equipment	
5.	Mechanic has to associate ten different wrenches with ten different uses	Mechanic has to associate ten blade and Phillips head screwdriver with appropriate screws	

SEE ANSWERS

IV.8

EXERCISE #27

1. Recognize

C. Put an X through the situation in which assistance in associating (or chaining) input and action is likely to be necessary. In the last column tell why.

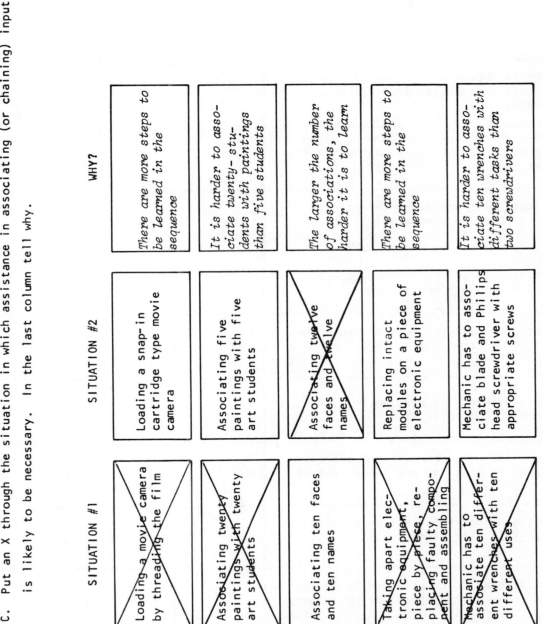

	SITUATION #1	SITUATION #2	WHY?
1.	Loading a movie camera by threading the film (X)	Loading a snap-in cartridge type movie camera	There are more steps to be learned in the sequence
2.	Associating twenty paintings with twenty art students (X)	Associating five paintings with five art students	It is harder to associate twenty-students with paintings than five students
3.	Associating ten faces and ten names	Associating twelve faces and twelve names (X)	The larger the number of associations, the harder it is to learn
4.	Taking apart electronic equipment, piece by piece, replacing faulty component and assembling (X)	Replacing intact modules on a piece of electronic equipment	There are more steps to be learned in the sequence
5.	Mechanic has to associate ten different wrenches with ten different uses (X)	Mechanic has to associate blade and Phillips head screwdriver with appropriate screws	It is harder to associate ten wrenches with different tasks than two screwdrivers

RESUME READING
ON PAGE IV.19
IN THE HANDBOOK.

IV.9

EXERCISE #28

1. Recognize

A. Classify the visual practice used in training as either Criterion, Simulated,
   or Mediating.

VISUALS USED IN TRAINING	CRITERION VISUAL	SIMULATED VISUAL	MEDIATING VISUAL
1. Black cardboard silhouttes of planes are used to practice identifying enemy aircraft.			
2. Microscope is used to compare blood samples of patients with and without leukemia.			
3. Projectionist practices threading a Bell & Howell projector.			
4. Electrician refers to photograph to tie underwriters knot in cord.			
5. Tobacco roller practices making corona roll using brown paper.			
6. Mechanic refers to diagram to dis-assemble carburetor.			
7. Dancer imitates movements of choreo-grapher in learning new dance routine.			
8. Draftsman spaces letters on tracing paper laid over standard title block.			
9. Chemist uses dust collected in gathering cups to determine makeup of pollutants.			
10. Scuba diver practices using face mask in swimming pool.			

SEE ANSWERS

EXERCISE #28

1. Recognize

A. Classify the visual practice used in training as either Criterion, Simulated, or Mediating.

VISUALS USED IN TRAINING	CRITERION VISUAL	SIMULATED VISUAL	MEDIATING VISUAL
1. Black cardboard silhouttes of planes are used to practice identifying enemy aircraft.		X	
2. Microscope is used to compare blood samples of patients with and without leukemia.	X		
3. Projectionist practices threading a Bell & Howell projector.	X		
4. Electrician refers to photograph to tie underwriters knot in cord.			X
5. Tobacco roller practices making corona roll using brown paper.		X	
6. Mechanic refers to diagram to dis-assemble carburetor.			X
7. Dancer imitates movements of choreo-grapher in learning new dance routine.			X
8. Draftsman spaces letters on tracing paper laid over standard title block.			X
9. Chemist uses dust collected in gathering cups to determine makeup of pollutants.	X		
10. Scuba diver practices using face mask in swimming pool.		X	

RESUME READING ON PAGE IV.22 IN THE HANDBOOK.

EXERCISE #29

I. Recognize

A. For each of the mediating visuals below, put an X in the column which
describes the type of assistance it is designed to provide.

	ASSISTANCE FOR:		
	DISTINCTIONS AMONG INPUTS	SIMILARITIES AMONG INPUTS	CONNECTIONS BETWEEN INPUTS AND ACTIONS
1. Transparent plastic model engines: showing the differences in construction of diesel engine and of internal combustion engine.			
2. A series of X-ray pictures: showing all the varieties of "hairline" fractures.			
3. [he she it] → A rectangle enclosing all the singular personal pronouns that take the verb "is."			
4. All foot positions in a dance step are laid out on floor for learner to follow.			
5. The parts of a rifle to be assembled are spatially arranged from left to right in the order in which they are to be assembled.			
6. The name of an animal that is a vertebrate is enclosed in one square, that of a non-vertebrate is enclosed in a second, separate square.			
7. Two squares joined by arrows: one square contains an example; the second contains a label (a term for the example).			
8. Arrows on parts to be assembled: allow the learner to line up parts so that he can tell if they are oriented properly.			
9. Color coding of female and male electrical terminals.			
10. On desk calculator, a column of "tens" digits is colored the same (but different from "hundreds").			

SEE ANSWERS

EXERCISE #29

I. Recognize

A. For each of the mediating visuals below, put an X in the column which describes the type of assistance it is designed to provide.

ASSISTANCE FOR:

		DISTINCTIONS AMONG INPUTS	SIMILARITIES AMONG INPUTS	CONNECTIONS BETWEEN INPUTS AND ACTIONS
1.	Transparent plastic model engines: showing the differences in construction of diesel engine and of internal combustion engine.	X		
2.	A series of X-ray pictures: showing all the varieties of "hairline" fractures.		X	
3.	he she it → A rectangle enclosing all the singular personal pronouns that take the verb "is."		X	
4.	All foot positions in a dance step are laid out on floor for learner to follow.			X
5.	The parts of a rifle to be assembled are spatially arranged from left to right in the order in which they are to be assembled.			X
6.	The name of an animal that is a vertebrate is enclosed in one square, that of a non-vertebrate is enclosed in a second, separate square.	X		
7.	Two squares joined by arrows: one square contains an example; the second contains a label (a tern for the example).			X
8.	Arrows on parts to be assembled: allow the learner to line up parts so that he can tell if they are oriented properly.	X		
9.	Color coding of female and male electrical terminals.			X
10.	On desk calculator, a column of "tens" digits is colored the same (but different from "hundreds").		X	

RESUME READING ON PAGE IV.28 IN THE HANDBOOK.

IV.13

EXERCISE #30

I. Recognize

A. Classify the mediating visuals below as being designed to provide
   assistance in <u>Visual</u>, <u>Verbal</u>, or <u>Motor</u> performance. Put an X in the
   appropriate column.

	MEDIATING VISUAL CUES AND PERFORMANCE THEY ARE DESIGNED TO ASSIST	CRITERION PERFORMANCE		
		VISUAL	VERBAL	MOTOR
1.	A list of animals that all can be classified as "mammals" is enclosed in a <u>box</u> (to facilitate the generalization).			
2.	Picture of seating to assume when walking, trotting, or galloping on horses with Western and English saddles.			
3.	<u>Map</u> of U.S. during colonial times facilitates learning about the comparative land holdings of England, France, and Spain.			
4.	<u>Exploded view</u> of valve facilitates discriminations about the correct position of valve in equipment.			
5.	To facilitate learning spelling or pronunciation, similarities in the "a-t" in cat, hat, sat, and mat, are printed in <u>red</u>.			
6.	A slow motion film is used to analyze an opponent's serve (to discriminate between a serve that results in the ball bouncing high and the ball bouncing low).			
7.	To facilitate learning to identify stages in life cycle of a mammal, <u>drawings</u> are used.			
8.	Writing on tracing paper that allows child learning to write to determine whether he is writing within the lines or whether it is going below or above the lines.			
9.	Art student learning to mix paint tries to match paints to <u>samples</u> mixed by instructor.			
10.	Photographs or film of different stirring motions used in cooking.			

SEE ANSWERS

I. Recognize

A. Classify the mediating visuals below as being designed to provide assistance in <u>Visual</u>, <u>Verbal</u>, or <u>Motor</u> performance. Put an X in the appropriate column.

	MEDIATING VISUAL CUES AND PERFORMANCE THEY ARE DESIGNED TO ASSIST	CRITERION PERFORMANCE		
		VISUAL	VERBAL	MOTOR
1.	A list of animals that all can be classified as "mammals" is enclosed in a <u>box</u> (to facilitate the generalization).		X	
2.	Picture of seating to assume when walking, trotting, or galloping on horses with Western and English saddles.			X
3.	<u>Map</u> of U.S. during colonial times facilitates learning about the comparative land holdings of England, France, and Spain.		X	
4.	<u>Exploded view</u> of valve facilitates discriminations about the correct position of valve in equipment.	X		
5.	To facilitate learning spelling or pronunciation, similarities in the "a-t" in cat, hat, sat, and mat, are printed in <u>red</u>.		X	
6.	A slow motion film is used to analyze an opponent's serve (to discriminate between a serve that results in the ball bouncing high and the ball bouncing low).	X		
7.	To facilitate learning to identify stages in life cycle of a mammal, <u>drawings</u> are used.		X	
8.	Writing on tracing paper that allows child learning to write to determine whether he is writing within the lines or whether it is going below or above the lines.	X		
9.	Art student learning to mix paint tries to match paints to <u>samples</u> mixed by instructor.	X		
10.	Photographs or film of different stirring motions used in cooking.			X

RESUME READING ON PAGE <u>IV.31</u> IN THE HANDBOOK.

EXERCISE #31

I. Produce

A. For each of the following examples produce a mediating visual
   cue to precede and assist criterion practice.

CRITERION
PERFORMANCE

1. A man starts with a
   lump of clay and takes
   all the steps involved
   in making a bowl on a
   potters wheel.

2. Seamstress must thread
   thread through sewing
   machine in specific
   sequence.

3. Man assembles a bicycle
   following a specific
   sequence.

4. Secretary must follow
   procedure to take out
   old ribbon and replace
   new one in typewriter.

5. Apprentice craftsman
   must follow correct
   steps in applying two
   fluids to erase line
   on "clear line" print.

SEE ANSWERS

EXERCISE #31

1. Produce

A. For each of the following examples produce a mediating visual
   cue to precede and assist criterion practice.

CRITERION PERFORMANCE	PRIOR USE OF VISUAL CUE
1. A man starts with a lump of clay and takes all the steps involved in making a bowl on a potters wheel.	*An expert potter first demonstrates the complete (live or on film) procedure, then student practices same steps.*
2. Seamstress must thread thread through sewing machine in specific sequence.	*An expert demonstrates (live or on film) the complete operation beforehand and then learner practices.*
3. Man assembles a bicycle following a specific sequence.	*An expert demonstrates (live or on film) the complete operation beforehand and then learner practices.*
4. Secretary must follow procedure to take out old ribbon and replace new one in typewriter.	*Experienced secretary demonstrates (live or on film) steps and new girl then performs steps.*
5. Apprentice craftsman must follow correct steps in applying two fluids to erase line on "clear line" print.	*The instructor demonstrates procedure (live or on film) and apprentice erases line exactly as instructor did.*

RESUME READING ON PAGE
IV.40 IN THE HANDBOOK.

EXERCISE #32

I. __Recognize__

A. Identify the following mediating visual cues which accompany practice as __content__ or __attentional__ cues. (Put an X in the appropriate column.) In Column A, tell how the visual cues assist practice of discriminations, generalizations, or chains.

	CRITERION PERFORMANCE	MEDIATING VISUAL CUE	A. TYPE OF ASSISTANCE	CONTENT CUE	ATTEN-TIONAL CUE
1.	Use <, > signs in arithmetic	80 > 60 (more than) 70 < 90 (less than) Examples written on blackboard			
2.	Edit out inferior quality film from used film	Back-lighted slide showing examples of inferior and quality film			
3.	Verbal contrasts of speed of air moving above and below air-plane wing	Arrows superimposed on TV image show points at under and upper side of wing			
4.	Classify all plant types belonging to the same family	Series of pictures belonging to the same family __enclosed in a box__			
5.	Florist contructs a "totem" arrangement in which vines are wrapped around pole	Six photographs sequen-tially numbered showing steps in construction			

SEE ANSWERS

EXERCISE #32

I. Recognize

A. Identify the following mediating visual cues which accompany practice as content or attentional cues. (Put an X in the appropriate column.) In Column A, tell how the visual cues assist practice of discriminations, generalizations, or chains.

	CRITERION PERFORMANCE	MEDIATING VISUAL CUE	A. TYPE OF ASSISTANCE	CONTENT CUE	ATTENTIONAL CUE
1.	Use <, > signs in arithmetic	80 > 60 (more than) 70 < 90 (less than) Examples written on blackboard	Presence of examples helps learner to associate the signs and the situations in which they are used	X	
2.	Edit out inferior quality film from used film	Back-lighted slide showing examples of inferior and quality film	Presence of examples helps the learner to discriminate between quality and inferior film	X	
3.	Verbal contrasts of speed of air moving above and below airplane wing	Arrows superimposed on TV image show points at under and upper side of wing	Arrow helps learner to discriminate between events above and below the wing		X
4.	Classify all plant types belonging to the same family	Series of pictures belonging to the same family enclosed in a box	Box helps the generalization by including in it all the relevant types		X
5.	Florist constructs a "totem" arrangement in which vines are wrapped around pole	Six photographs sequentially numbered showing steps in construction	Sequence of photographs helps the learner to practice the steps in the chain in the correct order	X	

RESUME READING ON PAGE IV.44 IN THE HANDBOOK.

```
┌─────────────────────────────┐
│   FOLD OUT THE DIAGRAM       │
│   ON THE BACK OF THIS PAGE.  │
└─────────────────────────────┘
```

I. Recognize

A. The problems below are based on the adjacent diagram which serves as a mediating visual cue for the student of English grammar. For each problem, put an X through the best answer.

PROBLEMS	ANSWER #1	#2	#3
1. The discrimination between classes of subjects used in sentences is facilitated by:	Four separate boxes in the subject columns	Multiple examples in boxes in the subject columns	Pairing of boxes in the subject/verb columns
2. The generalization across instances belonging to a single class of subjects is facilitated by:	Four separate boxes in the subject columns	Multiple examples in boxes in the subject columns	Pairing of boxes in the subject/verb columns
3. The associations between classes of subjects and the verbs they go with is facilitated by:	Four separate boxes in the subject columns	Multiple examples in boxes in the subject columns	Pairing of boxes in the subject/verb columns
4. Associations are facilitated by the following visual property of the diagrams:	Isolation of inputs in separate boxes	Inclusion of multiple examples of inputs in the same box	Joining of boxes by arrows
5. Discriminations are facilitated by the following visual property of the diagrams:	Isolation of inputs in separate boxes	Inclusion of multiple examples of inputs in the same box	Joining of boxes by arrows
6. Generalizations are facilitated by the following visual property of the diagrams:	Isolation of inputs in separate boxes	Inclusion of multiple examples of inputs in the same box	Joining of boxes by arrows
7.* The reason(s) the diagram facilitates discriminations among subjects is that the learner can already:	Associate spatially separate with different	Discriminate spatially separate boxes	Discriminate between columns and rows
8.* The reason(s) the diagram facilitates generalizations across subjects is that the learner can already:	Discriminate between what is and is not enclosed together	Discriminate between what is and is not linked together	Associate enclosure with sameness
9.* The reason(s) the diagram faciliates associations between subjects and verbs is that the learner can already:	Discriminate between boxes that are and are not labeled	Associate "linked" with "together"	Discriminate between what is and is not labeled
10.* The facilitating visual properties of diagrams are:	Spatial separation	Enclosure	Linkage

*Problems 7-10 can have 1, 2, or 3 correct choices.

IV.22

SEE ANSWERS

STUDY THIS DIAGRAM, AND THEN DO THE PROBLEMS ON THE NEXT PAGE.

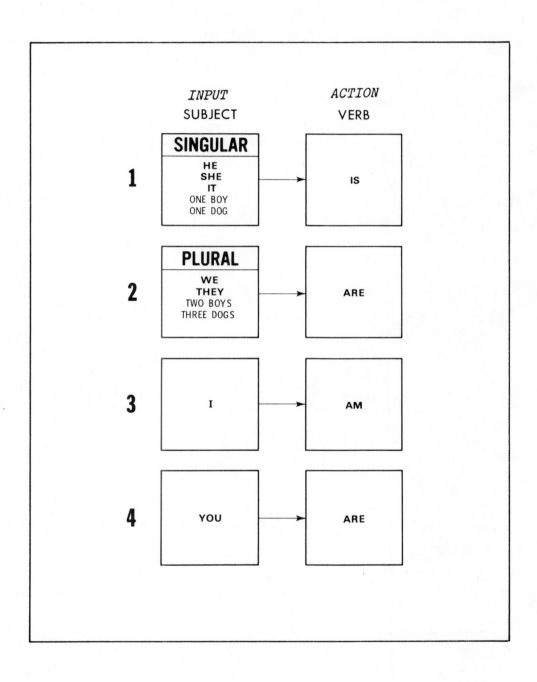

I. Recognize

A. The problems below are based on the adjacent diagram which serves as a
mediating visual cue for the student of English grammar. For each
problem, put an X through the best answer.

ANSWER

PROBLEMS	#1	#2	#3
1. The discrimination between classes of subjects used in sentences is facilitated by:	Four separate boxes in the subject columns	Multiple examples in boxes in the subject columns	Pairing of boxes in the subject/verb columns
2. The generalization across instances belonging to a single class of subjects is facilitated by:	Four separate boxes in the subject columns	Multiple examples in boxes in the subject columns	Pairing of boxes in the subject/verb columns
3. The associations between classes of subjects and the verbs they go with is faciliated by:	Four separate boxes in the subject columns	Multiple examples in boxes in the subject columns	Pairing of boxes in the subject/verb columns
4. Associations are facilitated by the following visual property of the diagrams:	Isolation of inputs in separate boxes	Inclusion of multiple examples of inputs in the same box	Joining of boxes by arrows
5. Discriminations are facilitated by the following visual property of the diagrams:	Isolation of inputs in separate boxes	Inclusion of multiple examples of inputs in the same box	Joining of boxes by arrows
6. Generalizations are facilitated by the following visual property of the diagrams:	Isolation of inputs in separate boxes	Inclusion of multiple examples of inputs in the same box	Joining of boxes by arrows
7.* The reason(s) the diagram facilitates discriminations among subjects is that the learner can already:	Associate spatially separate with different	Discriminate spatially separate boxes	Discriminate between columns and rows
8.* The reason(s) the diagram facilitates generalizations across subjects is that the learner can already:	Discriminate between what is and is not enclosed together	Discriminate between what is and is not linked together	Associate enclosure with sameness
9.* The reason(s) the diagram faciliates associations between subjects and verbs is that the learner can already:	Discriminate between boxes that are and are not labeled	Associate "linked" with "together"	Discriminate between what is and is not labeled
10.* The facilitating visual properties of diagrams are:	Spatial separation	Enclosure	Linkage

* Problems 7-10 can have 1, 2, or 3 correct choices.

EXERCISE #33

II. Produce

A. For each of the following training situations, describe why the particular mediating visual was chosen to facilitate learning of a particular skill.

#	INPUT	ACTION	OUTPUT	MEDIATING VISUAL CUE	CRITERION SKILL IT IS FACILITATING	WHY WAS IT CHOSEN TO SERVE THIS FUNCTION?
1.	superior, peer, subordinate	report to, cooperate with, direct	work performed	Table of Organization	Facilitates discriminating among people according to level in organization and subsequently how to behave toward them	
2.	primary, high school, college	X%, Y%, Z%	identification of percent attaining levels of education		Facilitates associating a relative percentage with degrees of education	
3.	vertical symptoms, horizontal symptoms	adjusts vertical, adjusts horizontal	diagnosis and adjustment	A series of photographs of all the vertical symptoms that require the same adjustment	Facilitates a generalization, e.g., all symptoms meaning a vertical hold problem	
4.	voter preference for candidates	compares relative standing of candidates	comparison	#1, #2, #3	Facilitates associating a numerical value with each candidate	
5.	film loop	threads projector	threaded projector	Numbered path and visual cues to guide forming a loop of correct height	Facilitates the practice of a long chain in the correct sequence and taking the right actions	

SEE ANSWERS

IV.24

EXERCISE #33

II. Produce

A. For each of the following training situations, describe why the particular mediating visual was chosen to facilitate learning of a particular skill.

	INPUT	ACTION	OUTPUT	MEDIATING VISUAL CUE	CRITERION SKILL IT IS FACILITATING	WHY WAS IT CHOSEN TO SERVE THIS FUNCTION?
1.	superior, peer, subordinate	report to, cooperate with, direct	work performed	Table of Organization	Facilitates discriminating among people according to level in organization and subsequently how to behave toward them	The learner can respond to the spatial relationship of the squares which represent vertical and horizontal relationships
2.	primary, high school, college	X%, Y%, Z%	identification of percent attaining levels of education	(pie chart: X%, Y%, Z%)	Facilitates associating a relative percentage with degrees of education	The learner can respond to relative areas representing relative percentages
3.	vertical symptoms, horizontal symptoms	adjusts vertical, adjusts horizontal	diagnosis and adjustment	A series of photographs of all the vertical symptoms that require the same adjustment	Facilitates a generalization, e.g., all symptoms meaning a vertical hold problem	The sample photographs allow the learner to compare a symptom he is faced with with the same types. Comparison is easy
4.	voter preference for candidates	compares relative standing of candidates	comparison	#1, #2, #3 (stick figures)	Facilitates associating a numerical value with each candidate	Number of stick figures is used because the learner can easily discriminate between numbers
5.	film loop	threads projector	threaded projector	Numbered path and visual cues to guide forming a loop of correct height	Facilitates the practice of a long chain in the correct sequence and taking the right actions	Can match his loop with a standard (discriminating whether they match or not is something he can already do)

EXERCISE #33

II. Produce

B. For each of the following jobs, devise a mediating visual cue that can facilitate the criterion performance that has been identified. Also, indicate why it is likely to be effective in this role.

JOB	INPUT	ACTION	CRITERION PERFORMANCE	PROPOSED VISUAL CUE	WHY IT FACILITATES CRITERION PERFORMANCE
1. highway patrol-man	moving viola-tion / moving non-vio-lation	tickets / does not ticket	Discriminating between moving violations and non-violations		
2. mechanic	parts of trans-mission	assem-bles	Performs the chain correctly; assembles the parts in the cor-rect sequence		
3. X-ray special-ist	duodenal ulcer / no duodenal ulcer	identi-fies condi-tion	Discriminating between evidence of ulcer and evidence of no ulcer in X-rays		
4. chemis-try student	organic com-pounds / inorgan-ic com-pounds	labels "organ-ic" / labels "inor-ganic"	Verbally defines organic and inorganic compounds		
5. elec-tronics mainte-nance man	differ-ent leads to be con-nected	connects leads appro-priately	Associating which leads get attached (or in-serted) to which other leads (or connections)		

SEE ANSWERS

IV.26

EXERCISE #33

II. Produce

B. For each of the following jobs, devise a mediating visual cue that can facilitate the criterion performance that has been identified. Also, indicate why it is likely to be effective in this role.

	JOB	INPUT	ACTION	CRITERION PERFORMANCE	PROPOSED VISUAL CUE	WHY IT FACILITATES CRITERION PERFORMANCE
1.	highway patrolman	moving violation / moving non-violation	tickets / does not ticket	Discriminating between moving violations and non-violations	Film showing the difference between them	Examples provide a standard of comparison; easy to compare a practice problem with the standard
2.	mechanic	parts of transmission	assembles	Performs the chain correctly; assembles the parts in the correct sequence	Divides parts into groups--laying out groups spatially to suggest order of assembly	Spatial arrangement facilitates practicing the chain in the correct order
3.	X-ray specialist	duodenal ulcer / no duodenal ulcer	identifies condition	Discriminating between evidence of ulcer and evidence of no ulcer in X-rays	Sample X-rays showing symptoms or lack of them	Learner can easily compare a practice problem with the standardized samples
4.	chemistry student	organic compounds / inorganic compounds	labels "organic" / labels "inorganic"	Verbally defines organic and inorganic compounds	EXAMPLES / LABEL — organic, inorganic (boxes)	The boxes facilitate the discriminations, generalizations, and associations involved in the definition
5.	electronics maintenance man	different leads / leads to be connected	connects / appropriately	Associating which leads get attached (or inserted) to which other leads (or connections)	Color-coded leads to be connected	Easy to associate, for example, blue leads with other blue leads

RESUME READING ON PAGE IV.53 IN THE HANDBOOK.

I. Recognize

A. Below are visual examples that are used to illustrate abstract, verbal concepts and principle. The visual examples serve as mediating visuals that facilitate the learning of concepts or principles. Put an X through the relevant property (or properties) of the visual example that the learner can readily respond to, thereby making it easier for him to learn the more abstract, verbal materials.

1. **Principle**: relationship between heat and molecular movement. **Visual**: animation showing faster vibrations of molecules in steel bar following application of flame.	Relative speed of moving objects.	Relationship between cause (before) and effect (after).	Learner already associates flame and heat.
2. **Fact**: proportion of income spent on goods and services. Food Other Goods Services Savings %	Relative area sizes.	Number of markings in areas	Differences in shading.
3. **Principle**: relating "hardness" to arrangement of atoms in molecules. **Visual**: Graphite Diamond	Difference in color.	Difference in spatial arrangement.	Learner already associates narrow layers of atoms with hardness.
4. **Fact**: wind breaks up water drops; negative charges go to top of cloud, positive, to bottom of cloud. **Visual**:	Differences in number.	Differences in left and right.	Difference between up and down.
5. **Concept**: positively and negatively charged objects. Negative Positive	Differences in number.	Differences in areas.	Differences in left to right arrangement.

SEE ANSWERS

I. **Recognize**

A. Below are visual examples that are used to illustrate abstract, verbal concepts and principle. The visual examples serve as mediating visuals that facilitate the learning of concepts or principles. Put an X through the <u>relevant property</u> (or <u>properties</u>) of the visual example that the learner can readily respond to, thereby making it <u>easier</u> for him to learn the more abstract, verbal materials.

VISUAL EXAMPLES	PROPERTY OF VISUAL EXAMPLE		
1. <u>Principle</u>: relationship between heat and molecular movement. <u>Visual</u>: animation showing faster vibrations of molecules in steel bar following application of flame.	⊠ Relative speed of moving objects.	⊠ Relationship between cause (before) and effect (after).	⊠ Learner already associates flame and heat.
2. <u>Fact</u>: proportion of income spent on goods and services. <u>Visual</u>: Food Other Goods Services Savings %	⊠ Relative area sizes.	⊠ Number of markings in areas.	⊠ Differences in shading.
3. <u>Principle</u>: relating "hardness" to arrangement of atoms in molecules. <u>Visual</u>: Graphite Diamond	Difference in color.	⊠ Difference in spatial arrangement.	⊠ Learner already associates narrow layers of atoms with hardness.
4. <u>Fact</u>: wind breaks up water drops; negative charges go to top of cloud, positive, to bottom of cloud. <u>Visual</u>:	Differences in number.	Differences in left and right.	⊠ Difference between up and down.
5. <u>Concept</u>: positively and negatively charged objects. Negative Positive	⊠ Differences in number.	Differences in areas.	Differences in left to right arrangement.

I. Recognize

B. For each problem below, put an X through the example which is likely to make the concept easier for the learner. In the last column, state why it is easier and the other is harder.

EXERCISE #34

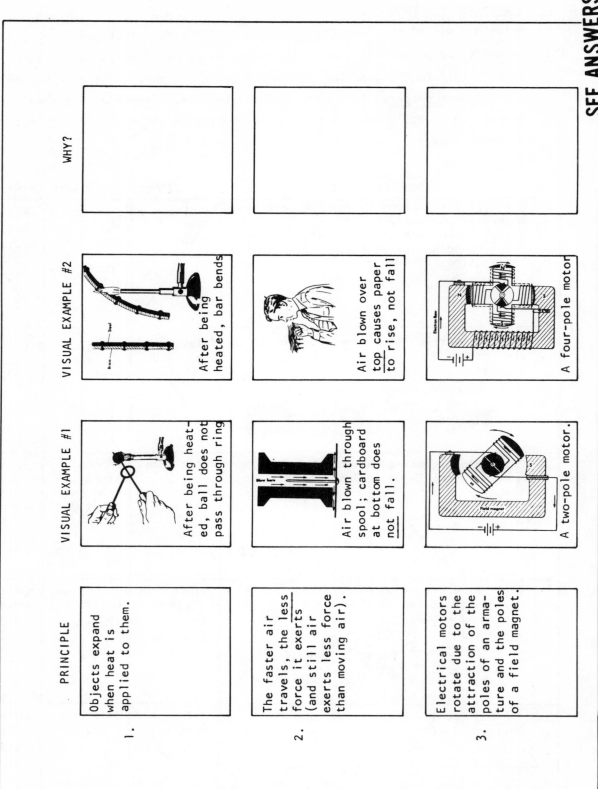

PRINCIPLE	VISUAL EXAMPLE #1	VISUAL EXAMPLE #2	WHY?
1. Objects expand when heat is applied to them.	After being heated, ball does not pass through ring.	After being heated, bar bends	
2. The faster air travels, the less force it exerts (and still air exerts less force than moving air).	Air blown through spool; cardboard at bottom does not fall.	Air blown over top causes paper to rise, not fall	
3. Electrical motors rotate due to the attraction of the poles of an armature and the poles of a field magnet.	A two-pole motor.	A four-pole motor	

SEE ANSWERS

EXERCISE #34

I. Recognize

B. For each problem below, put an X through the example which is likely to make the concept _easier_ for the learner. In the last column, state why it is easier and the other is harder.

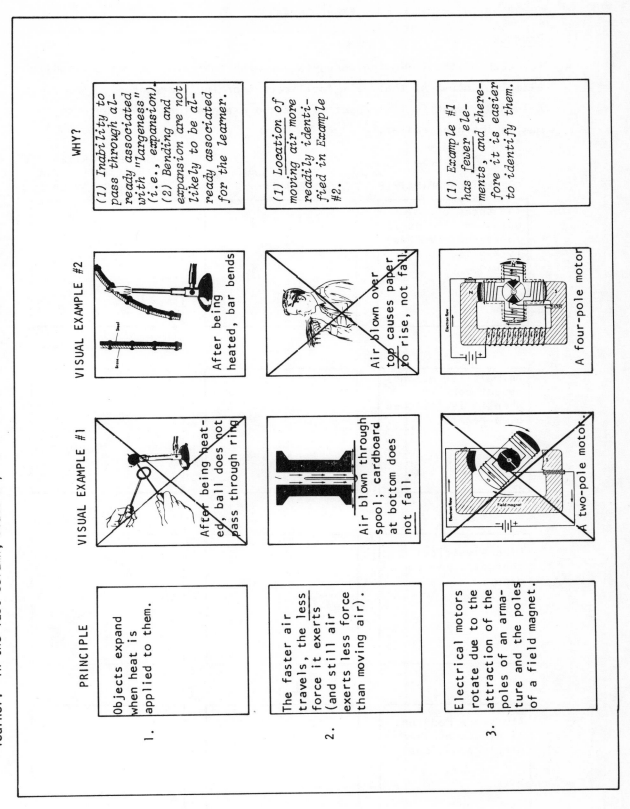

PRINCIPLE	VISUAL EXAMPLE #1	VISUAL EXAMPLE #2	WHY?
1. Objects expand when heat is applied to them.	After being heated, ball does not pass through ring	After being heated, bar bends	_(1) Inability to pass through already associated with "largeness" (i.e., expansion)._ _(2) Bending and expansion are not likely to be already associated for the learner._
2. The faster air travels, the less force it exerts (and still air exerts less force than moving air).	Air blown through spool; cardboard at bottom does _not fall._	Air blown over top causes paper to rise, not fall.	_(1) Location of moving air more readily identified in Example #2._
3. Electrical motors rotate due to the attraction of the poles of an armature and the poles of a field magnet.	A two-pole motor	A four-pole motor	_(1) Example #1 has fewer elements, and therefore it is easier to identify them._

EXERCISE #34

II. Produce

A. For each of the following concepts you wish to teach, create a visual example (Column A) that will facilitate learning the concept. In Column B, identify the properties of the example that contribute to making learning easier.

	CONCEPT OR PRINCIPLE	A. YOUR VISUAL EXAMPLE	B. WHAT PROPERTIES OF THE EXAMPLE MAKE LEARNING EASIER?
1.	The speed of molecules in liquids is increased when heat is applied to the liquid.		
2.	Animals (or humans) repeat behavior when it is followed by a reward.		
3.	Like electrical charges repel each other.		
4.	Atoms are made up of electrons which circle a nucleus.		

SEE ANSWERS

IV.32

EXERCISE #34

II. Produce

A. For each of the following concepts you wish to teach, create a <u>visual</u>
example (Column A) that will facilitate learning the concept. In
Column B, identify the properties of the example that contribute to
making learning easier.

CONCEPT OR PRINCIPLE	A. YOUR VISUAL EXAMPLE	B. WHAT PROPERTIES OF THE EXAMPLE MAKE LEARNING EASIER?
1. The speed of mole-cules in liquids is increased when heat is applied to the liquid.	*e.g., animation of flask of water and flame applied; mole-cules (dots) speed up.*	*(1) Flame and heat are associated* *(2) Faster movement is easily seen* *(3) Learner can identify cause and effect*
2. Animals (or humans) repeat behavior when it is followed by a reward.	*e.g., film of parent praising child for doing an arithmetic problem; child does another problem.*	*(1) Learner already associates various objects with concept "reward"* *(2) Learner can identify repetition of same behavior*
3. Like electrical charges repel each other.	*e.g., live demon-stration* *Positively charged object causes positively charged balls to move apart*	*(1) Learner can already identify "moving apart"*
4. Atoms are made up of electrons which circle a nucleus.	*e.g., animation:*  *Dot circling another dot.*	*(1) Learner can already identify circling motions*

IV.33

RESUME READING
ON PAGE IV.62
IN THE HANDBOOK.

I. Recognize

A. For each of the following learning tasks, put an X through the example you would first present to the learner. State why.

LEARNING TASK		EXAMPLE A	EXAMPLE B	WHY?
1. discrimination about statistical distribution	INPUT #1 "positive skewness" — INPUT #2 "negative skewness"	curve; positive skewness / negative skewness	"Negative skewness means that scores pile up at the top of the distribution; positive, at the bottom"	
2. discrimination about weights of objects	INPUT #1 "weight in air" — INPUT #2 "weight in water"	"An object weighed 30 pounds in air, but only 20 pounds when submerged"		
3. associating procedures with a label (definition)	INPUT provides reward for behavior — ACTION applies label: "reinforcement"	"Whenever the parent rewards a child immediately after he does something desirable, we say the parent reinforced the child"	"A film showing a parent giving a child a nickel after cleaning up his room; word "reinforcement" shown"	
4. discrimination between concepts	INPUT #1 "forward bias" — INPUT #2 "reverse bias"	P N / P N — forward reverse	"In forward bias, like poles are connected; in reverse bias, opposite poles are attached"	
5. producing a verbal chain	molecules move faster when heated — what happens to molecules when heated	Animated sequence showing speed-up of molecular movement when heat is applied to an object	"The molecules in a metal bar move faster when heat is applied to it"	

SEE ANSWERS

EXERCISE #35

I. Recognize

A. For each of the following learning tasks, put an X through the example you would first present to the learner. State why.

LEARNING TASK			EXAMPLE A	EXAMPLE B	WHY?
1. discrimination about statistical distribution	INPUT #1 "positive skewness"	INPUT #2 "negative skewness"	(positive skewness / negative skewness)	"Negative skewness means that scores pile up at the top of the distribution; positive, at the bottom"	Learner can more easily respond to the spatial properties of the curves than to the abstract words of Example B.
2. discrimination about weights of objects	INPUT #1 "weight in air"	INPUT #2 "weight in water"	"An object weighed 30 pounds in air, but only 20 pounds when submerged"		A concrete example makes a concept easier to understand; easy to see the change in scale reading
3. associating procedures with a label (definition)	INPUT provides reward for behavior	ACTION applies label: "reinforcement"	"Whenever the parent rewards a child immediately after he does something desirable, we say the parent reinforced the child"	A film showing a parent giving a child a nickel after cleaning up his room; word "reinforcement" shown	The events on film are concrete and meaningful to the viewer; thus the label is associated with something familiar
4. discrimination between concepts	INPUT #1 "forward bias"	INPUT #2 "reverse bias"	forward reverse	"In forward bias, like poles are connected; in reverse bias, opposite poles are attached"	The concrete example facilitates the discrimination more readily than the verbal description
5. producing a verbal chain	molecules move faster when heated		Animated sequence showing speed-up of molecular movement when heat is applied to an object	"The molecules in a metal bar move faster when heat is applied to it"	The learner can respond to the faster movement and more readily associate it with the applied heat (also concretely shown)

EXERCISE #35

I. Recognize

B. For each VISUAL example below, put an X through the preferred type of response you would require of a learner when the material to be learned is difficult or he is in an early learning stage.

LEARNING TASK	INPUT #1	INPUT #2	VISUAL EXAMPLE	RESPONSE A	RESPONSE B
1. discrimination about weights of objects	weight in air	weight in water	"What will happen when I lower the object in water?"	"Which way will the scale look like?"	"Will the scale reading stay the same, increase, or decrease?"
2. producing a verbal chain	what happens to molecules when heated	molecules move faster when heated	Animated sequence "What will happen to the molecules if I heat the water in this flask?"	"The molecules in the water will stop moving, slow down, stay the same, or speed up."	Animation showing speed up, slow down, the same. "Which way will it be?" (Student picks out right way)
3. associating procedures with a label (definition)	INPUT provides reward for behavior	ACTION applies label: "reinforcement"	Film: parent rewards a child "Which of these situations is an example of reinforcement?"	Student picks out the reinforcement situation from two verbal examples.	Student picks from two filmed sequences showing examples of reinforcement and non-reinforcement.
4. discrimination about statistical distribution	positive skewness	negative skewness	"What will happen if this curve becomes negatively skewed?"	"Which way will it be like?"	"Will the scores pile up at the top or bottom of the distribution?"
5. discrimination between concepts	forward bias	reverse bias	"What will the connections be like in forward bias?"		"Will like poles be connected or will opposite poles be connected?"

SEE ANSWERS

IV.36

I. Recognize

B. For each VISUAL example below, put an X through the preferred type of response you would require of a learner when the material to be learned is difficult or he is in an early learning stage.

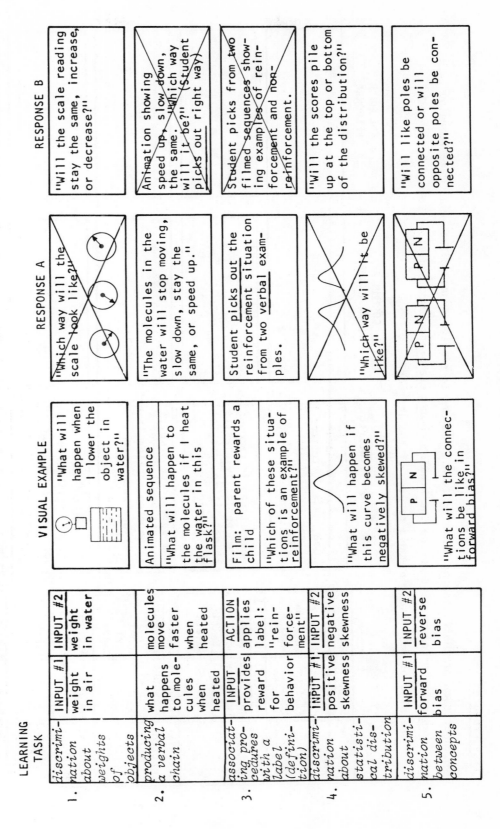

LEARNING TASK			VISUAL EXAMPLE	RESPONSE A	RESPONSE B
1. discrimination about weights of objects	INPUT #1 weight in air	INPUT #2 weight in water	"What will happen when I lower the object in water?"	"Which way will the scale look like?"	"Will the scale reading stay the same, increase, or decrease?"
2. producing a verbal chain	what happens to molecules when heated	molecules move faster when heated	Animated sequence "What will happen to the molecules if I heat the water in this flask?"	"The molecules in the water will stop moving, slow down, stay the same, or speed up."	Animation showing speed up, slow down, the same. "Which way will it be?" (Student picks out right way)
3. associating procedures with a label (definition)	INPUT provides reward for behavior	INPUT ACTION applies label: "reinforcement"	Film: parent rewards a child "Which of these situations is an example of reinforcement?"	Student picks out the reinforcement situation from two verbal examples.	Student picks from two filmed sequences showing examples of reinforcement and non-reinforcement.
4. discrimination about statistical distribution	INPUT #1 positive skewness	INPUT #2 negative skewness	"What will happen if this curve becomes negatively skewed?"	"Which way will it be like?"	"Will the scores pile up at the top or bottom of the distribution?"
5. discrimination between concepts	INPUT #1 forward bias	INPUT #2 reverse bias	"What will the connections be like in forward bias?"		"Will like poles be connected or will opposite poles be connected?"

EXERCISE #35

II. Produce

A. For each of the following learning tasks, you are to provide practice that will make learning easier. In Column A, describe the kind of visual example you would use; in Column B, describe the kind of response you would require of the learner.

	TASK		CONCEPT OR PRINCIPLE	COLUMN A VISUAL EXAMPLE	COLUMN B RESPONSE
1.	Discrim- ination	Input #1 fulcrum distance #1 from load	Input #1 fulcrum distance #2 from load	Closer fulcrum is to load, less force re-quired to lift it.		
2.	Discrim- ination	Input #1 "perfect- ly elas- tic ob- ject"	Input #2 "non- perfectly elastic object"	When stress is removed from perfectly elastic object, it returns to the original shape		
3.	Discrim- ination	Input #1 pressure that will tear paper	Input #3 pressure that won't tear paper	The same force (i.e., weight) applied over a large area applies less pressure than over a small area.		
4.	Associ- ation	Input ignoring behavior	Action label "extinc- tion"	"Extinction" means to ignore (neither reward nor punish) behavior.		
5.	Associ- ation	Input weight of dis- placed water	Action says "equal to loss of weight of object"	Weight of water dis-placed by submerged object is equal to the loss of weight when object is submerged.		

SEE ANSWERS

EXERCISE #35

II. Produce

A. For each of the following learning tasks, you are to provide practice that will make learning easier. In Column A, describe the kind of visual example you would use; in Column B, describe the kind of response you would require of the learner.

	TASK		CONCEPT OR PRINCIPLE	COLUMN A VISUAL EXAMPLE	COLUMN B RESPONSE
1.	Discrimination — Input #1 fulcrum distance #1 from load	Input #1 fulcrum distance #2 from load	Closer fulcrum is to load, less force required to lift it.	Live or on film: lever about to lift a load.	"In order to use less force, in which position should lever be, here or here?"
2.	Discrimination — Input #1 "perfectly elastic object"	Input #2 "non-perfectly elastic object"	When stress is removed from perfectly elastic object, it returns to the original shape	Live or on film: Stress applied to an object identified as "perfectly elastic"	"If I remove the stress, will the object look like this or this?"
3.	Discrimination — Input #1 pressure that will tear paper	Input #3 pressure that won't tear paper	The same force (i.e., weight) applied over a large area applies less pressure than over a small area.	Live or on film: Wooden oblong block held over paper.	"Which way should I rest this on the paper-- this way ☐ or this way ☐ --in order for the paper to tear?"
4.	Association — Input ignoring behavior	Action Label "extinction"	"Extinction" means to ignore (neither reward nor punish) behavior.	On film: Child seeks attention from teacher.	"Which of these is an example of extinction?" (On film, teacher ignores completely; teacher tells child to go to seat)
5.	Association — Input weight of displaced water	Action Says "equal to loss of weight of object"	Weight of water displaced by submerged object is equal to the loss of weight when object is submerged.	On film: Object submerged and reading on scale goes down.	"How much will this overflow weigh--as it is on this scale face or this one?"

RESUME READING ON PAGE IV.69 IN THE HANDBOOK.

I. Produce

A. For each of the following job tasks, develop editing practice and production practice.

	JOB	TASK	COMMON ERRORS	EDITING PRACTICE	PRODUCTION PRACTICE
1.	operator of desk computer	computes statistics	omission: failure to clear out previous results		
2.	filing clerk	filing at the end of the day	wrong action: puts correspondence in wrong place		
3.	electronic maintenance man	checks out equipment	wrong sequence: safety precaution too late		
4.	pilot	take-off	omitted step: check of indicator		
5.	teacher	handling problem behavior	wrong action: ignores instead of rewarding child		

SEE ANSWERS

I. Produce

A. For each of the following job tasks, develop editing practice and production practice.

JOB	TASK	COMMON ERRORS	EDITING PRACTICE	PRODUCTION PRACTICE
1. operator of desk computer	computes statistics	omission: failure to clear out previous results	"Watch this performance and then correct it." Omitted step is built into a live or filmed demonstration.	"Compute a correlation."
2. filing clerk	filing at the end of the day	wrong action: puts correspondence in wrong place	"Watch this demonstration, and if it's incorrect, indicate what you would do differently." (wrong action shown)	"File these papers."
3. electronic maintenance man	checks out equipment	wrong sequence: safety precaution too late	"Look at this film and then tell me what you would do differently."	"Check out this equipment."
4. pilot	take-off	omitted step: check of indicator	"Look at this film and then indicate what you would do differently."	"Take off" (in simulator or in trainer).
5. teacher	handling problem behavior	wrong action: ignores instead of rewarding child	"Look at this film of how you dealt with this situation. What would you do differently now?"	"Solve this case study problem. What would you do?"

RESUME READING ON PAGE IV.75 IN THE HANDBOOK.

EXERCISE #37

I. Recognize

A. For each of the following job tasks, three types of practice have been devised. Indicate by writing the sequence, 1, 2, or 3, in which you would have the learner engage in the three types of practice.

JOB	TASK	COMMON ERRORS	TYPE A	TYPE B	TYPE C
1. Movie projectionist	Threading film through projector	Sprocket holes in film facing wrong way	The film in this projector has been threaded incorrectly. Diagnose the problem and rethread it properly ____	"Thread the film through the projector" ____	"Which is the correct way for the sprockets to be facing--A or B?" (Demonstrated live or in photographs) ____
2. IBM card equipment operator	Feeding cards into	Sequence of steps incorrect	"Which is the correct sequence of steps to take--as in A or as in B?" (Demonstate or on film) ____	"Feed these cards into the sorter" ____	"One step was taken out of sequence. Which one? When should it be taken? ____
3. Mechanic	Assemble a carburetor	Parts assembled in wrong sequence	"Assemble this carburetor" ____	"What's wrong with the way this carburetor has been assembled?" (Film of assembly; learner writes answer) ____	"Which is the correct way to assemble the four parts of the carburetor?" (Show alternative film sequences). ____
4. Teacher	Rewarding a child for gradual improvement	Rewarding an insufficient amount of improvement	"In this film of you, did you reward the child at the right time? If you didn't, when should you have rewarded him? ____	"In which of these two situations would you reward a child?" ____	"Observe this child and reward him for appropriate amounts of improvement" ____
5. Soldier	Disassembly of rifle	Failure to tear down all parts	"Which of these parts was not torn down in the demonstration?" (Choose from actual parts) ____	"What was wrong in the film you saw? What would you have done differently?" ____	"Disassemble this rifle" ____

SEE ANSWERS

IV.42

EXERCISE #37

I. Recognize

A. For each of the following job tasks, three types of practice have been devised. Indicate by writing the sequence, 1, 2, or 3, in which you would have the learner engage in the three types of practice.

	JOB	TASK	COMMON ERRORS	TYPE A	TYPE B	TYPE C
1.	Movie projectionist	Threading film through projector	Sprocket holes in film facing wrong way	"The film in this projector has been threaded incorrectly. Diagnose the problem and rethread it properly" _2_	"Thread the film through the projector" _3_	"Which is the correct way for the sprockets to be facing--A or B?" (Demonstrated live or in photographs) _1_
2.	IBM card equipment operator	Feeding cards into	Sequence of steps incorrect	"Which is the correct sequence of steps to take--as in A or as in B?" (Demonstrate or on film) _1_	"Feed these cards into the sorter" _3_	"One step was taken out of sequence. Which one? When should it be taken? _2_
3.	Mechanic	Assemble a carburetor	Parts assembled in wrong sequence	"Assemble this carburetor" _3_	"What's wrong with the way this carburetor has been assembled?" (Film of assembly; learner writes answer) _2_	"Which is the correct way to assemble the four parts of the carburetor?" (Show alternative film sequences). _1_
4.	Teacher	Rewarding a child for gradual improvement	Rewarding an insufficient amount of improvement	"In this film of you, did you reward the child at the right time? If you didn't, when should you have rewarded him? _2_	"In which of these two situations would you reward a child?" _1_	"Observe this child and reward him for appropriate amounts of improvement." _3_
5.	Soldier	Disassembly of rifle	Failure to tear down all parts	"Which of these parts was not torn down in the demonstration?" (Choose from actual parts) _1_	"What was wrong in the film you saw? What would you have done differently?" _2_	"Disassemble this rifle." _3_

EXERCISE #37

II. Produce

A. For each of the job tasks below, create three different types of practice you would use. Start easy (#1) and end hard (#3).

	JOB	TASK	COMMON ERRORS	#1	#2	#3
1.	Operator of missile support equipment	Check operability of support equipment	An omitted step (safety precaution)			
2.	Seamstress	Sews clothes	Wrong step			
3.	Auto engine repair	Adjust distributor to improve timing	Step in wrong sequence			
4.	Electronics maintenance	Troubleshoot malfunction	Incomplete chain (stops too soon)			
5.	Chef	Prepare food	Wrong sequence: ingredient added too soon			

SEE ANSWERS

IV.44

EXERCISE #37

II. Produce

A. For each of the job tasks below, create three different types of practice you would use. Start easy (#1) and end hard (#3).

JOB	TASK	COMMON ERRORS	#1	#2	#3
1. Operator of missile-support equipment	Check operability of support equipment	An omitted step (safety precaution)	On film: "Which of these two operations has been performed correctly?"	On film: "What is wrong with this performance? What would you do differently?"	Live: "Check the operability of the equipment."
2. Seamstress	Sews clothes	Wrong step	On film: "In which example was a wrong step taken, A or B?"	On film: "One step was wrong; correct it."	Live: "Cut and sew this dress.
3. Auto engine repair	Adjust distributor to improve timing	Step in wrong sequence	Live demonstration: "Which is the correct procedure to follow; A or B?"	Live demonstration: "Did I adjust the distributor properly? If not, where did I go wrong and what should I have done?"	Live: "Adjust the timing of this engine."
4. Electronics maintenance	Troubleshoot malfunction	Incomplete chain (stops too soon)	On film: "Is this procedure complete or incomplete?"	On film: "The maintenance man did something wrong. What should he have done?"	Live: "Troubleshoot this equipment."
5. Chef	Prepare food	Wrong sequence: ingredient added too soon	On film: "In which sequence (A, B or C) were the ingredients added in the right order?"	Live demonstration: "There was an error; how would you add the ingredients?" (Verbal answer)	Live: "Make a hollandaise sauce."

RESUME READING ON PAGE IV.81 IN THE HANDBOOK.

EXERCISE #38

I. Produce

A. For each of the following practice situations, describe the feedback you would provide.

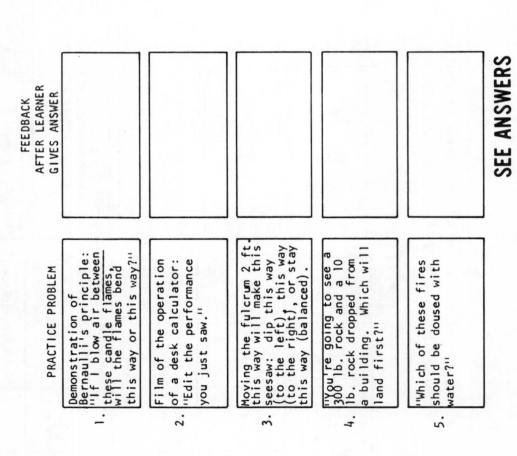

PRACTICE PROBLEM	FEEDBACK AFTER LEARNER GIVES ANSWER
1. Demonstration of Bernoulli's principle: "If I blow air between these candle flames, will the flames bend this way or this way?"	
2. Film of the operation of a desk calculator: "Edit the performance you just saw."	
3. Moving the fulcrum 2 ft. this way will make this seesaw: dip this way (to the left), this way (to the right), or stay this way (balanced).	
4. "You're going to see a 300 lb. rock and a 10 lb. rock dropped from a building. Which will land first?"	
5. "Which of these fires should be doused with water?"	

SEE ANSWERS

IV.46

EXERCISE #38

I. Produce

A. For each of the following practice situations, describe the feedback you would provide.

	PRACTICE PROBLEM	FEEDBACK AFTER LEARNER GIVES ANSWER
1.	Demonstration of Bernoulli's principle: "If I blow air between these candle flames, will the flames bend this way or this way?"	*Show the way the flames actually bend (i.e., inward).*
2.	Film of the operation of a desk calculator: "Edit the performance you just saw."	*Show the learner the correct editing, i.e., the change in the performance he should have made.*
3.	Moving the fulcrum 2 ft this way will make this seesaw: dip this way (to the left), this way (to the right), or stay this way (balanced).	*Move the fulcrum and show the results.*
4.	"You're going to see a 300 lb. rock and a 10 lb. rock dropped from a building. Which will land first?"	*Show the results of simultaneous landing.*
5.	"Which of these fires should be doused with water?"	*Show which fire should be doused with water.*

RESUME READING
ON PAGE IV.89
IN THE HANDBOOK.

I. Recognize

A. For each of the following uses of mediating visuals, check the appropriate "media display requirements."

MEDIATING VISUALS   MEDIA DISPLAY REQUIREMENTS

#	Mediating Visuals			
1.	CUE the boy → was the boys → were	Film	Actual people	Paper-and-pencil drawing
2.	CUE function: a live demonstration of operations involved in using a sewing machine (which the learner then imitates).	Actual people, objects, events	Film of people, objects, events	Drawings
3.	RESPONSE to visuals: animated sequence showing what happens to molecules when matter is heated; learner selects from pictorial options	Photographs of objects	Actual objects, events	Animation
4.	RESPONSE to visuals: an immediate record of learner's performance which he critiques or edits.	TV tape	Actual people, events	Paper-and-pencil description of performance
5.	FEEDBACK function: learner predicts what will happen in live demonstration of objects weighed in air; then he is shown what happens.	TV tape	Film	Actual objects, events
6.	FEEDBACK function: learner critiques immediate playback of his own performance (saying what he would do correctly) and shows what he should have done.	Actual objects, people, events	Film	TV tape
7.	RESPONSE to visuals: learner is shown alternative ways to assemble equipment and then selects the correct way; performed live.	Film	Actual objects, people, events	Photographs
8.	CUE function: learner has to identify types of plants. Types are contrasted in high-fidelity reproductions.	Actual objects	Black and white drawings	Colored photographs
9.	CUE function: tinker toy model is used to facilitate discriminations about structures of different molecules.	Actual objects	Model	Black and white photographs
10.	RESPONSE to visuals: learner is required to predict what will happen to rubber ball when stress is applied and then removed.	TV tape	Film	Actual operating events

SEE ANSWERS

I. Recognize

A. For each of the following uses of mediating visuals, check the appropriate "media display requirements."

MEDIATING VISUALS   MEDIA DISPLAY REQUIREMENTS

	MEDIATING VISUALS			
1.	CUE the boy → was the boys → were	Film	Actual people	Paper-and-pencil drawing ⊠
2.	CUE function: a live demonstration of operations involved in using a sewing machine (which the learner then imitates).	Actual people, objects, events ⊠	Film of people, objects, events	Drawings
3.	RESPONSE to visuals: animated sequence showing what happens to molecules when matter is heated; learner selects from pictorial options	Photographs of objects	Actual objects, events	Animation ⊠
4.	RESPONSE to visuals: an immediate record of learner's performance which he critiques or edits.	TV tape ⊠	Actual people, events ⊠	Paper-and-pencil description of performance
5.	FEEDBACK function: learner predicts what will happen in live demonstration of objects weighed in air; then he is shown what happens.	TV tape	Film	Actual objects, events ⊠
6.	FEEDBACK function: learner critiques immediate palyback of his own performance (saying what he would do correctly) and shows what he should have done.	Actual objects, people, events	Film	TV tape ⊠
7.	RESPONSE to visuals: learner is shown alternative ways to assemble equipment and then selects the correct way; performed live.	Film	Actual objects, people, events ⊠	Photographs
8.	CUE function: learner has to identify types of plants. Types are contrasted in high-fidelity reproductions.	Actual objects	Black and white drawings	Colored photographs ⊠
9.	CUE function: tinker toy model is used to facilitate discriminations about structures of different molecules.	Actual objects	Model ⊠	Black and white photographs
10.	RESPONSE to visuals: learner is required to predict what will happen to rubber ball when stress is applied and then removed.	TV tape	Film	Actual operating events ⊠

RESUME READING
ON PAGE V.1
IN THE HANDBOOK.

PART V

EXERCISE
40

EXERCISE #40

Produce

1. This is an unstructured exercise. Your task is to select a small
   section from a training development effort you are currently engaged
   in and apply the procedures outlined in Part V to it.

2. There are three subtasks to this exercise:

   a. You are to follow the procedures listed on page V.8, applying
      them to appropriate training materials in your own work.

   b. You are to follow the procedures listed on page V.9, applying
      them to appropriate training materials in your own work.

   c. You are to follow the procedures listed on page V.10, applying
      them to appropriate training materials in your own work.

3. Deal with only a small amount of training materials so that you can
   complete the exercise in a small amount of time.

3a. Do not develop complete learning exercises. Concentrate on the planning
    elements in selecting and using visuals (e.g., identifying criterion
    visuals; assessing the logistical burden; identifying discriminations,
    generalizations, chains, and barriers to them; and designing mediating
    visuals to overcome them).